PRENTICE-HALL FOUNDATIONS OF MODERN BIOLOGY SERIES

William D. McElroy and Carl P. Swanson, Editors

NEW VOLUME

Chemical Background for the Biological Sciences, *Emil H. White*

SECOND EDITIONS

The Cell, *Carl P. Swanson*

Cell Physiology and Biochemistry, *William D. McElroy*

Heredity, *David M. Bonner and Stanley E. Mills*

Adaptation, *Bruce Wallace and Adrian M. Srb*

Growth and Development, *Maurice Sussman*

Animal Physiology, *Knut Schmidt-Nielsen*

Animal Diversity, *Earl D. Hanson*

Animal Behavior, *V. G. Dethier and Eliot Stellar*

The Life of the Green Plant, *Arthur W. Galston*

The Plant Kingdom, *Harold C. Bold*

Man in Nature, *Marston Bates*

EMIL H. WHITE   *The Johns Hopkins University*

Englewood Cliffs, New Jersey   **PRENTICE-HALL, INC.**

Chemical Background for the Biological Sciences

FOUNDATIONS OF MODERN BIOLOGY SERIES

Chemical Background for the Biological Sciences, *Emil H. White*

FOUNDATIONS OF MODERN BIOLOGY SERIES

William D. McElroy and Carl P. Swanson, Editors

Design by Walter Behnke

Drawings by Felix Cooper

PRENTICE-HALL INTERNATIONAL, INC., *London*

PRENTICE-HALL OF AUSTRALIA, PTY., LTD., *Sydney*

PRENTICE-HALL OF CANADA, LTD., *Toronto*

PRENTICE-HALL OF INDIA PVT. LTD., *New Delhi*

PRENTICE-HALL OF JAPAN, INC., *Tokyo*

PRENTICE-HALL DE MEXICO, S. A., *Mexico City*

C-12845(p)   *C-12846(c)*

Foundations of Modern Biology Series

PREFACE TO THE FIRST EDITION

The science of biology today is *not* the same science of fifty, twenty-five, or even ten years ago. Today's accelerated pace of research, aided by new instruments, techniques, and points of view, imparts to biology a rapidly changing character as discoveries pile one on top of the other. All of us are aware, however, that each new and important discovery is not just a mere addition to our knowledge; it also throws our established beliefs into question, and forces us constantly to reappraise and often to reshape the foundations upon which biology rests. An adequate presentation of the dynamic state of modern biology is, therefore, a formidable task and a challenge worthy of our best teachers.

The authors of this series believe that a new approach to the organization of the subject matter of biology is urgently needed to meet this challenge, an approach that introduces the student to biology as a growing, active science, and that also *permits each teacher of biology to determine the level and structure of his own course.* A single textbook cannot provide such flexibility, and it is the authors' strong conviction that these student needs and teacher prerogatives can best be met by a series of short, inexpensive, well-written, and well-illustrated books so planned as to encompass those

v

areas of study central to an understanding of the content, state, and direction of modern biology. The FOUNDATIONS OF MODERN BIOLOGY SERIES represents the translation of these ideas into print, with each volume being complete in itself yet at the same time serving as an integral part of the series as a whole.

PREFACE TO THE SECOND EDITION

The first edition of the FOUNDATIONS OF MODERN BIOLOGY SERIES represented a marked departure from the traditions of textbook writing. The enthusiastic acceptance of the Series by teachers of biology, here and abroad, has been most heartening, and confirms our belief that there was a long-felt need for flexible teaching units based on current views and concepts. The second edition of all volumes in the Series retains the earlier flexibility, eliminates certain unnecessary overlaps of content, introduces new and relevant information, and provides more meaningful illustrative material.

The Series has also been strengthened by the inclusion of a new volume, *Chemical Background for the Biological Sciences* by Dr. Emil White. The dependence of modern biology on a sound foundation in physics and chemistry is obvious; this volume is designed to provide the necessary background in these areas.

In preparing the second edition of the Series, the authors and editors gratefully acknowledge the many constructive criticisms that have been made by hundreds of teaching biologists. Their interest and aid have made the task of writing more a pleasure than a burden.

Contents

Introduction

This volume is a brief outline of chemistry. It was written for the student of biochemistry and biology, and for others wishing an introduction to the subject. Included are concise, systematic treatments of atomic structure and inorganic chemistry, and a somewhat lengthier treatment of organic chemistry; applications of chemistry to biology have been given wherever possible. A short summary of the metric system and of the use of exponents and logarithms completes the volume. The approach throughout has been to emphasize the most important aspects of chemistry, and to treat selected topics in depth, consistent with the limited space available. As in any introductory work, the use of a large number of new terms has been necessary. These are indicated in bold type at the point of first use and they are listed in the index to facilitate the location of the definitions. Drawings, figures, and equations have been freely used to illustrate points in the text; they have been designed as integral parts of the volume and they should be studied as carefully as the material in the text. The author hopes that this attempt to show how and why chemical substances react will enable the reader to get a fuller and richer understanding of biochemistry and biology; the aim has been to show that chemistry is, in fact, one of the foundations of biology.

Matter, Atoms, and Molecules

Chemistry is the science that deals with the composition and structure of matter and with the transformations that matter undergoes. Chemistry is a rather broad field; at one extreme, in theoretical chemistry and spectroscopy, it borders on physics, and at the other extreme, in organic chemistry, it borders on biochemistry and biology. The problems that chemists work on reflect this broad range; in recent years, for example, chemists have published research papers on a mathematical model of methane, the generation of the chemical elements by the reaction of high-energy protons with iron, the infrared detection of water in the atmosphere of Venus, the preparation of compounds of xenon and krypton, the action of light on benzene, the mechanism of the oxidation of ethyl alcohol, the determination of the formula and structure of firefly luciferin, the synthesis of penicillin, and studies of the mode of action of the enzyme chymotrypsin. Despite the apparent variety of these investigations, however, chemistry is united by a relatively small number of basic principles; these principles are the subject of the present volume.

Chemistry became a science during the latter part of the eighteenth century, largely as a result of the application of quantitative methods to chemical phenomena by the French scientist Lavoisier. It is proper, therefore, that we begin this volume with a section on the measurement of matter.

WEIGHTS AND MEASURES

The quantity of matter in any given system is the **mass** of that system, where mass is measured in terms of a standard unit, the **kilogram.** Two other important standard units of measurement in the sciences are that of length, the **meter,** and that of time, the **second.** These units have been variously defined in the past. At the present time, a kilogram is defined as a mass equal to that of a block of platinum-iridium alloy kept at Sèvres, France, the meter is defined as a length equal to 1,650,763.73 times the wave length of the orange-red light emitted by the element krypton (Kr^{86}), and the second is defined as a time interval equal to 1/86,400 of the mean solar day (24 hours = 1440 minutes = 86,400 seconds). Two important subunits of this system are the **gram** (g), which is $\frac{1}{1000}$ of a kilogram, and the **centimeter** (cm), which is $\frac{1}{100}$ of a meter.

The kilogram, meter, and second are the fundamental units of the **metric system*** of measurement, a system used by scientists throughout the world. The metric system is also used as the standard system of weights and measures in many countries. In the commercial affairs of the United States and England, however, the British system of measurement is used; the fundamental units of this system are the pound, the foot, and the second.

ATOMS AND ELEMENTS

A casual examination of the outward appearance of an object usually leads to the conclusion that matter is continuous in nature. That is, the average person would conclude from such an observation that a block of a substance such as pure copper could be divided in half an infinite number of times. This view of matter is incorrect. If the copper block were to be divided enough times, a stage would ultimately be reached at which no further division could be effected. Similarly, the division of other substances would yield other indivisible particles. These indivisible particles, the building blocks of all matter, are called **atoms.** Of course, atoms can be split in nuclear reactions and in other high-energy processes, but as long as we restrict ourselves to chemical reactions, our notion of indivisible atoms is correct.

Atoms are exceedingly small. A block of ordinary copper weighing 63.5 grams (slightly more than two ounces) contains 602,000,000,000,000,000,000,-000 atoms of copper;† the reason for picking this particular weight of copper and number of atoms will be given in a later section. This large a number cannot be comprehended meaningfully. Suppose that we had 6.02×10^{23} peas; what volume would they occupy? Assuming that the peas were average in size (about 100, or 10^2 peas per cubic inch), how many peas would completely fill a household refrigerator? About 10^6. How many would fill an ordinary house from cellar to attic? 10^9. How many would be required to fill all the houses in a city the size of Chicago? 10^{15}. How many would be required to form a uniform layer ten feet deep over the entire surface of the earth? 10^{22}. At this point, most of our peas still remain! To use up

* See Appendix A.
† Expressed in powers of 10, this number becomes 6.02×10^{23}; see Appendix B.

6.02×10^{23} peas, we would have to blanket with 10 feet of peas about 60 planets the size of the earth!*

We are dealing here with very large numbers, and it is the very large number of atoms in even a microscopic piece of matter that leads to our erroneous impression that matter is continuous. We see now that it would be impossible to divide a copper block down to its constituent atoms with a knife, or some other crude device. Using more subtle approaches, however, scientists can readily detect and work with individual atoms in the cyclotron and in the mass spectrometer, and in fact, most of the information we have concerning atoms comes from such experiments.

A substance composed of a single kind of atom is called an **element;** copper, iron, and oxygen, for example, are elements. It is a surprising fact that all the matter in the earth, in the solar system, and in the universe, is made up of just 103 elements. All of the compounds that we are familiar with derive from various combinations of these 103 elements. Actually, a few of the elements are synthetic, or man-made, and others are quite rare. About 98 per cent of the mass of the earth is composed of just 7 different elements; these are, in order of decreasing abundance, iron, oxygen, silicon, magnesium, nickel, calcium, and aluminum.

ATOMIC STRUCTURE

Atoms are not hard, homogeneous spheres. Experiments with high-energy particles have shown that atoms are complex systems made up of a number of smaller particles; of these, the **electron** (e), the **proton** (p), and the **neutron** (n) are the most important. The atoms of the 103 elements are composed of different numbers and proportions of these 3 fundamental particles. The proton, which bears a positive electrical charge, and the neutron, which bears no charge, have approximately the same mass. On the other hand, the electron, which has a negative charge equal in magnitude to the positive charge on the proton, has a mass of only 1/1836 that of the proton. Since atoms are electrically neutral, they must contain equal numbers of electrons and protons.

Our understanding of the way these fundamental particles are arranged in the atom is due largely to the work of the English physicist Ernest Rutherford and the Danish physicist Niels Bohr. In the model of the atom developed by these scientists, the protons and neutrons are concentrated in a small volume at the center of the atom (called the **nucleus** of the atom), and the electrons move in regular, defined orbits about the nucleus. For convenience, we shall refer to this as the planetary model of the atom.

The smallest and simplest atom of all is the hydrogen atom, which consists of a single proton and a single electron. The structure of this atom is given in Fig. 1-1 along with the structures of the second and third lightest atoms, helium and lithium. Note that the size of the nuclei is exaggerated in the figures; the nucleus of the hydrogen atom has a diameter of about 10^{-13} cm, whereas the diameter of the atom itself is about 100,000 times larger (10^{-8} cm). The helium atom consists of 2 protons, 2 neutrons, and 2 electrons, and the most common type of lithium atom consists of 3 protons, 4 neutrons, and 3 electrons. If this listing of the fundamental particles is continued for the

* Adapted from D. H. Andrews and R. J. Kokes, *Fundamental Chemistry* (New York: John Wiley and Sons, Inc., 1962), pp. 9–10.

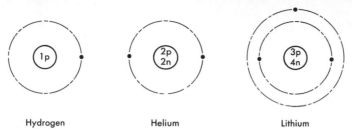

Hydrogen   Helium   Lithium

Fig. 1-1. Planetary models of various atoms. The black dots represent electrons.

remaining elements, a graded series is formed in which the nuclei of the atoms contain from 1 to 103 protons plus a slightly larger number of neutrons. The number of protons in the nucleus is called the **atomic number** of the element; for our 3 examples, then, the atomic numbers are 1, 2, and 3, respectively. A convenient way of representing the elements consists of the symbol for that element, a subscript giving the atomic number of the element, and a superscript giving the total number of protons and neutrons in the nucleus. Thus, the 3 elements in Fig. 1-1 and also their individual atoms, are designated by the symbols $_1H^1$, $_2He^4$, and $_3Li^7$.

Isotopes

Although ordinary hydrogen is largely $_1H^1$, careful analyses have demonstrated the presence of 2 other varieties of the element with slightly different properties. The atomic structures for these 3 varieties are shown in Fig. 1-2. It can be seen that they differ only in the number of neutrons in the nucleus. Forms of an element with the same nuclear charge but with different numbers of neutrons in the nucleus are called **isotopes;** other examples are $_3Li^6$, $_3Li^7$; $_6C^{12}$, $_6C^{14}$; and $_8O^{16}$, $_8O^{17}$, $_8O^{18}$. The isotopes of hydrogen each bear a different name, but this practice is not continued for the heavier elements.

Atomic Weight

A list of the 103 elements, along with their symbols, atomic numbers, and atomic weights, is given in Table 1-1. The atomic weights are derived in the following way. It would be inconvenient to use the absolute weights of the atoms in laboratory work; the hydrogen atom weighs 1.67×10^{-24} g, for example, and it would be impossible to measure out such a small quantity of matter. Therefore, a set of useful weights has been devised for the elements in which relative atomic weights are assigned to the elements, starting with a value near 1 for hydrogen, in an order parallel to the absolute weights of their atoms. The scale has been defined with respect to several different elements in the past. At the present time, the **atomic weight** of an element is defined as the weight of a representative atom of that element relative to the

Fig. 1-2. The three isotopes of hydrogen.

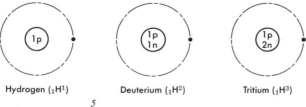

Hydrogen ($_1H^1$)   Deuterium ($_1H^2$)   Tritium ($_1H^3$)

Table 1-1

TABLE OF ATOMIC WEIGHTS (Based on Carbon-12)

Element	Symbol	Atomic Number	Atomic Weight	Element	Symbol	Atomic Number	Atomic Weight
Actinium	Ac	89	[227]c	Mercury	Hg	80	200.59
Aluminum	Al	13	26.9815	Molybdenum	Mo	42	95.94
Americium	Am	95	[243]c	Neodymium	Nd	60	144.24
Antimony	Sb	51	121.75	Neon	Ne	10	20.183
Argon	Ar	18	39.948	Neptunium	Np	93	[237]c
Arsenic	As	33	74.9216	Nickel	Ni	28	58.71
Astatine	At	85	[210]c	Niobium	Nb	41	92.906
Barium	Ba	56	137.34	Nitrogen	N	7	14.0067
Berkelium	Bk	97	[249]c	Nobelium	No	102	[254]c
Beryllium	Be	4	9.0122	Osmium	Os	76	190.2
Bismuth	Bi	83	208.980	Oxygen	O	8	15.9994a
Boron	B	5	10.811a	Palladium	Pd	46	106.4
Bromine	Br	35	79.909b	Phosphorus	P	15	30.9738
Cadmium	Cd	48	112.40	Platinum	Pt	78	195.09
Calcium	Ca	20	40.08	Plutonium	Pu	94	[242]c
Californium	Cf	98	[251]c	Polonium	Po	84	[210]c
Carbon	C	6	12.01115a	Potassium	K	19	39.102
Cerium	Ce	58	140.12	Praseodymium	Pr	59	140.907
Cesium	Cs	55	132.905	Promethium	Pm	61	[147]c
Chlorine	Cl	17	35.453b	Protactinium	Pa	91	[231]c
Chromium	Cr	24	51.996b	Radium	Ra	88	[226]c
Cobalt	Co	27	58.9332	Radon	Rn	86	[222]c
Copper	Cu	29	63.54	Rhenium	Re	75	186.2
Curium	Cm	96	[247]c	Rhodium	Rh	45	102.905
Dysprosium	Dy	66	162.50	Rubidium	Rb	37	85.47
Einsteinium	Es	99	[254]c	Ruthenium	Ru	44	101.07
Erbium	Er	68	167.26	Samarium	Sm	62	150.35
Europium	Eu	63	151.96	Scandium	Sc	21	44.956
Fermium	Fm	100	[253]c	Selenium	Se	34	78.96
Fluorine	F	9	18.9984	Silicon	Si	14	28.086a
Francium	Fr	87	[223]c	Silver	Ag	47	107.870b
Gadolinium	Gd	64	157.25	Sodium	Na	11	22.9898
Gallium	Ga	31	69.72	Strontium	Sr	38	87.62
Germanium	Ge	32	72.59	Sulfur	S	16	32.064a
Gold	Au	79	196.967	Tantalum	Ta	73	180.948
Hafnium	Hf	72	178.49	Technetium	Tc	43	[99]c
Helium	He	2	4.0026	Tellurium	Te	52	127.60
Holmium	Ho	67	164.930	Terbium	Tb	65	158.924
Hydrogen	H	1	1.00797a	Thallium	Tl	81	204.37
Indium	In	49	114.82	Thorium	Th	90	232.038
Iodine	I	53	126.9044	Thulium	Tm	69	168.934
Iridium	Ir	77	192.2	Tin	Sn	50	118.69
Iron	Fe	26	55.847b	Titanium	Ti	22	47.90
Krypton	Kr	36	83.80	Tungsten	W	74	183.85
Lanthanum	La	57	138.91	Uranium	U	92	238.03
Lawrencium	Lw	103	[257]c	Vanadium	V	23	50.942
Lead	Pb	82	207.19	Xenon	Xe	54	131.30
Lithium	Li	3	6.939	Ytterbium	Yb	70	173.04
Lutetium	Lu	71	174.97	Yttrium	Y	39	88.905
Magnesium	Mg	12	24.312	Zinc	Zn	30	65.37
Manganese	Mn	25	54.9380	Zirconium	Zr	40	91.22
Mendelevium	Md	101	[256]c				

Adapted from *Chemical and Engineering News,* November 20, 1961, p. 43.

a The atomic weight varies because of natural variations in the isotopic composition of the element. The observed ranges are boron, ±0.003; carbon, ±0.00005; hydrogen, ±0.00001; oxygen, ±0.0001; silicon, ±0.001; sulfur, ±0.003.

b The atomic weight is believed to have an experimental uncertainty of the following magnitude: bromine, ±0.002; chlorine, ±0.001; chromium, ±0.001; iron, ±0.003; silver, ±0.003. For other elements the last digit given is believed to be reliable to ±0.5.

c A value given in brackets is the mass number of the isotope of longest known lifetime.

weight of a $_6C^{12}$ atom assigned the integral value 12.* The units for the atomic weight scale are called atomic mass units (a.m.u.). On the scale just defined, the atomic weight of hydrogen is 1.00797 a.m.u., that of helium is 4.0026 a.m.u., and that of lithium is 6.939 a.m.u. The mass of the proton on this scale is 1.0073 a.m.u. and the mass of the neutron is 1.0087 a.m.u. Since these masses are very close to the value 1 and since the mass of the electron is small enough to be neglected, the atomic weights of individual isotopes should have very nearly integral values. Many elements, as they occur in nature, consist of largely one isotope, and the atomic weights of these elements are in fact very close to integers (e.g., H, He, N, O, and F). Other elements, as they occur in nature, consist of mixtures of isotopes. Ordinary magnesium, for example, contains 78.7% of $_{12}Mg^{24}$, 10.1% of $_{12}Mg^{25}$, and 11.2% of $_{12}Mg^{26}$; the atomic weight of magnesium, 24.312, is a proportional average of the atomic weights of the isotopes present. The atomic weight of ordinary carbon is 12.01115 and not 12 for the same reason.

Atomic weights are useful to the chemist in that they permit him to work in a quantitative fashion with weighable quantities of matter. A weight in grams of an element numerically equal to the atomic weight of that element is called a **gram atomic weight,** or a **gram atom.** A gram atom of each and every element contains the same number of atoms, since the atomic weights are assigned in proportion to the masses of single atoms. The number of particles in a gram atom of an element, 6.02×10^{23}, is known as **Avogadro's Number.**

In practice, the symbols we use for the elements have three meanings. The symbol Li, for example, stands for the element lithium in a general way; it stands for a single atom of lithium; and it also stands for a gram atom of lithium. If we know that 1 atom of lithium reacts with 1 atom of hydrogen, then we know from our definitions that 1 gram atom of lithium will react with 1 gram atom of hydrogen, and also that 6.939 g of lithium will react with exactly 1.008 g of hydrogen.

RADIOACTIVITY

In 1896, the French scientist Becquerel found that the element uranium and its salts were able to produce an image on a photographic plate and that this exposure could take place through thick layers of paper and other materials. Shortly afterward, Marie and Pierre Curie discovered two other elements capable of the same action, polonium and radium. We recognize now that these elements, called radioactive elements, emit one or more of 3 types of penetrating rays: α rays, which are composed of streams of α particles (positively charged helium atoms stripped of their 2 planetary electrons); β rays, composed of electrons; and γ rays, composed of short-wave-length X-rays. These rays originate in the nuclei of the radioactive atoms. The nucleus is thought to be in an unstable state, and the ejection of the α, β, and γ rays leads to a more stable nucleus.

Most of the naturally occurring elements are not radioactive. All of the elements, however, have 1 or more isotopes which are radioactive; these are prepared synthetically today in nuclear reactors or in cyclotrons (several of the synthetic radioactive elements are listed in Table 1-1, identified by the superscript ^{c}). Since radioactive elements are easy to detect in very low con-

---

* 12 = 12.0000 · · · · · · · ; similarly, other integral values are indicated by an underscore.

centrations, they are often used to "tag" molecules. For example, the fate of aspirin in the human body has been determined by tagging aspirin with a radioactive isotope of carbon, $_6C^{14}$; the excreta of the test subject are then examined for radioactivity, and the radioactive products are isolated and identified (in this case, the products happen to be salicylic and gentisic acids).

Radiation has a profound disruptive effect on the chemistry of living organisms and general exposure to radiation from radioactive elements or from nuclear explosions can be fatal. The selective irradiation of malignant tissue to destroy it (a technique used in cancer therapy) is another example, on the other hand, of the controlled and beneficial use of radioactivity.

THE PERIODIC TABLE

By the middle of the nineteenth century, it had been recognized that members of certain groups of elements—such as lithium, sodium, and potassium or chlorine, bromine, and iodine—have very similar properties. Considerable effort was then expended to devise a general scheme to correlate the properties of the then-known elements. The most useful arrangement of this type, the **Periodic Table,** was developed by the Russian chemist Mendeleev in 1869. In the periodic table, the elements are listed in order of their atomic numbers and arranged in such a way that similarities become apparent; a modern version is given in Table 1-2. The vertical columns, called **groups,** contain elements with similar properties, which usually vary in a systematic way from top to bottom. Group I, for example, contains highly reactive elements called the alkali metals. They all react violently with water, chlorine, etc., and the rates of these reactions increase with increasing atomic number. The horizontal rows of the table, called **periods,** contain series of elements in which the chemical properties change in discrete steps. For example, in the third period, the first 3 elements (Na, Mg, and Al) are metals, and they appear in order of decreasing reactivity with a reagent such as water. The next 4 elements are nonmetals, and they are listed in order of increasing reactivity with a reagent such as sodium. The last element, argon, is rather unreactive, and as we shall see later, it represents the logical end of a period in the periodic table. This arrangement of the elements is not an accident; instead, it is a direct consequence of the structures of the atoms.

THE ELECTRONIC CONFIGURATION OF THE ATOMS

The electrons of an atom are not distributed uniformly about the nucleus, nor are they distributed randomly. They occupy, in fact, certain fixed orbits (or shells) of different energies and these orbits contain certain fixed numbers of electrons. In Fig. 1-1, for example, the third electron of lithium was not placed in the shell already containing 2 electrons, but it was placed in a second shell. This second shell can contain a maximum of 8 electrons. Since the number of electrons in an atom equals the number of protons (the atomic number), we readily see from the periodic table that all the electrons of the elements up to neon will fit into these 2 electron shells. Sodium, the first element of the third period, contains 1 electron in a third shell.

Actually, all electron shells beyond the first one are further divided into subshells containing electrons that differ slightly in energy. The second shell is made up of 1 subshell containing a maximum of 2 electrons (designated an s subshell) and a second subshell at a higher energy that can hold a

Table 1-2

THE PERIODIC TABLE

Metalloids and Nonmetals — Transition Metals

Period	I	II												III	IV	V	VI	VII	VIII
1	1 H Hydrogen																		2 He Helium
2	3 Li Lithium	4 Be Beryllium												5 B Boron	6 C Carbon	7 N Nitrogen	8 O Oxygen	9 F Fluorine	10 Ne Neon
3	11 Na Sodium	12 Mg Magnesium												13 Al Aluminum	14 Si Silicon	15 P Phosphorus	16 S Sulfur	17 Cl Chlorine	18 Ar Argon
4	19 K Potassium	20 Ca Calcium	21 Sc Scandium	22 Ti Titanium	23 V Vanadium	24 Cr Chromium	25 Mn Manganese	26 Fe Iron	27 Co Cobalt	28 Ni Nickel	29 Cu Copper	30 Zn Zinc		31 Ga Gallium	32 Ge Germanium	33 As Arsenic	34 Se Selenium	35 Br Bromine	36 Kr Krypton
5	37 Rb Rubidium	38 Sr Strontium	39 Y Yttrium	40 Zr Zirconium	41 Nb Niobium	42 Mo Molybdenum	43 Tc Technetium	44 Ru Ruthenium	45 Rh Rhodium	46 Pd Palladium	47 Ag Silver	48 Cd Cadmium		49 In Indium	50 Sn Tin	51 Sb Antimony	52 Te Tellurium	53 I Iodine	54 Xe Xenon
6	55 Cs Cesium	56 Ba Barium	57 La Lanthanum	72 Hf Hafnium	73 Ta Tantalum	74 W Tungsten	75 Re Rhenium	76 Os Osmium	77 Ir Iridium	78 Pt Platinum	79 Au Gold	80 Hg Mercury		81 Tl Thallium	82 Pb Lead	83 Bi Bismuth	84 Po Polonium	85 At Astatine	86 Rn Radon
7	87 Fr Francium	88 Ra Radium	89 Ac Actinium																

Lanthanides (Rare Earth Metals)

58 Ce Cerium	59 Pr Praseodymium	60 Nd Neodymium	61 Pm Promethium	62 Sm Samarium	63 Eu Europium	64 Gd Gadolinium	65 Tb Terbium	66 Dy Dysprosium	67 Ho Holmium	68 Er Erbium	69 Tm Thulium	70 Yb Ytterbium	71 Lu Lutetium

Actinides

90 Th Thorium	91 Pa Protoactinium	92 U Uranium	93 Np Neptunium	94 Pu Plutonium	95 Am Americium	96 Cm Curium	97 Bk Berkelium	98 Cf Californium	99 Es Einsteinium	100 Fm Fermium	101 Md Mendelevium	102 No Nobelium	103 Lw Lawrencium

Adapted from Ernest Grunwald and Russell H. Johnsen, *Atoms, Molecules, and Chemical Change* (Englewood Cliffs, N.J.: Prentice-Hall, 1960).

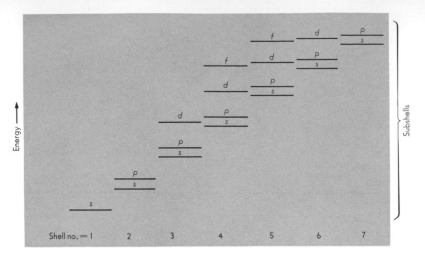

Fig. 1-3. Relative energies of the electron shells and subshells.

maximum of 6 electrons (designated a *p* subshell). The third shell is made up of 3 subshells (called *s*, *p*, and *d*) containing a maximum of 2, 6, and 10 electrons, respectively. A complete listing of the electron subshells, along with an indication of their relative energies, is given in Fig. 1-3. The symbols *s*, *p*, *d*, *f* were introduced by spectroscopists long ago to indicate the character of lines in the emission spectra of the elements (*s*harp, *p*rincipal, *d*iffuse, and *f*undamental).

The systematic development of the electron arrangements for the first 50 elements is given in Table 1-3. The filling of the subshells is straightforward up to argon (A). At this point, our simple order is interrupted; the 4*s* subshell is of lower energy than the 3*d* subshell (Fig. 1-3), and the next 2 electrons go into the fourth shell. The 3*d* subshell is filled next. Note that for elements with an incomplete 3*d* subshell, the electron distribution is irregular and either 1 or 2 electrons are found in the 4*s* subshell. The order in which the remaining subshells are filled is rather complex. A simple scheme for determining the general order is given in Fig. 1-4 to aid the reader in outlining the electronic configurations of the heavier 53 elements not listed in Table 1-3.

To use the chart, distribute the total number of electrons in an atom among the sublevels in the order indicated by the arrows, starting at the top of the figure and working downwards until the electrons are exhausted. The arrows in Fig. 1-4 stop at the 5*f* level, since atoms have not been detected or synthesized yet with electrons in higher energy sublevels. That is, the highest energy electrons of lawrencium ($_{103}$Lw) are in the 5*f* sublevel (note: *f* subshells contain a maximum of 14 electrons).

Fig. 1-4. The electron subshells listed in order of increasing energy.

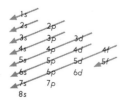

The electronic structures of the atoms (Table 1-3) and the positions of the elements in the periodic table are directly related. A correlation of Tables 1-2 and 1-3 will show, for example, that all the alkali metals (group I) contain a single electron in an outer *s* subshell; further, all the halogens (group VII) contain 5 electrons in an outer *p* subshell, and all the noble gases (group VIII)

MATTER, ATOMS, AND MOLECULES

Table 1-3

ELECTRONIC STRUCTURES OF THE ATOMS

Element	Atomic No.	1s	2s	2p	3s	3p	3d	4s	4p	4d	4f	5s	5p	5d
H	1	1												
He	2	2												
Li	3	2	1											
Be	4	2	2											
B	5	2	2	1										
C	6	2	2	2										
N	7	2	2	3										
O	8	2	2	4										
F	9	2	2	5										
Ne	10	2	2	6										
Na	11	Neon Core of 10 electrons			1									
Mg	12				2									
Al	13				2	1								
Si	14				2	2								
P	15				2	3								
S	16				2	4								
Cl	17				2	5								
A	18				2	6								
K	19	Argon Core of 18 electrons						1						
Ca	20							2						
Sc	21						1	2						
Ti	22						2	2						
V	23						3	2						
Cr	24						5	1						
Mn	25						5	2						
Fe	26						6	2						
Co	27						7	2						
Ni	28						8	2						
Cu	29						10	1						
Zn	30						10	2						
Gd	31						10	2	1					
Ge	32						10	2	2					
As	33						10	2	3					
Se	34						10	2	4					
Br	35						10	2	5					
Kr	36						10	2	6					
Rb	37	Krypton Core of 36 electrons										1		
Sr	38											2		
Y	39									1		2		
Zr	40									2		2		
Cb	41									4		1		
Mo	42									5		1		
Tc	43									6		1		
Ru	44									7		1		
Rh	45									8		1		
Pd	46									10				
Ag	47									10		1		
Cd	48									10		2		
In	49									10		2	1	
Sn	50									10		2	2	

have a filled set of *s* and *p* subshells. In general, in each group of the periodic table, all the members have the same number and distribution of electrons in the outermost shell, and in each period, the number of electrons in this outermost shell increases in a regular way. The periodicity of the elements is therefore accounted for by the periodicity of the electronic structures.

The outermost shell of electrons, called the **valence shell,** determines the chemical behavior of the elements (in the transition metals and the rare earths, however, the valence *shell* often includes the partially filled *d* or *f* subshells of the underlying level). Since the inner shells are not directly involved in chemical bonding (with the exception just noted), they are usually omitted from electron diagrams of the atom. A simple way to represent the atoms is given below.

·Li　:Be　:B·　:C:　:N:　:Ö:　:F:　:Ne:

Usually no attempt is made to distinguish the sublevels in these simple representations of the atom; their chief value lies in focusing attention on the total number of electrons in the valence shell. This number is of importance in determining the types of chemical reactions that an element undergoes.

MODERN THEORY OF THE ATOM

In the 1920's, the French physicist Louis de Broglie proposed that electrons should show wave-like properties; that is, that a beam of electrons should have many of the properties of a beam of light. Within a few years, this view of the electron was verified experimentally, and today the electron microscope, which is based on this principle, may be found in most research laboratories. Also in the 1920's, a model of the atom was developed, based on this concept of the wave nature of electrons, in particular by the German physicist Erwin Schrödinger. Fundamental to the modern picture of the atom is the Schrödinger equation, which describes the properties of the electron

Fig. 1-5. Probability of finding a 1s electron in a shell of unit thickness around the nucleus of an atom plotted against the radius of this shell.

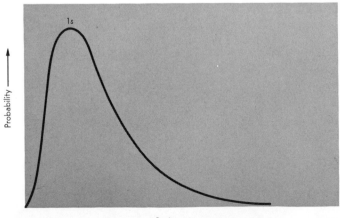

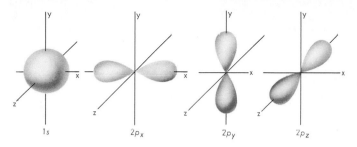

Fig. 1-6. Representations of the 1s and 2p orbitals.

waves in atoms. Solutions to this equation are called wave functions, or **orbitals,** and they are a measure of the probability of finding an electron in a given region in space. That is, the definite, planar orbits of the Bohr (or planetary) atom are abandoned in favor of certain volumes in space in which the electrons move. The orbital that holds the 1s electrons is represented reasonably accurately by a sphere, for example. The probability distribution for a 1s electron as a function of the radius of this sphere is given in Fig. 1-5. It can be seen from the diagram that the probability of finding the electron is a maximum at a certain distance (which would correspond to the radius of the 1s electron shell in the planetary model of the atom) and that the probability drops off slowly, although it never vanishes. Strictly speaking, to account quantitatively for the one electron, the 1s orbital would have to be infinite in size. For representational purposes, however, a radius is usually chosen so there is a 90 per cent probability of finding the electron within the volume determined by that radius.

The shapes of the 1s and 2p orbitals are represented in Fig. 1-6. The p orbitals are shaped somewhat like dumbbells. There are three 2p orbitals, and these are oriented perpendicularly to one another. As we will see in the next few sections, this orientation provides an explanation for the 90° bond angles often found in compounds of the group V and VI elements.

An orbital can be occupied by either 1 electron or by 2 paired electrons, where a pair of electrons is defined as a set with opposite spins; this can be represented conveniently in diagrams of the atom by a pair of opposed arrows, ⥮. The spin of an electron describes its behavior in a magnetic field; a simplified view is that the electron is spinning on its axis in either a clockwise or a counterclockwise position. We can now restate the electronic configurations of the atoms given in Table 1-3 in terms of the atomic orbitals involved (Table 1-4). It should be noted that electrons tend to remain unpaired in orbitals of the same subshell (for example, the p electrons in C, N, and O).

As we shall see later, the modern picture of the atom gives us a much better understanding of matter than the old planetary model. The usefulness of a theory is determined largely by what it can predict, and the new model of the atom is eminently successful in that respect.

CHEMICAL REACTIONS

It is easily verifiable that mixtures of many of the elements are unstable, and that reactions, often of a violent nature, occur when such mixtures are prepared. Furthermore, most of the other elements can be made to react with one another through the use of heat, light, or other forms of energy. The products of these reactions are called **compounds.** The properties

Table 1-4

ELECTRONIC CONFIGURATION
OF THE SECOND-PERIOD ELEMENTS

Element	Electron Distribution		
	1s	2s	2p
Li	⇅	↑	
Be	⇅	⇅	
B	⇅	⇅	↑
C	⇅	⇅	↑ ↑
N	⇅	⇅	↑ ↑ ↑
O	⇅	⇅	⇅ ↑ ↑
F	⇅	⇅	⇅ ⇅ ↑
Ne	⇅	⇅	⇅ ⇅ ⇅

of compounds are usually quite different from those of the constituent elements. For example, the reaction of the highly active, silvery metal sodium with the greenish gas chlorine yields sodium chloride (common table salt), a white, crystalline solid with a very high melting point.

Three elements in the periodic table have never been brought into chemical combination, however, despite intensive efforts to achieve this result. These elements are helium, neon, and argon, members of group VIII of the periodic table (the noble gases). The other elements in the group—krypton, xenon, and radon—are also very inert, and compounds of these elements were not prepared until 1962, and then only under very special conditions. This reluctance of the noble gases to react with the other elements indicates that the electronic configurations of these elements are particularly stable ones. It suggests, furthermore, that the other elements will react in such a way as to gain or approach the nearest noble gas electron configuration. By and large, the facts support this conclusion. The elements listed in the left-hand portion of the periodic table tend to reach the noble gas configuration by loosing electrons, whereas those in the right-hand portion tend to reach that configuration by gaining electrons. For example, energy is required to remove one electron from a lithium atom, $Li \cdot + energy \longrightarrow Li^+ + 1\,e$. Energy is set free, however, when a fluorine atom gains one electron, $: \overset{..}{F} \cdot + 1\,e \longrightarrow : \overset{..}{F} : ^- + energy$. Now if fluorine atoms are mixed with lithium atoms, $Li \cdot + : \overset{..}{F} \cdot \longrightarrow Li^+ : \overset{..}{F} : ^- + energy$, the compound lithium fluoride will be formed with the liberation of considerable energy (a part of this energy comes from the attraction of the particles bearing opposite charges). In this process, lithium has gained the helium electron configuration with a full, or closed, 1s shell, and fluorine has gained the neon electron configuration with closed 2s and 2p subshells.

IONIC COMPOUNDS

The charged particles formed by the loss and gain of electrons from the respective lithium and fluorine atoms are called **ions,** and the product, $Li^+ F^-$, is called an **ionic compound.** Other ionic compounds may be prepared by the reaction of the various metals (chiefly the elements in the left side of the periodic table) with the elements in group VII or with the lighter elements in groups V and VI. The formulas for most of the possible combinations can be determined from the electronic configurations listed in Table 1-3, that is, from the number of electrons that must be lost or gained to reach a noble gas configuration. A number of compounds of this type are given below:

Na$^+$:F̈:$^-$, Sodium fluoride $\qquad$ (Cs$^+$)$_3$:N̈:$^≡$, Cesium nitride

K$^+$:Cl̈:$^-$, Potassium chloride $\qquad$ Ba^{++} :Ö:$^=$, Barium oxide

(Rb$^+$)$_2$:Ö:$^=$, Rubidium oxide $\qquad$ Sc^{+++}(:B̈r:$^-$)$_3$, Scandium bromide

Quite often, however, the ions in a compound only approximate a noble gas configuration. This behavior is especially common among the ions of the transition metals and the rare earths (Table 1-2), although it is reasonably common in the group V and VI elements as well. A few examples are given:

K$^+$:Ö:Ö·$^-$, Potassium superoxide $\qquad$ Fe^{++}(:Cl̈:$^-$)$_2$, Ferrous chloride

Cu$^+$:B̈r:$^-$, Cuprous bromide $\qquad$ Fe^{+++}(:Cl̈:$^-$)$_3$, Ferric chloride

Iron can combine with chlorine in 2 different ratios (as shown in the 2 formulas given above). This combining capacity of an element in an ionic compound is called its **valence;** it is represented normally by a number bearing a $+$ or $-$ sign to represent the charges on the ion. Thus, the elements listed above have the following valences: sodium ($+1$), fluorine (-1), potassium ($+1$), chlorine (-1), rubidium ($+1$), oxygen (-2; rarely -1), cesium ($+1$), nitrogen (-3; also higher values in certain compounds), barium ($+2$), scandium ($+3$), iron ($+2$ and $+3$), etc. In naming compounds of metals with a variable valence, the lower valence state is usually given the ending **-ous** and the upper valence state the ending **-ic;** for example, ferrous and ferric chlorides, cuprous and cupric bromides, etc. The relationship of the valence of an element to the electronic structure of its atoms, and to the group number of the element in the periodic table should be noted. The electronic structures of certain atoms and their ions are given in Table 1-5.

Since the ions in an ionic compound bear opposite charges, they are attracted to one another by a considerable electrostatic force, and a bond can be said to exist between the ions. The charges on the ions are usually spherical in distribution and each positive ion can, therefore, attract several negative ions and each negative ion can attract several positive ions. The result is that in ionic compounds, the charged ions tend to form aggregates in which the ions alternate in the structure. A three-dimensional solid aggregate of this type with a regular structure is called a **crystal**. An example of this regular structure is found in the sodium chloride crystal, a representation of which is given in Fig. 1-7.

Ionic compounds tend to be high-melting, hard substances which are insoluble in nonpolar solvents, but soluble in polar solvents such as water (polar solvents are made up of molecules with partially ionic bonds; see next section). These properties are consistent with the crystalline structures of the

Table 1-5

A COMPARISON OF THE ELECTRONIC STRUCTURES
OF CERTAIN ATOMS AND THEIR IONS

Element	Subshell						
	1s	2s	2p	3s	3p	3d	4s
Li	2	1					
Li+	2						
F	2	2	5				
F−	2	2	6				
Na	2	2	6	1			
Na+	2	2	6				
Cl	2	2	6	2	5		
Cl−	2	2	6	2	6		
Fe	2	2	6	2	6	6	2
Fe++	2	2	6	2	6	6	

ionic compounds. In order to remove an ion from the crystal, or to melt it, a number of bonds must be broken and this process requires a considerable amount of energy. Ionic compounds dissolve in water and in other polar solvents because a number of polar solvent molecules can form weak bonds with each ion. The net energy gained is enough to offset the energy required to remove the ion from the crystal.

COVALENT COMPOUNDS

Atoms can reach the noble gas configuration not only through the gain or loss of electrons, but also through the sharing of electrons ($:\ddot{F}\cdot$ + $:\ddot{F}\cdot \longrightarrow$ $:\ddot{F}:\ddot{F}:$). The shared electrons circulate about both nuclei and they are treated as if they were in the valence shell of each atom. The attractive force of the two nuclei for the shared electrons holds the unit, or molecule, together (where we define a **molecule** as a particle made up of two or more atoms).

Bond formation of this type accounts for the fact that most of the

Fig. 1-7. The arrangement of ions in a crystal of sodium chloride.

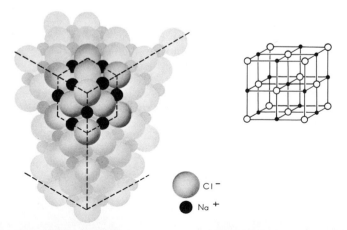

Cl−
Na+

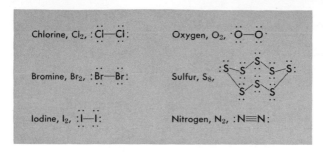

Fig. 1-8. Molecular forms of some common elements in Groups V, VI, and VII of the periodic table. The covalent bonds are represented by a dash, one dash for each electron pair involved.

nonmetals exist in nature not as collections of atoms, but as collections of molecules. The atoms in molecules of the shared-electron type are said to be connected by **covalent bonds** and the substances formed with this type of bonding are called **covalent compounds.** The molecular forms of various nonmetals are given in Fig. 1-8 along with their structures.

The **molecular weight** of a covalently bonded compound is defined as the sum of the atomic weights of all the atoms in the molecule. A second useful unit is the **gram molecular weight,** or **mole** for short, which is a weight in grams of the compound numerically equal to the molecular weight; such a quantity of matter contains 6.02×10^{23} molecules. Very often the term g molecular weight is used when the weight aspect of this quantity is to be emphasized, and the term mole when the number aspect (i.e., the number of particles) is the most important. A summary of these and other chemical units is given in Table 1-6.

Table 1-6

SUMMARY OF CHEMICAL UNITS

		Elements			Compounds
		Examples			Example
Quantity	*Term*	*C*	*Cl*	*Term*	*CCl₄*
Smallest particle	1 atom	1 atom of C	1 atom of Cl	1 molecule	1 molecule of CCl₄
Weight of particle relative to $_6C^{12}$ as $\underline{12}$ a.m.u.	atomic weight	12.01115 a.m.u.	35.453 a.m.u.	molecular weight	12.01115 + 4(35.453) = 153.823 a.m.u.
6.02×10^{23} particles (Avogadro's Number)	1 g atomic weight or 1 g atom	12.01115 g of C	35.453 g of Cl	1 g molecular weight or 1 mole	1 g atom C + 4 g atoms Cl = 12.01115 g + 4(35.453) g = 153.823 g of CCl₄

The absolute weight of a molecule may be found by dividing the g molecular weight by 6.02×10^{23}, just as the absolute weight of an atom may be found by dividing the g atomic weight by the same number.

Covalent molecules may also be formed by the combination of different kinds of atoms, principally from the elements located in the right-hand por-

17

tion of the periodic table. For example, 1 mole of nitrogen reacts with 3 moles of hydrogen to give 2 moles (34.061 g) of ammonia (NH_3).

$$:N\equiv N: \quad [2 :\overset{..}{\underset{.}{N}}\cdot] + 3\text{ H}-\text{H} \quad [6\text{ H}\cdot] \longrightarrow 2 \overset{\text{H}}{\underset{\text{H}}{:N-\text{H}}}$$

It is convenient to visualize the reaction in terms of the electronic structures of the atoms involved, as if the molecules broke up into atoms first, and these reacted to give ammonia. It should be recognized, however, that the reaction as it actually occurs may involve a direct interaction of the intact nitrogen molecules with hydrogen.

The formation of covalent compounds can be profitably reconsidered from the standpoint of the atomic orbitals involved. For example, the formation of a hydrogen molecule from 2 hydrogen atoms can be represented as:

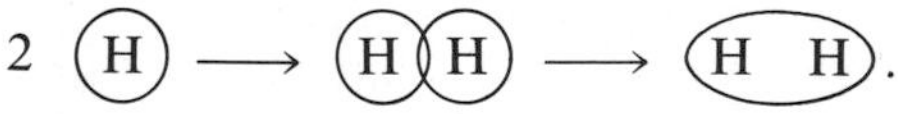

2 (H) $\longrightarrow$ (H)(H) $\longrightarrow$ (H H). The covalent bond is formed by the

coalescing or overlapping of the atomic orbitals. The new orbital is called a **molecular orbital** and it encompasses both of the nuclei in the molecule. There is a certain probability of finding the electron anywhere within the molecular orbital, although the probability is highest in the region between the nuclei; this is represented by a pulling in of the electron cloud from the far side of each atom to the center of the molecular orbital. In a similar fashion, the reaction of hydrogen atoms with nitrogen atoms to form ammonia can be represented as:

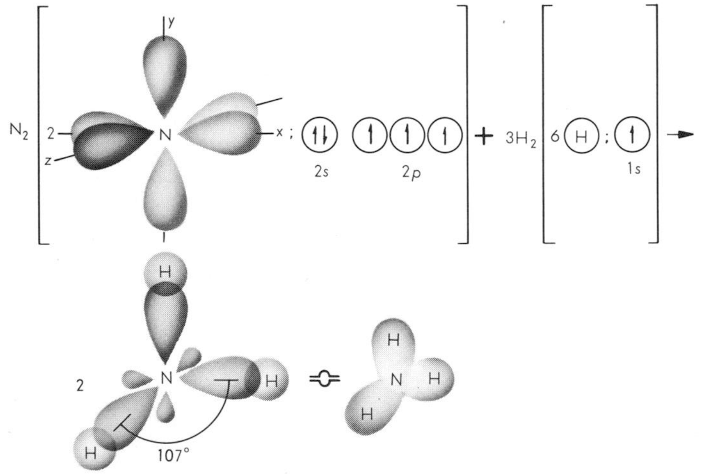

In this case, 3 molecular orbitals are formed by the overlapping of the $1s$ orbitals of hydrogen and the $2p$ orbitals of nitrogen; each molecular orbital can hold a maximum of 2 electrons (of opposite spin). For the sake of clarity, the $1s$ and $2s$ orbitals have been omitted from the figures of the nitrogen atoms, since to a first approximation, they are not involved in the bonding.

The length of a covalent bond is determined by a balance of forces: an attractive force resulting from the orbital overlap (the greater the overlap, the shorter and stronger the bond), and a repulsive force resulting from the charge interaction of the 2 positively charged nuclei. This balance results in a N—H bond length of 1.01×10^{-8} cm in ammonia, and a H—H bond length of 0.74×10^{-8} cm in hydrogen. Molecular orbitals formed by the overlap of s and p atomic orbitals in any combination (e.g., H_2 and NH molecular orbitals) are cylindrically symmetrical about the bond axes; such a molecular orbital is called a σ **(sigma)** orbital, and the bond that it represents is called a σ bond. A different type of molecular orbital, the π **(pi)** orbital, will be discussed in Chapter 3.

One might expect that the angles between the NH bonds in ammonia would be 90°, the value for the angles between the p orbitals of the nitrogen atom. But the experimental value, as determined by electron diffraction experiments, is 107° (all 3 HNH angles are the same). An explanation based on the polarity of the NH bonds has been advanced to account for this discrepancy. The electrons in a bond are shared equally by the 2 atoms only when those atoms are identical, as in H_2, F_2, etc. When different atoms are involved, one of the atoms forming the bond is likely to be more electronegative than the other (the **electronegativity** of an atom is the power of attraction of that atom for the bonding electrons). In this case, the nitrogen atom is more electronegative than the hydrogen atom with the result that in the NH bond, nitrogen bears a slight negative charge and the hydrogen bears a slight positive charge (symbolized by δ^- and δ^+,* as in $\overset{\delta^-}{N}—\overset{\delta^+}{H}$). Bonds of this type are known as **polar bonds**, and they represent a bridge between the symmetrical covalent bond (in H_2, F_2, etc.) and the ionic bond. To return to the HNH bond angles in the ammonia molecule, it has been proposed that the abnormally large bond angles (107°) result from the mutual repulsions of the 3 partially charged hydrogen atoms in the molecule. Some support for this argument comes from a study of the bond angles in the hydrides of 3 other group V elements. If our reasoning concerning the bond angles in ammonia is correct, the hydrides of these heavier elements should have bond angles nearer the theoretical value of 90° since these elements—phosphorus, arsenic, and antimony—are less electronegative than nitrogen, and since they have larger atomic radii (which would lead to greater hydrogen-hydrogen distances in the hydrides). The experimentally determined bond angles for these hydrides are indeed very close to the theoretical value; the experimental values are 93° for phosphine (PH_3), 92° for arsine (AsH_3), and 91° for stibine (SbH_3).

The reaction of hydrogen with oxygen to form water (H_2O) is similar to the hydrogen-nitrogen reaction outlined in this section and the details of the process are left to the reader as an exercise.

Covalent Compounds of Carbon

We might expect, in view of the distribution of valence electrons in the carbon atom ($2s$ ⑪ $2p$ ①①), that the derivatives of carbon would be divalent, where the **valence** of a covalently bonded atom is defined as the number of electron-pair bonds that it forms. In its stable compounds, however, carbon

* The Greek letter delta is often used to signify a small amount or a small change.

is predominantly tetravalent, and in compounds such as CH_4, CCl_4, etc., all 4 bonds are identical. These facts concerning the compounds of carbon are accounted for by the modern theories of bonding in the following way.

The electronic configurations listed in Tables 1-3 and 1-4 are the **ground state** configurations of the atoms, that is, the configurations of lowest energy. Other configurations can be obtained if enough energy is supplied; atoms with these different electronic configurations are said to be in an **excited state.** For example, in one of the excited states of the hydrogen atom, the electron is in a $2p$ orbital, whereas in the ground state, as we have seen from Table 1-3, it is in the $1s$ orbital. If energy is supplied to a carbon atom, one of the $2s$ electrons is "promoted" to a $2p$ orbital to give a carbon atom in an excited state. Thus: C(Ground State $2s$ ⑪ $2p$ ①①○) ⟶ C(Excited State $2s$ ① $2p$ ①①①). Four orbitals are now available and 4 bonds could in principle be formed with hydrogen. Considerable energy is released during the formation of a covalent bond, and the energy available from the formation of the 2 "extra" bonds to carbon would outweigh the energy required to promote a $2s$ electron to the $2p$ level. The explanation is still incomplete, however, because it would lead us to suspect that, in a molecule such as CH_4, 3 of the C—H bonds would be separated by 90° (the angle separating the p orbitals in the atom) and that the fourth C—H bond, involving the overlap of two s atomic orbitals, would have no particular angular dependence. We know, however, that all 4 bonds in CH_4 are identical and that the 4 bonds are separated by an angle of 109°28'. A second modification is required, and in this modification the $2s$ and the three $2p$ orbitals are combined to give a set of 4 equivalent orbitals, each with $1/4$ s character and $3/4$ p character: $2s$ ① $2p$ ①①① ⟶ sp^3 ①①①①. The four equivalent sp^3 orbitals are then used in bond formation:

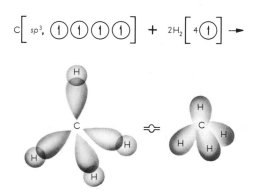

that is, in chemical terms, C + 2 H_2 ⟶ CH_4.

Orbitals formed by the combination of different types of orbitals are called **hybrid orbitals;** those of carbon that we have just discussed are known as sp^3 hybrid orbitals, in view of the type and number combined. The shape of an sp^3 orbital is shown in Fig. 1-9. The sp^3 orbital is greatly concentrated in the bond direction and it forms stronger bonds than a p orbital. Theory predicts that four sp^3 orbitals should be directed to the corners of a tetrahedron and that sp³ bonds should form an angle of 109°28′ (the value calculated from a regular tetrahedron). This is precisely the value that has been found by electron diffraction studies for the bond angles in CH_4 and related compounds. We shall make use of this bond angle in discussing the geometry of carbon compounds in Chapter 3.

The Physical Properties of Covalent Compounds

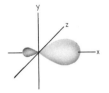

Fig. 1-9. An sp⁰ orbital (on the x axis).

The forces of attraction between adjacent covalent molecules are weak, and as a result most covalent compounds are gases, liquids of low boiling point, or solids with low melting points. Within this class, polar covalent compounds usually have higher boiling points and melting points than nonpolar compounds because of the electrostatic attraction of opposite charges. In contrast to these properties, the ionic compounds have very high boiling and melting points as mentioned earlier. The physical properties of the compounds listed in Table 1-7 illustrate these points.

Table 1-7

PHYSICAL PROPERTIES OF CERTAIN
COVALENT AND IONIC COMPOUNDS

| | | | | | Solubility in: | |
| | | | Melting Point | Boiling Point | Polar[a] Liquid | Nonpolar[b] Liquid |
Compound	Formula	Type of Bonding				
Hydrogen	H_2	Covalent nonpolar	−259° C	−253° C	——	——
Chlorine	Cl_2	Covalent nonpolar	−102° C	−35° C	——[c]	Soluble
Ammonia	NH_3	Covalent polar	−78° C	−33° C	Soluble	Soluble
Sulfur dichloride	SCl_2	Covalent polar	−78° C	59° C	——[c]	Soluble
Beryllium chloride	$Be^{++}(Cl^-)_2$	Ionic	440° C	520° C	Soluble	Insoluble
Lithium fluoride	Li^+F^-	Ionic	870° C	1670° C	Soluble	Insoluble

[a] Water (H_2O), for example.
[b] Carbon disulfide (CS_2) or hexane (C_6H_{14}), for example.
[c] The compound reacts with water and related solvents.

Chemical Reactions

In the last chapter, it was pointed out that most of the elements enter into chemical combination to form various ionic and covalent compounds. In this chapter, we shall be concerned with the further chemical reactions of these compounds, both with the elements and with other compounds. A very large number of combinations is possible—in fact, literally millions of chemical reactions are known. Here, obviously, we can discuss only the more important of these reactions; the references given at the end of this volume should be consulted for a more complete listing of others.

THE OXIDES

Virtually every element in the periodic table reacts with oxygen, and the products, called **oxides,** are of considerable theoretical and practical importance. The formulas for a few typical oxides are given in Table 2-1. A few of these oxides are widely distributed on earth: Water requires no comment; carbon dioxide is found in the atmosphere and also in the form of calcium carbonate in marine shells, limestone, and marble; silicon dioxide is found in the pure state as quartz and sand, and in the bound state in most rocks.

Table 2-1

OXIDES OF SOME OF THE MORE COMMON ELEMENTS

Water (H_2O)	Nitric oxide (NO)	Silicon dioxide (SiO_2)
Hydrogen peroxide (H_2O_2)	Nitrogen dioxide (NO_2)	Phosphorus pentoxide (P_2O_5)
Lithium oxide (Li_2O)	Dinitrogen tetroxide (N_2O_4)	Sulfur dioxide (SO_2)
Beryllium oxide (BeO)	Fluorine oxide (F_2O)	Sulfur trioxide (SO_3)
Boric oxide (B_2O_3)	Sodium oxide (Na_2O)	Chlorine monoxide (Cl_2O)
Carbon monoxide (CO)	Magnesium oxide (MgO)	Titanium dioxide (TiO_2)
Carbon dioxide (CO_2)	Aluminum oxide (Al_2O_3)	Zinc oxide (ZnO)
Nitrous oxide (N_2O)		

The oxides formed from the elements in the far left of the periodic table are ionic compounds, and the formulas, $(Li^+)_2:\overset{..}{\underset{..}{O}}:^=$, for example, are satisfactorily accounted for by the principles of bonding developed in the last chapter. The oxides formed from the elements in the upper right of the periodic table are covalently bonded compounds, and their formulas and structures ($H:\overset{..}{\underset{..}{O}}:H$, $:\overset{..}{\underset{..}{F}}:\overset{..}{\underset{..}{O}}:\overset{..}{\underset{..}{F}}:$, etc.) are also largely accounted for by those principles.

Certain other covalent compounds, however (in particular compounds of carbon, nitrogen, and oxygen), contain a third type of bond called a **multiple bond.** In this type, 2 or 3 electron pairs are shared by the atoms involved. Examples are carbon monoxide, which contains a triple bond ($:C::O:$, or $:C{\equiv}O:$), carbon dioxide, which contains 2 double bonds ($:\underset{..}{O}{=}C{=}\underset{..}{O}:$), and dinitrogen tetroxide, also with 2 double bonds (see diagram in the next paragraph). If only single bonds were present in these compounds ($:\overset{..}{\underset{..}{C}}:\overset{..}{\underset{..}{O}}:$, for example), the atoms involved would have electron structures quite far removed from those of the noble gases. Atoms of the elements in the second and third periods of the periodic table require 8 valence electrons to reach the noble gas configuration, and in the cases just cited, this "octet" of electrons is gained by multiple electron sharing. Note that pairs of electrons are normally involved in covalent bonding; bonds made up of an odd number of electrons are quite rare.

A few of the oxides of nitrogen and the halogens have rather unusual structures. The molecules NO, NO_2, and ClO_2, for example, contain an odd number of electrons ($\cdot\overset{..}{\underset{..}{N}}::\overset{..}{\underset{..}{O}}:$, $:\overset{..}{\underset{..}{O}}:\overset{..}{N}::\overset{..}{\underset{..}{O}}:$, and $:\overset{..}{\underset{..}{O}}:\overset{..}{\underset{..}{Cl}}:\overset{..}{\underset{..}{O}}:$). Molecules of this type are called **free radicals.** Free radicals have many properties in common with halogen atoms. For one, they tend to gain electrons in chemical reactions: $Na\cdot + \cdot\overset{..}{N}::\overset{..}{\underset{..}{O}}: \longrightarrow Na^+(:\overset{..}{N}::\overset{..}{\underset{..}{O}}:)^-$. For another, at low temperatures, they often double up to form a molecule with an even number of electrons:

$$2 \ \overset{\overset{..}{O}}{\underset{:\overset{..}{O}:}{\diagdown}}N\cdot \longrightarrow \overset{\overset{..}{O}}{\underset{:\overset{..}{O}:}{\diagdown}}N:N\overset{\diagup\overset{..}{O}:}{\diagdown_{\overset{..}{O}:}} = N_2O_4$$

The oxides formed from the elements in the center part of the periodic table are unusual for quite other reasons. Boric oxide, aluminum oxide, silicon

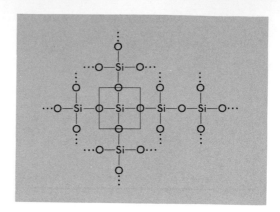

Fig. 2-1. Schematic diagram of the SiO_2 giant molecule. The repeat unit is shown within the rectangle; the dotted lines imply attachment to other SiO_2 groups.

dioxide, and oxides of most of the other elements in this group exist as giant molecules containing many thousands of atoms. The silicon dioxide molecule, for example, consists of a very large network of alternating oxygen and silicon atoms (see Fig. 2-1). The molecule is highly regular; it is made up of chains of a small "repeat unit," which in Fig. 2-1 is enclosed in a rectangle. Since each oxygen is shared by 2 silicon atoms (the rectangles shown bisect each oxygen), the repeat unit is SiO_2. The giant molecule, therefore, has a molecular formula of $(SiO_2)_n$, where n is some very large number. For convenience, oxides of this type are referred to by their repeat unit; that is, silicon dioxide (quartz) = SiO_2, and aluminum oxide = Al_2O_3. As a result of their extremely high molecular weights, these oxides are completely insoluble in ordinary solvents and they have very high melting points; because of these properties, they are used as insulation linings in furnaces.

A FEW CALCULATIONS

The formulas we have been using represent *pure* compounds—that is, substances containing only a single kind of molecule. The ratio of carbon atoms to oxygen atoms in a large sample of carbon dioxide (CO_2) is the same, therefore, as the ratio in the individual molecules, namely 1 to 2. It also follows that the weight ratio of the 2 elements in the large sample is the same as the weight ratio in the individual molecules. Thus:

Weight ratio of C to O in 1 molecule of CO_2 =

$$\frac{1 \text{ carbon atom} \times \dfrac{12 \text{ a.m.u.}}{1 \text{ carbon atom}}}{2 \text{ oxygen atoms} \times \dfrac{16 \text{ a.m.u.}}{1 \text{ oxygen atom}}} = \frac{12 \text{ a.m.u. of C}}{32 \text{ a.m.u. of O}} = \frac{1}{2.67} = \frac{0.375}{1} = \frac{0.38 \text{ a.m.u. of C}}{1 \text{ a.m.u. of O}}$$

[Note: $\frac{12 \text{ apples}}{1 \text{ dozen}}$ is read "12 apples per dozen" where the word *per* implies division.]

The weight ratio of C to O in 1 mole of CO_2 =

$$\frac{1 \text{ g atom of C} \times \dfrac{12 \text{ g of C}}{1 \text{ g atom of C}}}{2 \text{ g atoms of O} \times \dfrac{16 \text{ g of O}}{1 \text{ g atom of O}}} = \frac{12 \text{ g of C}}{32 \text{ g of O}} = \frac{0.38 \text{ g C}}{1 \text{ g O}}$$

That is, the weight ratio in any quantity of a pure compound can be calculated simply from the formula of the compound. Calculate the weight ratios of nitrogen to oxygen in N_2O, NO, NO_2, and N_2O_4. (Answers: 1.75,

0.875, 0.437, 0.437, respectively.) Now divide these numbers by the lowest value (.437). (Answers: 4, 2, 1, 1; this type of calculation, showing that the elements react in integral ratios by weight, provided one of the foundations —The Law of Multiple Proportions—for the atomic theory of matter as developed in the nineteenth century.)

Using a similar approach, we can calculate the percentage by weight of carbon in CO_2.

$$\% \text{ of x in y} = \text{parts of x per 100 parts of y} = \frac{\text{parts x by wt}}{1 \text{ part y by wt}} \text{ times } 100 - \frac{\text{wt of x}}{\text{wt of y}}(100)$$

From the formula of carbon dioxide:

$$\% \text{ C in } CO_2 = \frac{12 \text{ g C}}{44 \text{ g } CO_2}(100) = 27.3; \quad \% \text{ O in } CO_2 = 72.7$$

Carbon dioxide, therefore, is composed of 27.3% C and 72.7% O. Calculate the composition of NO, NO_2, and N_2O_4. (Answers: 46.7% N, 53.3% O; 30.4% N, 69.6% O; and 30.4% N, 69.6% O, respectively.)

The last calculation is often reversed, and the problem becomes one of determining the formula of a compound from the composition data. For example, what is the formula of a compound that contains, by analysis, 30.4% N and 69.6% O? To solve this sort of problem, it is convenient to use an arbitrary amount of the compound (100 g, for example) and to calculate the gram atom ratio of the elements in that amount:

100 g of the compound contains 30.4 g N and 69.6 g O

$$100 \text{ g contains } \frac{30.4}{14.0} = 2.17 \text{ g atoms of N}$$

$$100 \text{ g contains } \frac{69.6}{16.0} = 4.35 \text{ g atoms of O}$$

The ratio is 2.17 to 4.35, or 0.499; within experimental error, this value is 0.5, and the ratio, therefore, is $\frac{1}{2}$ to 1. This value is also the ratio of the atoms in the molecule (remember that a gram atom of every element has the same number of atoms). Since a molecule cannot contain a fraction of an atom, the atom ratio is really 1 to 2, and the simplest formula we can have for this compound is N_1O_2, or NO_2.

In the absence of further information, we cannot tell whether the formula of our compound is NO_2, N_2O_4, N_3O_6, or some higher formula with the same *ratio* of nitrogen to oxygen. We need to know the *molecular weight* of the compound to decide this point. There are several experimental methods for getting approximate values of the molecular weights of compounds. Usually, we use solutions of the compounds in some liquid. Certain properties of the solutions, such as the melting point, boiling point, and vapor pressure, are found to depend on the number of molecules in solution (and for a fixed weight of compound this number depends on the molecular weight of the compound). If, by one of these methods, we learn that the molecular weight of our compound $(NO_2)_n$ is 92, then we know that n = 2, and the compound is N_2O_4. If molecular weight information is not available, only the simplest formula, NO_2, is reported; this simplest formula is called the **empirical formula** of the compound. Problem: Calculate the empirical formulas of compounds A and B from the analytical data given.

Compound A: S, 40%; O, 60%. Compound B: P, 43.7%; O, 56.3%. (Answers: SO_3 and P_2O_5.)

CHEMICAL EQUATIONS

A considerable amount of information concerning chemical reactions is summarized in a chemical equation just as a considerable amount of mathematical information is summarized in an algebraic equation. Both types of equations must be balanced, however, before useful information can be obtained. The statement of fact that hydrogen reacts with oxygen to form water could be written as $H_2 + O_2 \longrightarrow H_2O$, but the equation would not be balanced (the 2 sides are not equal). The right side tells us that 2 hydrogen atoms are present per oxygen atom. Two-to-one then must have been the ratio in which they reacted, and, therefore, this must also be the ratio of atoms on the left side of the equation. That is, 4 hydrogen atoms, or 2 hydrogen molecules, must have reacted with 1 oxygen molecule: $2 H_2 + O_2 \longrightarrow H_2O$. The equation is still not complete, however, since 2 molecules of hydrogen and 1 molecule of oxygen yield not 1 molecule of water, but 2: $2 H_2 + O_2 \longrightarrow 2 H_2O$. The equation is now balanced; the 2 sides contain the same number of hydrogen atoms and the same number of oxygen atoms. Our equation is now consistent with the law of conservation of mass; that is, the total mass of the reactants equals the total mass of the products. We can now use the equation to calculate weight relations in chemical reactions. Our balanced equation tells us: (1) that hydrogen reacts with oxygen to form water, (2) that 2 molecules of hydrogen react with 1 molecule of oxygen to form 2 molecules of water, and (3) that 2 moles of hydrogen react with 1 mole of oxygen to give 2 moles of water. From our knowledge of atomic weights, molecular weights, and gram molecular weights, we can calculate, in addition, that 4.03 g of hydrogen react with exactly 32.00 g of oxygen to yield 36.03 g of water. These weight relations are very important in laboratory work since through their use, we can readily calculate the quantity of one chemical needed to react completely with a given quantity of another. It must be stressed, however, that the calculations can be carried out only on balanced equations. The balancing of equations is generally a process of trial and error, as we have indicated in the hydrogen-oxygen example. The reader should balance the following equations:

(A) $S_8 + O_2 \longrightarrow SO_2$ (B) $P_4 + O_2 \longrightarrow P_2O_3$ (C) $P_2O_5 + H_2O \longrightarrow H_3PO_4$

(Answers: The coefficients reading from left to right are 1, 8, 8 for A; 1, 3, 2 for B; and 1, 3, 2 for C.)

REDOX REACTIONS

Redox reactions are chemical reactions involving both reduction and oxidation. Oxidation originally meant reaction with oxygen, but today, in a chemical context, it means the loss of electrons by a molecule or atom: $Li\cdot \longrightarrow Li^+ + 1 e$. Reduction, on the other hand, means the gain of electrons by molecules or atoms, $:\ddot{C}l\cdot + 1\ e \longrightarrow :\ddot{C}l:^-$. The balancing of redox reactions involving only simple ions is straightforward (the reactants and products must, of course, be known): $Fe^{+++} + Sn^{++} \longrightarrow Fe^{++} + Sn^{++++}$. Simple inspection here indicates the proper coefficients needed for a balanced equation, since each stannous ion (Sn^{++}) loses 2 electrons (negative charges), whereas each ferric ion (Fe^{+++}) gains 1 electron. The balanced equation therefore reads: $2\ Fe^{+++} + Sn^{++} \longrightarrow 2\ Fe^{++} + Sn^{++++}$.

The reactions of the elements are by and large redox reactions and the balancing of these equations follows from the electron configurations of the elements and their ions. In the reaction of iron with chlorine, for example,

$$Fe + Cl_2 \longrightarrow Fe^{++} + 2\ :\ddot{C}l:^-$$

$$\overset{+\,2\,e}{}\quad\overset{-\,2\,e}{}$$

the iron atom has lost 2 electrons, and each chlorine atom has gained 1 electron. In this process the iron is oxidized, but it *acts* as a reducing agent (since it donates electrons); the chlorine, on the other hand, is reduced while *acting* as an oxidizing agent (since it gains electrons). Oxidation of one substance must necessarily accompany the reduction of another (hence the use of the single term redox) and the number of electrons lost by the reducing agent must be equal to the number of electrons gained by the oxidizing agent.

The product of the reaction of chlorine with an *excess* of iron is ferrous chloride ($FeCl_2$). If ferrous chloride is treated now with chlorine, the ferrous ion is oxidized to the ferric state: $2\ Fe^{++}(Cl^-)_2 + Cl_2 \longrightarrow 2\ Fe^{+++}(Cl^-)_3$. Many other oxidizing agents can convert ferrous ion into ferric ion; potassium permanganate is an example:

$$5\ Fe^{++}(Cl^-)_2 + K^+MnO_4^- + 8\ HCl \longrightarrow$$
$$5\ Fe^{+++}(Cl^-)_3 + K^+Cl^- + Mn^{++}(Cl^-)_2 + 4\ H_2O$$

When ionic compounds are dissolved in water, the ions have essentially a free existence in solution; this condition can be represented as:

$$\text{solid } Fe^{+++}(Cl^-)_3 \longrightarrow Fe^{+++} + 3\ Cl^-\ \text{(in solution)}$$

This interpretation accounts for the fact that a solution prepared by dissolving 1 mole of Li^+Cl^- and 1 mole of Na^+Br^- in 1 liter of water is identical to a solution prepared from 1 mole of Li^+Br^- and 1 mole of Na^+Cl^-.

With this in mind, we can rewrite our redox reaction to read:

$$5\ Fe^{++} + K^+ + 8\ H^+ + 18\ Cl^- + MnO_4^- \longrightarrow$$
$$5\ Fe^{+++} + K^+ + Mn^{++} + 18\ Cl^- + 4\ H_2O.$$

Since the K^+ and Cl^- ions are not directly involved in the reactions, we can simplify the equation by subtracting these ions from both sides.

$$5\ Fe^{++} + 8\ H^+ + MnO_4^- \longrightarrow 5\ Fe^{+++} + Mn^{++} + 4\ H_2O$$

In this reaction, the ferrous ion is oxidized and the manganese atom is reduced. (Hydrogen and oxygen rarely change valence states in these reactions.) The last equation, as written, is balanced materially (both sides of the equation contain the same number of atoms) and electrically (the sum of the charges is the same on both sides of the equation); the electrical balance indicates that electrons are not created or destroyed, but only transferred from one ion to the other.

Redox reactions involving complex ions and molecules are often difficult to balance by the trial-and-error method. To aid in balancing these equations, and also to aid in understanding the redox principles, the oxidation number concept is often used. The **oxidation number** is a number assigned to an atom or ion to reflect its stage of oxidation. The oxidation number of an element is 0, and that of a simple ion is the valence of the ion. The assignment of oxidation numbers to the atoms in molecules or complex ions is somewhat arbitrary, on the other hand; the method is, in effect, an attempt to apply the simple ionic valence rules to molecules. Molecules are treated as if they contained only ionic bonds, and the electron pair of each bond is assigned to the more electronegative of the atoms making up the bond. The charge that remains on each atom is its oxidation number. In general, the electronegativities of the elements increase from left to right within any period in the periodic table, and from bottom to top in any group (the electronegativity is determined largely by the number of protons in the nucleus, the distance of the valence electrons from the positively charged nucleus, and the number of full electron shells between the nucleus and the valence electrons). Some examples of oxidation numbers are given in Table 2-2. It can be seen that the sum of the oxidation numbers of the atoms in a molecule is 0 and the sum in an ion is equal to the charge on that ion.

Table 2-2

OXIDATION NUMBERS

Atom or Ion	Oxidation Number
Cl in Cl_2	0
Cl^-	-1
Na^+	$+1$
H in H—O—H	$+1$
O in H—O—H	-2
N in NH_3	-3
C in O=C=O	$+4$
Mn in MnO_2	$+4$
Mn in MnO_4^-	$+7$

$$MnO_4^- = \begin{bmatrix} & \overset{\cdot\cdot}{\underset{\cdot\cdot}{O}} : & \\ \cdot\cdot & | & \cdot\cdot \\ : \overset{\cdot\cdot}{\underset{\cdot\cdot}{O}} \!-\! Mn \!-\! \overset{\cdot\cdot}{\underset{\cdot\cdot}{O}} : & \\ & \overset{\cdot\cdot}{\underset{\cdot\cdot}{O}} : & \end{bmatrix}^-$$

A change in the oxidation number of an atom implies a gain or loss of electrons, and the magnitude of this change tells us how many electrons were exchanged. We can demonstrate the value of oxidation numbers in balancing redox reactions by an example in which the permanganate ion (MnO_4^-) is involved.

Suppose that we are to balance the equation for the oxidation of ferrous ion in acidic solutions by permanganate ion. In the laboratory, this reaction could be carried out with ferrous chloride and potassium permanganate, with ferrous sulfate and sodium permanganate, or with some other combination of reagents. In any case, the products of the redox reaction are ferric ion and manganous ion (in oxidation reactions in acid solutions, the manganese atom from the permanganate ion usually ends up in the $+2$ valence state).

$$\overset{+2}{Fe^{++}} + \overset{+7}{MnO_4^-} + H^+ \longrightarrow \overset{+3}{Fe^{+++}} + \overset{+2}{Mn^{++}} + H_2O \quad \longleftarrow \text{Oxidation Numbers}$$

(with $+5\,e$ gained above and $-1\,e$ lost below indicated)

We have indicated in the equation the oxidation numbers and also the number of electrons lost by each ferrous ion and the number gained by each manganese atom. It is obvious that 5 ferrous ions are oxidized by each permanganate ion:

$$5\,Fe^{++} + MnO_4^- + H^+ \longrightarrow 5\,Fe^{+++} + Mn^{++} + H_2O$$

(with $+5\,e$ above and $5(-1\,e)$ below)

The oxygen atoms in acid solutions appear either in the ion or as water; in our example 4 water molecules must be formed. Thus:

$$5\,Fe^{++} + MnO_4^- + H^+ \longrightarrow 5\,Fe^{+++} + Mn^{++} + 4\,H_2O$$

If the hydrogens are now balanced,

$$5\,Fe^{++} + MnO_4^- + 8\,H^+ \longrightarrow 5\,Fe^{+++} + Mn^{++} + 4\,H_2O$$

we find our equation balanced both materially and electrically.

The steps involved in balancing a redox reaction in basic solutions are the same with the exception that the "extra" oxygens in the complex ion must end up as hydroxide ion (OH^-), and occasionally water molecules must be added to the equation to balance the number of protons involved. The following redox reaction carried out in a basic solution should be balanced by the reader to gain a familiarity with the methods involved.

$$CO + MnO_4^- + H_2O \longrightarrow CO_2 + MnO_2 + OH^-$$

(Answer: The coefficients are 3, 2, 1, 3, 2, 2 in the order shown in the equation.)

ACIDS AND BASES

Alchemists of the Middle Ages, in their attempts to classify matter, recognized two groups of compounds that were easy to characterize in terms of their properties. Members of the first group, called acids, have a sour taste, turn certain vegetable coloring materials (indicators) the same color, tend to dissolve metals, and react with members of the second group. Members of the second group, called bases, have a brackish taste, turn indicators a different color, dissolve only a few special metals, and react with acids to give solutions that have neither acidic nor basic properties.

Somewhat later, it was recognized that acids are compounds that are capable of furnishing hydrogen ions and bases are compounds that can furnish hydroxide ions.

$$HCl \longrightarrow H^+ + Cl^- \quad \text{(acid)}$$

$$NaOH \longrightarrow Na^+ + OH^- \quad \text{(base)}$$

It was also recognized that many of the common acids and bases can be prepared by the reaction of water with the oxides of the elements. Bases are prepared, for example, from the oxides of the elements found in the left side of the periodic table:

$$(Li^+)_2O^= + H_2O \longrightarrow 2 \ Li^+OH^- \quad \text{(Lithium hydroxide)}$$

$$Ca^{++}O^= + H_2O \longrightarrow Ca^{++}(OH^-)_2 \quad \text{(Calcium hydroxide)}$$

Very often, the same bases can be prepared from the reaction of the elements themselves with water; for example:

$$2 \ Li + 2 \ H_2O \longrightarrow 2 \ Li^+OH^- + H_2$$

$$Ca + 2 \ H_2O \longrightarrow Ca^{++}(OH^-)_2 + H_2$$

Note that the reactions of the oxides with water are not redox reactions (no changes in the oxidation numbers occur), whereas the reactions of the elements with water are.

On the other hand, oxides of the elements in the right side of the periodic table react with water to form acids:

$$CO_2 + H_2O \longrightarrow H_2CO_3 \left(\text{Carbonic acid; } H-\ddot{O}-\overset{\overset{\ddot{O}}{\|}}{C}-\ddot{O}-H \right)$$

$$SO_2 + H_2O \longrightarrow H_2SO_3 \left(\text{Sulfurous acid; } H-\ddot{O}-\overset{\overset{\ddot{O}:}{|}}{S}-\ddot{O}-H \right)$$

$$SO_3 + H_2O \longrightarrow H_2SO_4 \left(\text{Sulfuric acid; } H-\ddot{O}-\overset{\overset{\ddot{O}:}{|}}{\underset{\underset{\ddot{O}:}{|}}{S}}-\ddot{O}-H \right)$$

$$N_2O_5 + H_2O \longrightarrow 2 \ HNO_3 \left(\text{Nitric acid; } H-\ddot{O}-N\overset{\nearrow O:}{\searrow_{\ddot{O}:}} \right)$$

$$P_2O_5 + 3 \ H_2O \longrightarrow 2 \ H_3PO_4 \left(\text{Phosphoric acid; } H-\ddot{O}-\overset{\overset{\ddot{O}:}{|}}{\underset{\underset{\ddot{O}-H}{|}}{P}}-\ddot{O}-H \right)$$

The oxides of the elements in the center part of the periodic table are either insoluble in water, or they yield hydroxides that have the properties of both weak acids and weak bases (they are called **amphoteric** compounds).

Structurally, H_2SO_4 is a hydroxide, and the question arises, why should $Ca(OH)_2$ be a base and $(HO)_2SO_2$ an acid? The answer has to do with the electronegativities of the Ca and S atoms. Calcium has a low electronegativity, and even in the solid state of calcium hydroxide the calcium is fully ionized, $Ca^{++}(OH^-)_2$. In contrast, the S—O bond is covalent. Since sulfur has a high electronegativity, a large amount of energy would be required to ionize H_2SO_4 in the following sense: $HO^{-+}\overset{\overset{\displaystyle O}{|}}{\underset{|}{S}^+}OH^-$. Instead, the electronega-

tivity of the sulfur augments the electronegativity of the oxygen atoms, and in pure liquid sulfuric acid, as a result, the OH bond is highly polar,

$\overset{\delta^+\ \ \delta^-}{H}\text{—}\overset{\delta^-\ \ \delta^+}{O}\text{—}\overset{\overset{\displaystyle O}{|}}{\underset{\underset{\displaystyle O}{|}}{S}}\text{—}O\text{—}H$; that is, the hydrogen atom has less than an equal share of

the electron pair between hydrogen and oxygen. Compounds of this type tend to give up hydrogen ions readily, leaving the electron pair on the oxygen atom.

A second group of acids of considerable importance is made up of the halogen derivatives of hydrogen; these compounds—HF, HCl, HBr, and HI —are called the **hydrohalic** acids. They can be prepared from the elements $(H_2 + Cl_2 \longrightarrow 2\ HCl)$, but a more convenient method for the 3 heaviest acids involves the **hydrolysis** (reaction with water) of the phosphorus halides: $PBr_3 + 3\ H_2O \longrightarrow 3\ HBr + H_3PO_3$.

The compounds HF, HCl, HBr, and HI are gases at room temperature, whereas H_2SO_4 and HNO_3 are liquids. It is a surprising fact that the pure compounds do not have the properties that we associate with acids. These properties develop only when the compounds are dissolved in water, or in some other very polar solvent. The dissolution is accompanied by the evolution of considerable heat, which, along with other evidence, indicates that a chemical reaction has occurred. This chemical reaction is the transfer of a proton from the acid to the solvent.

$$HNO_3 + H_2\overset{..}{O}\text{:} \longrightarrow H\text{—}\overset{..}{\underset{\underset{\displaystyle H}{|}}{O}}{}^{\pm}H + NO_3^-$$

$$HCl + H_2O \longrightarrow H_3O^+ + Cl^-$$

$$H_2SO_4 + H_2O \longrightarrow H_3O^+ + HSO_4^-$$

It is the **hydronium ions** (H_3O^+) that give the water solutions of these compounds "acidic" properties. The negative ions are not directly involved in reactions of acid solutions, as is shown by the fact that approximately the same amount of heat is liberated when we treat the solutions of any one of the hydrohalic acids with sodium hydroxide:

$$Na^+ + OH^- + H_3O^+(Cl, Br, I^-) \longrightarrow 2\ H_2O + Na^+(Cl, Br, I^-) + heat$$

One characteristic of acids and bases is their ability to neutralize one another. For example, 1 mole of any one of the hydrohalic acids will react with exactly 1 mole of any one of the Group I hydroxides:

$$H_3O^+Cl^- + Na^+OH^- \longrightarrow 2\ H_2O + Na^+Cl^-$$

The product in the example cited is a water solution which has neither acidic nor basic properties, that is, a neutral solution. The solution contains, in fact, only sodium chloride (common table salt). In general, the reactions of acids with bases yield ionic compounds (often called salts) and water:

$$H_3O^+NO_3^- + Li^+OH^- \longrightarrow Li^+NO_3^- + 2\ H_2O$$

$$(H_3O^+)_2SO_4^= + 2\ K^+OH^- \longrightarrow (K^+)_2SO_4^= + 4\ H_2O$$

Examples of salts prepared in this way are given in Table 2-3. The ionic charges are omitted from the formulas to emphasize the ratios in which the elements are bound.

Table 2-3

TYPICAL SALTS

NaI	Sodium iodide	$CaSO_4$	Calcium sulfate
$Ca(NO_3)_2$	Calcium nitrate	$Fe_2(SO_4)_3$	Ferric sulfate
$Al(NO_3)_3$	Aluminum nitrate	$NaHSO_4$	Sodium bisulfate
Na_2CO_3	Sodium carbonate		(or Sodium hydrogen sulfate)
$KHCO_3$	Potassium bicarbonate	K_3PO_4	Potassium phosphate
Li_2SO_3	Lithium sulfite	KH_2PO_4	Potassium dihydrogen phosphate

CONCENTRATION UNITS FOR SOLUTIONS

Molarity

It is often more convenient to use water solutions of acids and bases than the pure compounds. To do this conveniently, we employ a new unit, **molarity** (M), which is the number of moles of a compound dissolved in 1 liter of solution. For example, 1 liter of a one-molar (1 M) solution of nitric acid is prepared by adding water to 1 mole of nitric acid (63 g) until the volume of the solution reaches 1 liter. (This solution is slightly different in concentration from a solution prepared by adding 1 mole of nitric acid to 1 liter of pure water.) It follows from the definition that the product of the molarity of a solution and the volume of that solution (V) is equal to the number of moles of reagent in the system: $M \times V$ = moles. This interconversion of units can be demonstrated readily with the aid of a balanced equation:

$$H_2SO_4 + 2KOH \longrightarrow K_2SO_4 + 2\ H_2O$$

1 mole   2 moles

$\begin{cases} \text{or: 1 liter of 1 } M \text{ solution} + \text{1 liter of 2 } M \text{ solution} \\ \text{or: 1 liter of 1 } M \text{ solution} + \text{2 liters of 1 } M \text{ solution, etc.} \end{cases}$

Normality

One liter of 1 M H_2SO_4 contains twice as many hydrogen ions as one liter of 1 M HCl. We often find it convenient to deal with solutions containing the same number of hydrogen ions or hydroxide ions per liter. For this purpose we make use of a new unit, the **normality** (N). The normality of an acid solution is the number of moles of hydrogen ion present per liter of solution, and the normality of a base solution is the number of moles of hydroxide ion per liter. That is, a solution containing 1 mole of KOH per liter is a 1 normal (or 1 N) solution—as well as a 1 M solution. A solution that contains

1 mole of H_2SO_4 per liter, however, is a 2 N solution—since 2 moles of hydronium ion are supplied by each mole of sulfuric acid. It follows then that 1 liter of any 1 N acid solution will exactly neutralize 1 liter of any 1 N base solution. The **equivalent weight** of an acid is that weight of the substance which furnishes 1 mole of H_3O^+; of a base, that weight which furnishes 1 mole of OH^-. Thus, the equivalent weight of H_2SO_4 is $98/2 = 49$ g, the equivalent weight of NaOH is $40/1 = 40$ g, and the equivalent weight of H_3PO_4 is $98/3 = 32.7$ g. The general formula for this calculation is:

$$\text{Equivalent weight} = \frac{\text{Molecular weight}}{\text{Number of H or OH per molecule}}$$

One equivalent weight of any acid or base diluted to 1 liter final volume with water yields a 1 normal solution of the acid or base. The normality of a solution, therefore, may be defined as the number of equivalent weights in a liter of that solution (eq. wts./l). A convenient formula to use for calculating the amount of one solution required to neutralize another is: $N_{acid} \times$ Vol. of acid solution $= N_{base} \times$ Vol. of base solution. From our definition of normality, the equation states, in effect: Number of equivalents of acid $=$ Number of equivalents of base. It follows from these equations that 1 liter of 5 N HCl will exactly neutralize 2 liters of 2.5 N NaOH, for example.

pH

If all the ions that are not directly involved in a neutralization reaction are subtracted from both sides of the equation, a very simple equation results:

$$H_3O^+Br^- + K^+OH^- \longrightarrow 2\ H_2O + K^+Br^-$$

$$H_3O^+ + OH^- \longrightarrow 2\ H_2O$$

The important reaction in neutralization, then, is the proton transfer from a hydronium ion to a hydroxide ion. This simplified view of neutralization led the Danish chemist Brønsted to propose new, more general definitions of acids and bases in 1923. According to the **Brønsted definitions,** acids are proton donors and bases are proton acceptors. This definition is in better accord with chemical facts; for example, it makes clear why ammonia is a base even though it does *not* exist as a hydroxide. Thus:

$$H_3\overset{..}{O}{}^+:\overset{..}{\underset{..}{Br}}:^- + :NH_3 \longrightarrow NH_4^+:\overset{..}{\underset{..}{Br}}:^- + H_2\overset{..}{\underset{..}{O}}:$$

$$\text{or } H_3\overset{..}{O}{}^+ + :NH_3 \longrightarrow NH_4^+ + H_2\overset{..}{\underset{..}{O}}:$$

To return to our simple equation for acid-base reactions, we might suppose that pure water itself would contain small amounts of hydronium and hydroxide ions since water can act as both an acid and a base. Thus: $2\ H_2\overset{..}{\underset{..}{O}}: \longrightarrow H_3O:^+ + :\overset{..}{\underset{..}{O}}H^-$. Measurements of the conductance of pure water show this to be true, although the extent of dissociation is low; the concentrations of H_3O^+ and OH^- in pure water at $25°$ C are both equal to 10^{-7} M. The product of these concentrations is found to be a constant at any given temperature; the value of this constant at $25°$ is 10^{-14}. We can express this as $[H_3O^+][OH^-] = 10^{-14}$. The brackets in the expression signify concentrations expressed in molarity. This equation indicates that water

CHEMICAL REACTIONS

solutions never contain only H_3O^+ or OH^-, but always both ions, and the relative proportions of the 2 determine the acidity or basicity of the solution. If we know one of the values, we can readily calculate the other.

Suppose that a 0.1 M solution of HNO_3 is prepared by adding nitric acid to water. The nitric acid generates 0.1 mole of hydronium ion; this amount swamps the very small amount present in pure water (0.0000001 mole), and the final concentration of hydronium ion is, for all practical purposes, 0.1 M. If the final concentration of H_3O^+ is 0.1 M, then from the equation, the final concentration of OH^- must be 10^{-13} M:

$$[OH^-] = \frac{10^{-14}}{[H_3O^+]} = \frac{10^{-14}}{10^{-1}} = 10^{-13}$$

The ratio of the hydronium to hydroxide ion concentrations is extremely large ($[H_3O^+]/[OH^-] = 10^{12}$), and for most purposes, only the acidic properties of such a solution need be considered.

In a graded series of concentrations—for example, 10^{-4} molar $H_3O^+NO_3^-$, 10^{-3} molar $H_3O^+NO_3^-$, and 10^{-2} molar $H_3O^+NO_3^-$—the hydronium ion concentrations are a measure of the acidity of the solutions. These numbers are often cumbersome to use, and therefore another unit of acidity, the pH unit, has been devised. The **pH** of a solution is the negative logarithm* of the hydronium ion concentration: $pH = -\log [H_3O^+]$. For our three nitric acid solutions, the $\log [H_3O^+]$ would be -4, -3, and -2, respectively, and the pH's would be 4, 3, and 2; that is, the smaller the pH value, the greater the acidity. More detailed examples of the relationships between the hydroxide

Table 2-4

MEASURES OF ACIDITY

$[H_3O]^+$ Moles per Liter	$[OH^-]$ Moles per Liter	$Log [H_3O^+]$	$-Log [H_3O^+] = pH$
1×10^0	1×10^{-14}	0	0
1×10^{-1}	1×10^{-13}	-1	1
1×10^{-4}	1×10^{-10}	-4	4
1×10^{-7}	1×10^{-7}	-7	7
1×10^{-10}	1×10^{-4}	-10	10
1×10^{-13}	1×10^{-1}	-13	13
1×10^{-14}	1×10^0	-14	14

ion concentration, the hydronium ion concentration, and the pH of acid and base solutions are given in Table 2-4. More complex examples are handled in a similar way:

$[H_3O^+] = 5 \times 10^{-3}$; $pH = -\log 5 \times 10^{-3} = -1(\log 5 \times 10^{-3}) = -1(0.70 - 3) = 2.30$

The use of pH units allows one to refer conveniently, but quantitatively, to the acidity of a solution; acidic solutions have pH's less than 7, and basic solutions have pH's greater than 7.

WEAK ACIDS AND BASES AND THEIR DISSOCIATION

The acids and bases used as examples up to this point are essentially completely dissociated in solution; they are called **strong** acids and bases. A sec-

* See Appendix B.

ond group of compounds called **weak** acids and bases are only partially dissociated in solution. Acetic acid (CH_3CO_2H, which we will symbolize as HOAc) is a typical weak acid. A 0.1 M solution of HOAc does not have a pH of 1, but instead a pH of about 3. Since the hydronium ion concentration is low, we conclude that most of the acetic acid is present in solution in the undissociated form. We can indicate this state by an equation with double arrows to show that the species represented on both sides of the equation are present in solution at the same time: $HOAc + H_2O \rightleftharpoons H_3O^+ + OAc^-$.

When the acetic acid is first added to water, dissociation occurs to give hydronium and acetate ions. Acetate ion (OAc^-) happens to be a moderately strong base (by the Brønsted definition) and it reacts with the hydronium ion to give back acetic acid: $OAc^- + H_3O^+ \longrightarrow HOAc + H_2O$. As the acetic acid dissociates (actually only a fraction of a second may be required for this process) the concentrations of H_3O^+ and OAc^- increase, and therefore the rate of the reverse reaction increases. A point is reached at which the rate of the forward reaction (number of HOAc molecules dissociating per second) equals the rate of the reverse reaction (number of H_3O^+ and OAc^- ions reacting per second) and at this point, the system is said to be at **equilibrium** (represented by the double-arrow equation):

$$HOAc + H_2O \rightleftharpoons H_3O^+ + OAc^-.$$

A system in equilibrium shows no change in properties with time. The equilibrium ratio of reagents is fixed at a given temperature; this is expressed by the following equation:

$$\frac{\begin{bmatrix} \text{Product of the} \\ \text{concentrations} \\ \text{of the products} \end{bmatrix}}{\begin{bmatrix} \text{Product of the} \\ \text{concentrations} \\ \text{of the reactants} \end{bmatrix}} = \frac{[H_3O^+][OAc^-]}{[HOAc][H_2O]} = K'$$

where the brackets represent concentrations of the species at equilibrium, and K' is called the equilibrium constant. In a dilute solution in water, the concentration of water (55.6 M)* does not change appreciably during a chemical reaction. For convenience, then, the ionization equation is usually rearranged so that the water concentration is part of the constant.

$$\frac{[H_3O^+][OAc^-]}{[HOAc]} = K'[H_2O] = K$$

The dissociation constants (K) are measures of the acidity of acids. The values of K for strong acids such as HCl and H_2SO_4 are considerably greater than 1 (our previous assumption that these compounds are fully ionized in water was valid). The value of K for acetic acid (1.75×10^{-5}) is considerably less than 1. Other weak acids are carbonic acid (H_2CO_3, $K = 4.7 \times 10^{-7}$), nitrous acid (HNO_2, $K = 4.1 \times 10^{-4}$), and hydrogen sulfide (H_2S, $K = 1.1 \times 10^{-7}$).

The dissociation constants are easily calculated once the concentrations of the species present at equilibrium are known. For example, the following concentrations have been measured for a certain solution of nitrous acid:

* 1 liter of solution contains approx. 1000 g H_2O (mol. wt. of H_2O is 18) = 1000/18 = 55.6 moles H_2O.

$[HNO_2] = 0.98$; $[H_3O^+] = 0.02$; and $[NO_2^-] = 0.02$ M. If we substitute these values in our equilibrium expression,

$$K = \frac{[H_3O^+][NO_2^-]}{[HNO_2]} = \frac{(0.02)(0.02)}{0.98}$$

and perform the calculation, we get a dissociation constant for nitrous acid of 4.1×10^{-4}.

Once the dissociation constant is known, we can calculate the acidity of solutions of the acid. For example, suppose that we needed to know the hydronium ion concentration in a 0.1 M solution of acetic acid. The concentrations of the species present at equilibrium can be set up in terms of a single unknown quantity X, as shown in Table 2-5. The substitution of these values in our equilibrium expression gives us $X^2/(0.1 - X) = K = 1.75 \times 10^{-5}$. In the calculations for weak acids, X is normally dropped from

Table 2-5

CONCENTRATIONS (MOLAR)
IN THE ACETIC ACID EQUILIBRIUM

Component	Immediately after Mixing and before Dissociation Occurs	At Equilibrium
HOAc	0.1	$0.1 - X$
H_3O^+	10^{-7} [The value in pure water]	X [The trace of H_3O^+ coming from the dissociation of water is neglected]
OAc$^-$	0	X

the denominator since it is usually a relatively small number; that is, $0.1 - X$ is very nearly equal to 0.1. The equation then becomes $X^2/0.1 = 1.75 \times 10^{-5}$, and solving for X ($X^2 = 1.75 \times 10^{-6}$; $X = \sqrt{1.75 \times 10^{-6}} = \sqrt{1.75} \times 10^{-3} = 1.32 \times 10^{-3}$) gives us 1.32×10^{-3} M as the concentration of hydronium ion in this solution at equilibrium. The percentage of dissociation of acetic acid in a 0.1 molar solution can then be calculated.

$$\% \text{ dissociation} = \left(\frac{1.32 \times 10^{-3}}{0.1}\right) 100 = 1.32 \%$$

Only 1.32 per cent of the acetic acid, then, is ionized in a 0.1 M solution at 25°.

INDICATORS

Very often, it is necessary to determine the pH of a solution without any knowledge of the amounts and kinds of the acids present. A class of compounds called indicators are useful in this respect. **Indicators** are complex organic compounds (weak acids, HIn, and weak bases, In) that have different colors depending on whether they are in the ionized or nonionized form. That is, the colors depend on the pH of the system.

Phenolphthalein is an indicator that is colorless in acidic solutions and red in basic solutions:

$$HIn + OH^- \longrightarrow In^- + H_2O$$

Colorless   Red

This change in color occurs at a pH very near to 7. If a base is added slowly to a solution containing an acid and a small amount of phenolphthalein, the neutralization point will be reached at that instant the solution becomes red in color. This process of quantitative neutralization is called **titration.** The value of indicators in determining the neutralization point is apparent.

Methyl violet is an example of a weakly basic indicator:

$$In + H_3O^+ \longrightarrow HIn^+ + H_2O$$

Colorless   Violet

In basic solutions it is colorless and in acidic solutions it is violet. In addition to red and violet, indicators are available to give colors in the entire range of the visible spectrum. The pH at which an indicator changes color is determined by the chemical make-up of the indicator; enough indicators are available so that the correct one can be chosen to reveal a change anywhere on the pH scale.

The materials responsible for the colors of most fruits and vegetables are indicators and the color changes attendant on ripening are a result of the general lowering of acidity. Vegetable extracts, such as litmus and extracts of the red cabbage, have been used as indicators in chemistry since the days of the alchemists.

BUFFERS

The pH of mammalian blood is maintained at a value very close to 7.35. If the pH shifts by as small an amount as 0.2 of a unit, serious impairment of the functioning of the organism, or even death, may occur. Since the addition of as small an amount of HCl as 10^{-6} mole (about 0.00004 g) to one liter of water changes the pH by 1 full unit (from 7 to 6), it is apparent that living organisms must have some way of protecting themselves from sudden changes in acidity. The systems used to achieve this result are called buffers.

Buffers are mixtures of a weak acid and its salt. We can illustrate the action of buffers with the aid of the expression for the equilibrium constant of acetic acid developed earlier.

$$HOAc + H_2O \rightleftharpoons H_3O^+ + OAc^- \qquad K = \frac{[H_3O^+][OAc^-]}{[HOAc]}$$

We can rearrange the equation:

$$K[HOAc] = [H_3O^+][OAc^-] \text{ or } [H_3O^+] = K\frac{[HOAc]}{[OAc^-]}$$

and take logarithms of each side:*

$$\log [H_3O^+] = \log K + \log \frac{[HOAc]}{[OAc^-]}$$

* See Appendix B.

Multiplying each side of the equation by -1 gives us:

$$-\log [H_3O^+] = -\log K - \log \frac{[HOAc]}{[OAc^-]} = -\log K + \log \frac{[OAc^-]}{[HOAc]}$$

Given our definition of pH, and the further definition that $-\log K = pK$, our expression then becomes:

$$pH = pK + \log \frac{[OAc^-]}{[HOAc]}$$

Suppose we now add sodium acetate (Na^+OAc^-) to this solution of acetic acid. Salts are ionized in solution and the acetate ion added is indistinguishable from the acetate ion formed by the ionization of acetic acid. Furthermore, if a large amount of sodium acetate is added, the amount of acetate in our expression above can be set equal to the concentration of the sodium acetate added, since only a very small, and negligible, amount of acetate ion is formed by the dissociation of acetic acid itself. The expression then becomes:

$$pH = pK + \log \frac{\text{salt concentration}}{\text{acid concentration}} = pK + \log \frac{[OAc^-]}{[HOAc]}$$

Since K, and therefore pK, is a constant, the expression tells us that the pH of a buffer is determined by the ratio of the salt to the acid present. The determination of the pH of a solution is one of the functions of a buffer. The other function is the protection of the system against pH changes. It does this by virtue of the high concentrations of salt (OAc^-) and weak acid ($HOAc$) used in the buffer (about 0.1 M, for example). If strong acids are added, they are neutralized by the acetate ion to form HOAc, an essentially undissociated acid, $H_3O^+ + OAc^- \longrightarrow HOAc$, and if strong bases are added, they are neutralized by the acetic acid to form OAc^-:

$$OH^- + HOAc \longrightarrow H_2O + OAc^-$$

In either case, the strong acid or base is neutralized without an appreciable change in the ratio of $OAc^-/HOAc$, and consequently in the pH of the system.

Suppose we compare the effects of adding 10^{-3} moles of HCl (0.037 g) to a dilute acid solution and to a solution buffered with 0.175 M NaOAc and 0.100 M HOAc, both of which solutions have an initial pH of 5.

Nonbuffered System (10^{-5} M solution of HCl):

Initial pH $= \underline{5}$; $[H_3O^+] = 10^{-5}$

Final pH: $[H_3O^+] = 10^{-5} + 10^{-3} = 0.00101 = 1.01 \times 10^{-3}$

pH $= 2.996$

Total change $= \underline{5} - 2.996 = 2.004$ pH units

Buffered System (0.175 M NaOAc + 0.100 M HOAc):

Initial pH $= pK + \log \frac{[OAc^-]}{[HOAc]}$

$= -\log 1.75 \times 10^{-5} + \log \frac{0.175}{0.100}$

$= 4.757 + .243 = 5.000$

$$\text{Final pH} = pK + \log \frac{(.175 - .001)}{(.100 + .001)} \quad [\text{OAc}^- + \text{H}_3\text{O}^+\text{Cl}^- \longrightarrow$$

$$\text{HOAc} + \text{H}_2\text{O} + \text{Cl}^-]$$

$$= 4.757 + \log \frac{.174}{.101}$$
$$= 4.757 + \log 1.72$$
$$= 4.757 + .236 = 4.993$$

Total Change $= \underline{5} - 4.993 = 0.007$ pH units

The pH change in the unbuffered system is large, whereas the pH change in the buffered system is negligible.

A large number of different acid-salt pairs are used as buffers in chemical and biological systems; examples are $\text{H}_3\text{PO}_4 + \text{NaH}_2\text{PO}_4$, $\text{NaH}_2\text{PO}_4 + \text{Na}_2\text{HPO}_4$, $\text{NaHCO}_3 + \text{Na}_2\text{CO}_3$, and $\text{NH}_3 + \text{NH}_4\text{Cl}$.

CHEMICAL ENERGY

Energy is the capacity to do work, **work** being ultimately defined in terms of a force times a displacement. The work done in sliding a block along a surface, for example, is equal to the product of the force required to move the block and the distance it is moved.

The conversion of one form of energy into another is relatively straightforward in mechanical systems. A barrel of water on a mountain top has a certain amount of potential energy (energy of position), which is proportional to the height of the mountain (and, of course, to the quantity of water in the barrel). If the water is poured over the edge of a cliff, the potential energy drops as the water falls, but the kinetic energy (energy of motion) increases proportionately. When the water strikes the floor of the canyon, an amount of heat energy is released equal to the kinetic energy of the water just before it reached the canyon floor, and this amount, in turn, is equal to the potential energy the water had on the mountain top (we neglect the effect of air friction and otherwise assume ideal conditions). If the water is allowed to strike a paddle wheel, on the other hand, a part of the energy may be obtained as work, although the rest is still converted into heat. Energy, therefore, may be converted from one form to another but in these transformations, the total amount of energy remains constant. This is essentially a statement of the first law of thermodynamics, which is also quoted in the following form: "Energy may neither be created nor destroyed."

We are particularly interested, however, in the energy that can be obtained from chemical compounds. In this respect, chemical energy is the energy a molecule has by virtue of the kinds of atoms it contains and the manner in which they are linked together; chemical energy may be considered as a type of potential energy. Explosions and flames are dramatic examples of reactions in which chemical energy is released. The heat and light that are characteristic of these reactions comes from the breakdown or rearrangement of the chemicals involved; that is, the energy released was present originally in the starting molecules as chemical energy.

Silver azide is an explosive compound that breaks down into silver atoms and nitrogen molecules, and in the process liberates considerable energy in the form of heat and light, thus:

$$2 \; Ag\overset{\cdot\cdot}{-}N{=}N{=}\overset{\cdot\cdot}{N}: \longrightarrow 2 \; Ag + 3 : N{\equiv}N: + \text{heat} + \text{light}$$

Silver azide

The 3 nitrogen molecules and the 2 silver atoms contain much less chemical energy than the 2 silver azide molecules because of the different ways in which the atoms are bonded, and in a general sense, the products are more stable than the reactants. This energy difference represents the energy liberated during the explosion.

The amount of heat released or absorbed from the surroundings during a chemical reaction is characteristic of that reaction. Measured at constant pressure, this heat energy, which is called the **heat of reaction,** is given the symbol ΔH (delta H). The magnitude of this heat term depends on the state and the concentrations of the reactants and products, however, and these variables must be defined. In the remainder of this chapter, the energy terms will be given for reactions of compounds at standard, or unit, concentrations; a superscript zero will be attached to the symbols used to indicate this.

When 1 mole of methane (CH_4) is burned in air, exactly 213,000 calories* of heat energy are released.

$$1 \; CH_4 + 2 \; O_2 \longrightarrow 1 \; CO_2 + 2 \; H_2O$$

$$\Delta H^0 = -213,000 \text{ calories}$$

The negative sign here for ΔH^0 indicates that the heat is released by the reaction. A few reactions have a positive ΔH^0 and during the course of these reactions, heat is absorbed from the surroundings. These two types of reactions are called **exothermic** and **endothermic,** respectively.

The heat energy of a reaction can be used to perform work in a mechanical device. For example, the heat from the burning of methane (natural gas) can generate steam which can run a steam engine, which in turn can perform mechanical work. A second way of converting chemical energy into work involves the use of a battery. In this device, a chemical reaction produces an electric current; the energy of the current then can be used to run a motor, which in turn can perform mechanical work.

FREE ENERGY AND WORK

The amount of work that can be obtained from a chemical reaction (that is, the <u>usable</u> energy of the reaction) is not given by ΔH^0, the heat of the reaction, but instead by an energy term ΔF^0 which is called the **free-energy** change. The relationship of ΔF^0 to ΔH^0 is given by the expression $\Delta F^0 = \Delta H^0 - q_{rev}$, where q_{rev} is the heat absorbed from the surrounding medium, or the heat given up to the medium, as the case may be, for the reaction carried out in a reversible manner at constant temperature. The term q_{rev} is further equal to $T\Delta S$, where T is the absolute temperature (°Kelvin = °Centigrade + 273), and ΔS is a thermodynamic quantity called the change in **entropy.** Substitution of this definition of q_{rev} into our free-energy equation then gives the expression $\Delta F^0 = \Delta H^0 - T\Delta S$. That is, once ΔH^0 and

* A *calorie* is that quantity of heat required to raise the temperature of 1 gram of water from 14.5° C to 15.5° C.

ΔS^0 are measured for a reaction, ΔF^0, the usable energy can be readily calculated.

Since $T\Delta S^0 = q_{rev}$, ΔS^0 may be calculated when q_{rev} has been measured for a process, subject to the restrictions given above. For example, during the melting of 1 mole of ice at $0°$ C at 1 atmosphere pressure, 1447 calories of energy are absorbed from the surroundings. The entropy change for this process is then:

$$H_2O_{ice} \longrightarrow H_2O_{liq} \quad (q_{rev} = +1447 \text{ cal.})$$

$$\Delta S^0 = \frac{q_{rev}}{T} = \frac{1447}{0° + 273} = \frac{1447}{273} = 5.3 \text{ cal./degree}$$

$$\Delta S^0 = S^0_{liq} - S^0_{ice} = +5.3 \text{ cal./degree}$$

The entropy of a system tells us how disordered that system is. The water molecules in an ice crystal are arranged in a very regular way, just as the sodium and chloride ions are arranged regularly in a crystal of sodium chloride (Fig. 1-7). In liquid water, on the other hand, the arrangement of water molecules is more haphazard and the molecules are essentially free to move about. Ice crystals and other crystals with ordered structures have low entropies, whereas the corresponding liquids with more random structures have high entropies. In general, systems tend to move from a more ordered structure to a less ordered one, and in this process the entropy increases.

Two general methods are available for the calculation of the maximum amount of work obtainable from a reaction. The first depends on the measurement of ΔS^0 and ΔH^0. For example, these quantities have been determined for the decomposition of nitrous oxide (N_2O): $N_2O \longrightarrow N_2 + \frac{1}{2}O_2$; $\Delta H^0 = -19,500$ cal; $\Delta S^0 = +18$ calories per degree; $T = 25°$ C or $298°$ Kelvin. From our equation for the free-energy change then, $\Delta F^0 = \Delta H^0 - T\Delta S^0 = -19,500 - 298 (18) = -24,864$ calories. If a battery were constructed based on this reaction, the maximum electrical work that we could obtain from it would be equivalent to 24,864 cal. The sign of ΔF^0 for a reaction is important; if ΔF^0 is a negative quantity, the reaction is spontaneous and work can be obtained from the system. If ΔF^0 is a positive quantity, on the other hand, the reaction will not proceed under standard conditions unless free energy is supplied from some outside source.

A second, more direct method for obtaining ΔF^0 is available if the reaction reaches equilibrium, since a simple relationship exists between ΔF^0 and the equilibrium constant K: $\Delta F^0 = -2.3$ RT log K. R in the equation is a constant with the value 1.99 cal/mole deg. As an example, consider the decomposition of hydrogen iodide in the gas phase at $25°$ C. The equilibrium constant for this reaction is 2.9.

$$2 \text{ HI} \rightleftharpoons \text{H}_2 + \text{I}_2 \qquad K = \frac{[H_2][I_2]}{[HI][HI]} = \frac{[0.77][0.77]}{[0.46][0.46]} = 2.8$$

0.46 moles   0.77 moles   0.77 moles

Given under the chemical symbols in the equation are the equilibrium quantities—that is, the number of moles of each component obtained when 2 moles of HI (or 1 mole H_2 + 1 mole I_2) are allowed to decompose until equilibrium is reached.

Substitution of the value of K (2.8) into our free-energy equation leads to a

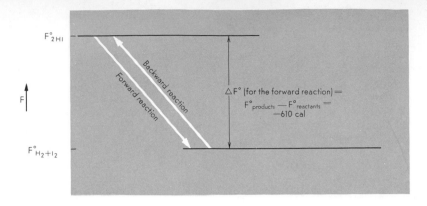

F°_{2HI}

F

$F^{\circ}_{H_2+I_2}$

Forward reaction

Backward reaction

ΔF° (for the forward reaction) =
$F^{\circ}_{products} - F^{\circ}_{reactants}$ =
-610 cal

Fig. 2-2. Free-energy change in the decomposition of HI.

ΔF^0 of -610 calories; this value means that when 2 moles of HI are converted into 1 mole of H_2 + 1 mole of I_2 under standard conditions, the maximum amount of work that can be done is equal to 630 calories. The changes in free energy occurring in this reaction are illustrated in Fig. 2-2.

Two moles of HI have a higher free energy than 1 mole of H_2 + 1 mole of I_2, and the conversion of two moles of HI to H_2 and I_2 yields 610 calories of energy. It is obvious that if we wished to convert a mixture of 1 mole of H_2 and 1 mole of I_2 to HI (an "uphill" process), it would be necessary to supply 610 calories of free energy from an outside source.

The relationship of the equilibrium constant for a reaction and the free-energy change can be outlined in the following way. Equilibria in which most of the reactant is converted into product (indicated by the relative lengths of the arrows in the equilibrium), A $\rightleftharpoons$ B, have large equilibrium constants, and negative values of ΔF indicating that free energy is liberated. On the other hand, equilibria in which very little of the reactant is converted into product, B $\rightleftharpoons$ A, have small equilibrium constants and positive values of ΔF.

The equilibrium constants, or the relative values of the free energies ($F^0_{H_2+I_2} - F^0_{2HI}$), tell us how much product can be found at equilibrium, but neither variable can tell us anything about how fast a reaction approaches equilibrium. Some reactions require a fraction of a second to reach equilibrium, others require centuries. Additional information is necessary before the <u>rate</u> at which equilibrium is reached can be discussed.

RATES OF REACTIONS

A few chemical reactions are extremely fast. The combination of iodine atoms in solution to form molecular iodine is an example ($:\overset{..}{I}\cdot + \cdot\overset{..}{I}: \longrightarrow$ $:\overset{..}{I}:\overset{..}{I}:$). In this case, virtually every collision of the iodine atoms leads to an iodine molecule. Most reactions of simple ions are also very fast:

$$I^- + Ag^+ \longrightarrow AgI \quad \text{(precipitate)}$$

Most of the reactions of organic compounds of biological interest are comparatively slow, on the other hand, and the time needed for the reactions to proceed to 50 per cent completion ranges from seconds to years, depending on the particular chemicals involved. Why are these reactions so slow? They are slow because, on the one hand, not every collision of large species can lead to a chemical reaction. If, for example, we are concerned with the ionization of a methyl alcohol molecule:

$$\begin{matrix} & H & & & & & H & & \\ & | & \ddot{} & & & & | & \ddot{} & \\ H-&C&-\ddot{O}-H\leftarrow:\ddot{O}-H & \rightleftharpoons & H-&C&-\ddot{O}:^- & + & H-\ddot{O}^{\pm}-H \\ & | & \ddot{} & \ddot{} & & & | & \ddot{} & \\ & H & & H & & & H & & H \end{matrix}$$

the collision of a water molecule on the wrong side of the molecule obviously cannot lead to the CH_3O^- ion:

$$\begin{matrix} & & & H & \\ & \ddot{} & & | & \\ H-\ddot{O}:&\rightarrow&H-C&-O-H & \quad \text{(no chemical reaction occurs)} \\ & & & | & \\ & H & & H & \end{matrix}$$

A second reason why reactions are slow is that molecules very often must be given a special amount of energy (by collision with neighboring molecules) to overcome the repulsion of the electrons on the two reactants. These effects lead to a free-energy barrier between reactants and products. This point is illustrated in Fig. 2-3. The free-energy barriers (F of activation) determine the speed of reactions; the higher the barrier, the slower the reaction. Path "c" represents a reaction mode with zero activation energy, and a reaction following this path would be immeasurably fast. The HI decomposition is a slow reaction, however, and it follows not this path, but path "a," which contains a reasonably large energy barrier. This barrier can be

Fig. 2-3. Three paths for the interconversion of HI and $H_2 + I_2$.

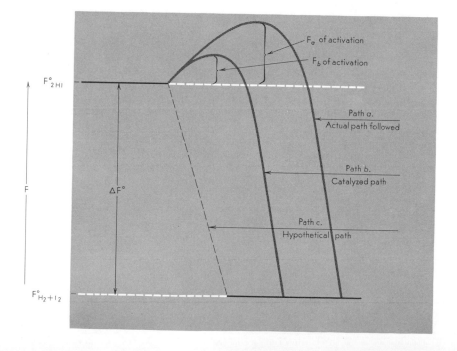

decreased and the rate of the reaction increased through the use of a catalyst, as we shall see in the next section. An increase in the rate of a reaction may also be brought about by an increase in the temperature or in the concentrations of the reactants; the references listed in the bibliography should be consulted for further information about the latter variables.

Catalysts

Certain substances called **catalysts** are able to lower the energy of activation of a reaction. In Fig. 2-3, this is illustrated by the effect of a catalyst in lowering the barrier from the value in path "a" to that in path "b." The new catalyzed reaction proceeds much faster than the old reaction. Notice that the barrier is lowered by the same amount (by the same number of calories) for the forward reaction, $2 HI \longrightarrow H_2 + I_2$, as for the backward reaction, $H_2 + I_2 \longrightarrow 2 HI$. This equal lowering means that although both reactions are speeded up by the catalyst, the equilibrium constant K is unchanged, since K is determined solely by ΔF^0. In other words, a catalyst can speed up the rate at which equilibrium is established, but it has no effect on the concentrations present at equilibrium. In the HI reaction, platinum and certain other metals act as catalysts. For reactions that occur in solution, acids and bases are very often used as catalysts; the rate at which carbonic acid is formed from CO_2 and H_2O, for example, $CO_2 + H_2O \xrightarrow{H_3O^+} H_2CO_3$, is increased by acids. In biological systems, complex proteins called enzymes serve as reaction catalysts. Other examples of catalysis are given in the following chapters. It should be noted that the catalyst is not consumed during the reaction; its final and initial concentrations are the same, and therefore only a very small quantity of the catalyst is usually required.

Energy Utilization in Biological Systems

Living organisms are extremely complex systems that are run by the chemical energy in the food ingested. The specific energy measure of interest here is the free energy of the food. A delicate balance exists between the free-energy input and the free-energy output (heat, motion, energy of excreted products, etc.), and if the energy output exceeds the input for any appreciable period of time, the organism dies. For this reason, a living organism must make efficient use of the energy in its food. A few examples of the chemical reactions in which this energy is released or transferred are given in Chapter 5; details, however, are given in a different volume of this series.*

* W. D. McElroy, *Cell Physiology and Biochemistry,* 2nd. ed., (Englewood Cliffs, N.J.: Prentice-Hall, 1964).

Organic Chemistry: The Hydrocarbons

Organic chemistry is the chemistry of carbon compounds. The name was assigned in the early part of the eighteenth century when the distinction was made between inorganic chemistry, which dealt with the mineral kingdom, and organic chemistry, which dealt with the plant and animal kingdoms. Organic compounds had been isolated only from plant and animal sources at that time, and the synthesis of organic compounds from carbon, hydrogen, and inorganic compounds was considered impossible. The synthesis of urea by Wohler in 1828 and acetic acid by Kolbe in 1845 served to overthrow these ideas and today we recognize that although carbon compounds are essential for life there are no intrinsic differences, in a philosophical sense, between inorganic and organic compounds.

The number of carbon compounds known today exceeds the number of compounds prepared from the other 102 elements. This complexity of carbon chemistry is a result of three properties of the element: the high covalency of carbon (4), which permits the attachment of a large number of groups to carbon in a large number of different combinations; the great strength of the carbon-carbon bond, which permits the formation of chains of carbon atoms of unlimited

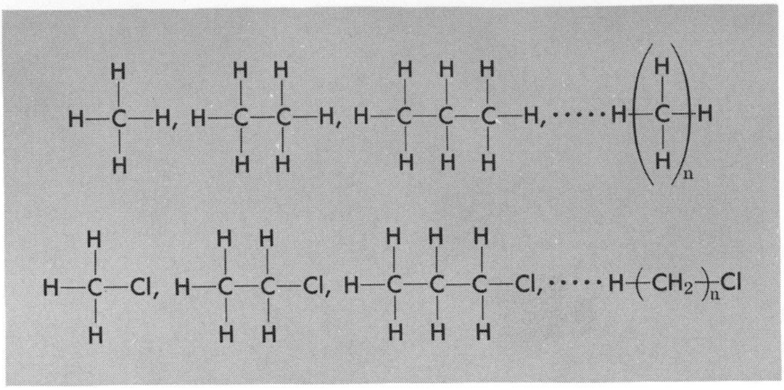

Fig. 3-1. A homologous series of alkanes, and a homologous series of chlorine compounds.

length; and the formation of multiple bonds by carbon, which further increases the number of possible organic compounds. A few of the other elements have one or two of these characteristics, but none has all three.

The organization of organic chemistry was vastly simplified by the recognition of **homologous series** of compounds; in these series, the members differ only by the number of building blocks, such as CH_2 groups, per molecule (Fig. 3-1). In general, the members of a homologous series have similar properties that are very often determined not by the carbon chain, which is rather inert, but by some small group, such as OH, Cl, NO_2, $CH\equiv C$, etc., called a **functional group,** attached to the chain. In this volume we shall organize our discussion primarily by functional groups; the number of specific compounds mentioned will be kept to a minimum through the use of a few examples and through the extrapolation of the facts covered to the other members of each homologous series.

This chapter on organic chemistry will deal with the hydrocarbons, which are defined as compounds containing only carbon and hydrogen, and the subject will be subdivided in the following way.

I. Aliphatic Hydrocarbons.
   A. Alkanes. Compounds related to methane, CH_4.
   B. Alkenes. Compounds related to ethylene, $CH_2{=}CH_2$.
   C. Alkynes. Compounds related to acetylene, $CH\equiv CH$.

II. Aromatic Hydrocarbons.
         Compounds related to benzene, C_6H_6.

THE ALKANES

The alkanes, also called saturated hydrocarbons or paraffins, are those hydrocarbons with a maximum ratio of hydrogen to carbon (general formula C_nH_{2n+2}). The simplest alkane, CH_4, is the principal constituent of natural gas, and most of the other members of the series have been isolated from such natural sources as beeswax and the plant waxes. The principal source, however, is petroleum, which is a complex mixture of various hydrocarbons and certain other compounds containing oxygen, nitrogen, sulfur, and small amounts of the other elements.

The simplest homologous series of alkanes is the straight-chain series, which as the name implies, contains members with a single chain of CH_2 groups capped at each end by a hydrogen atom (hence the general formula

46

Table 3-1

STRAIGHT-CHAIN ALKANES

Formula	Name	Melting Point, °C	Boiling Point, °C	Formula	Name	Melting Point, °C	Boiling Point, °C
CH_4	Methane	−183	−161	$C_{10}H_{22}$	n-Decane	−30	174
C_2H_6	Ethane	−172	−89	$C_{11}H_{24}$	n-Undecane	−26	196
C_3H_8	Propane	−188	−43	$C_{12}H_{26}$	n-Dodecane	−10	216
C_4H_{10}	n-Butane	−137	0	$C_{13}H_{28}$	n-Tridecane	−6	232
C_5H_{12}	n-Pentane	−130	36	$C_{20}H_{42}$	n-Eicosane	37	—
C_6H_{14}	n-Hexane	−94	69	$C_{21}H_{44}$	n-Heneicosane	40	—
C_7H_{16}	n-Heptane	−91	98	$C_{22}H_{46}$	n-Docosane	44	—
C_8H_{18}	n-Octane	−57	126	$C_{30}H_{62}$	n-Triacontane	68	—
C_9H_{20}	n-Nonane	−54	151	$C_{40}H_{82}$	n-Tetracontane	81	—

C_nH_{2n+2}). A listing of some members of this series is given in Table 3-1. The lower members are assigned specific names (devised before the existence of homologous series was recognized) whereas the higher members are assigned systematic names based on the Greek and Latin numerical prefixes and the general suffix **ane**, which stands for saturated hydrocarbons; the prefix *n* (normal) indicates that the molecule has a straight unbranched chain.

The Shapes of Organic Molecules

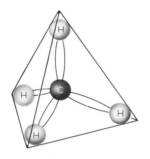

Fig. 3-2. A methane molecule inscribed in a regular tetrahedron.

The shapes of the alkanes may be derived from the shape of the methane molecule. In the first chapter, we saw that the 4 bonds in methane are directed to the corners of a regular tetrahedron; this geometry is represented in Fig. 3-2. The higher hydrocarbons are made up of chains of these tetrahedral units.

Simpler methods are available today for indicating the geometry of the hydrocarbons; three of these methods are given in Fig. 3-3. The drawings in the first column of Fig. 3-3 are based on models of the methane molecule in which the diameters of the carbon and hydrogen atoms, and the bond lengths are constructed to scale as accurately as possible. The figures in the second column represent "ball and stick" models which illustrate more clearly the bond angles involved. The figures in the third column are "projection" formulas that are drawn so as to aid in visualizing the geometry of the molecules. In addition to these methods of representation, we very often, for convenience, use graphic formulas such as $H—\overset{\displaystyle H}{\underset{\displaystyle H}{C}}—H$, and molecular formulas such as CH_4, C_2H_5, etc. In order to grasp more fully the structures represented by the projection or graphic formulas, ball and stick models of these compounds should be constructed out of wax or clay and match sticks or wire whenever they appear in the text.

A set of drawings representing the ethane molecule is given in Fig. 3-4.

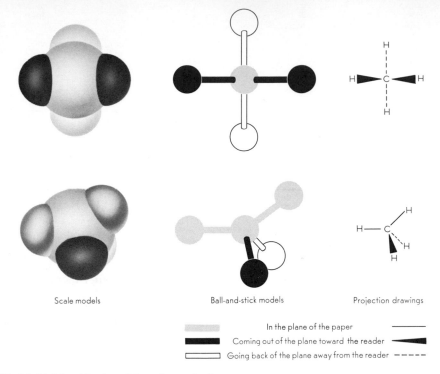

Scale models   Ball-and-stick models   Projection drawings

In the plane of the paper

Coming out of the plane toward the reader

Going back of the plane away from the reader

Fig. 3-3. Models and drawings of the methane molecule.

Side views

Fig. 3-4. Conformations of ethane,

$$C_2H_6, \quad H—\overset{\overset{\displaystyle H \quad H}{|\quad\;|}}{\underset{\underset{\displaystyle H \quad H}{|\quad\;|}}{C—C}}—H.$$

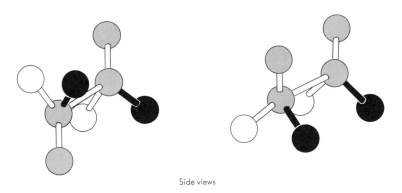

End view   End view

Staggered form   Eclipsed form

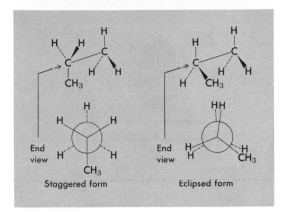

End view
Staggered form

End view
Eclipsed form

Fig. 3-5. Conformations of propane,

$$C_3H_8, \quad H-\overset{\overset{\displaystyle H}{|}}{\underset{\underset{\displaystyle H}{|}}{C}}-\overset{\overset{\displaystyle H}{|}}{\underset{\underset{\displaystyle H}{|}}{C}}-\overset{\overset{\displaystyle H}{|}}{\underset{\underset{\displaystyle H}{|}}{C}}-H.$$

Certain physical measurements indicate that at room temperature, essentially free rotation about single bonds (σ bonds) is possible. In this rotation about the single bond in ethane, two extreme structures are possible. The first set of drawings in Fig. 3-4 represents an ethane molecule in which the hydrogens on adjacent carbon atoms are as far apart as possible (see end view); this is the **staggered** form of ethane. The second set represents an ethane molecule in which the hydrogens are as close as possible; this is the **eclipsed** form of ethane. Forms of a molecule that differ only by rotation about single bonds are called **conformations** of that molecule. The eclipsed conformations are the highest energy forms, whereas the staggered conformations are the lowest energy forms obtained by rotation about the C—C bond. At room temperature, therefore, the equilibrium between the conformations favors the staggered form. It should be pointed out, however, that individual conformations cannot be isolated at room temperature since the forms are interconverted at too rapid a rate.

Similar representations of the conformations of propane and n-butane are given in Figs. 3-5 and 3-6. If we extrapolate the carbon backbone of the most stable form of butane to the longer chain hydrocarbons, we find that the lowest energy form is the extended one in which the carbon atoms trace out, as it were, the points on a saw (Fig. 3-7).

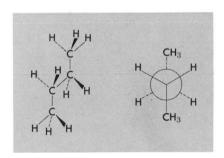

Fig. 3-6. The most stable conformation of

$$n\text{-butane}, \ C_4H_{10}, \ H-\overset{\overset{\displaystyle H}{|}}{\underset{\underset{\displaystyle H}{|}}{C}}-\overset{\overset{\displaystyle H}{|}}{\underset{\underset{\displaystyle H}{|}}{C}}-\overset{\overset{\displaystyle H}{|}}{\underset{\underset{\displaystyle H}{|}}{C}}-\overset{\overset{\displaystyle H}{|}}{\underset{\underset{\displaystyle H}{|}}{C}}-H.$$

The Branched-Chain Hydrocarbons

Many alkanes contain carbon branches attached to the long chain. The simplest branched-chain hydrocarbon is given in Fig. 3-8 along with a hypothethical scheme for making the compound that illustrates how these compounds are named. The radical (or group) formed by the loss of a hydrogen atom from a hydrocarbon is named by dropping the alkane ending **ane** and adding the ending **yl.** Complex hydrocarbons are then named as radical

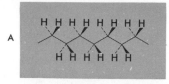

A

B

Fig. 3-7. (A) The most stable conformation of the carbon chain in the high-molecular-weight alkanes. (B) A molecular model of this carbon chain.

derivatives of the longest chain of carbon atoms. For example, compound A in Fig. 3-9 is named as a derivative of hexane, not of butane or pentane. The longest chain is then numbered from one end to the other, and the positions of the substituents are given by citing that number; for example, compound A is 3-methylhexane. The carbons are numbered from that end of the chain that gives the lowest set of numbers; that is, compound A is 3-methylhexane and not 4-methylhexane. If two substituents are present, each is given a number as in compounds C and D (Fig. 3-9). Note that there can be only one monomethyl propane (Fig. 3-8), and only one monomethyl *n*-butane (namely 2-methylbutane). There are no methyl-substituted methanes or ethanes, since substitution leads merely to ethane and propane respectively.

Isomers

Note that both *n*-butane and 2-methylpropane have the same molecular formula, C_4H_{10}. Different compounds with the same molecular formula are called **isomers.** In this particular case, the isomers differ only with respect to the position of the methyl group in the chain; in the butane molecule, the methyl group is attached to the end of a propane chain, whereas in methylpropane, it is attached to the central atom. Isomerism of this type is called **structural isomerism.** Similarly, *n*-hexane, 2-methylpentane, 3-methylpentane, 2,3-dimethylbutane, and 2,2-dimethylbutane are isomers with the molecular formula C_6H_{14}; they are referred to collectively as isomers of hexane. The number of possible structural isomers increases rapidly with molecular size; there are 2 isomeric butanes, 3 pentanes, 5 hexanes (listed above), 9 heptanes, 18 octanes, 35 nonanes, and a calculated number of

Fig. 3-8. Hypothetical path for the preparation of a branched-chain hydrocarbon.

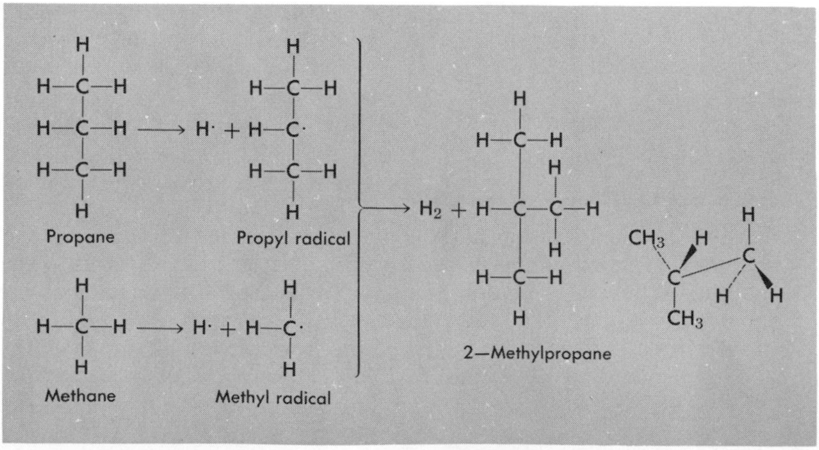

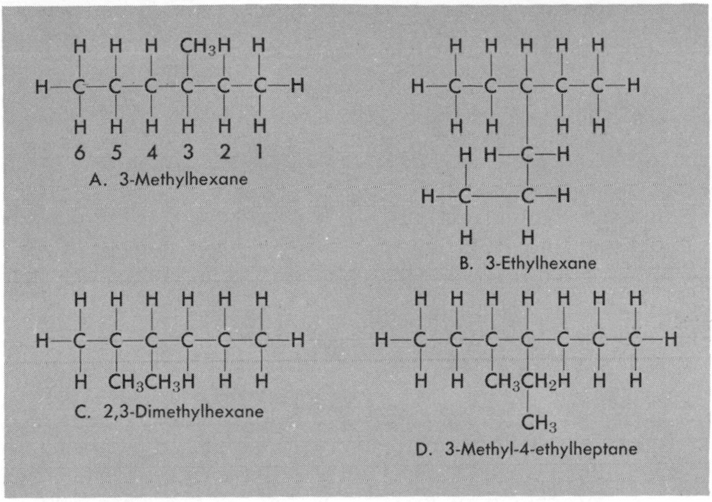

Fig. 3-9. Branched-chain hydrocarbons.

62,491,178,805,831 structural isomers with the general formula $C_{40}H_{82}$! The reader should write out structures for the isomeric heptanes and octanes.

Cyclic Alkanes

A third class of alkanes is made up of the cyclic hydrocarbons; a number of examples are given in Fig. 3-10. These compounds are named by appending the prefix **cyclo** to the name of the corresponding straight-chain alkane. The

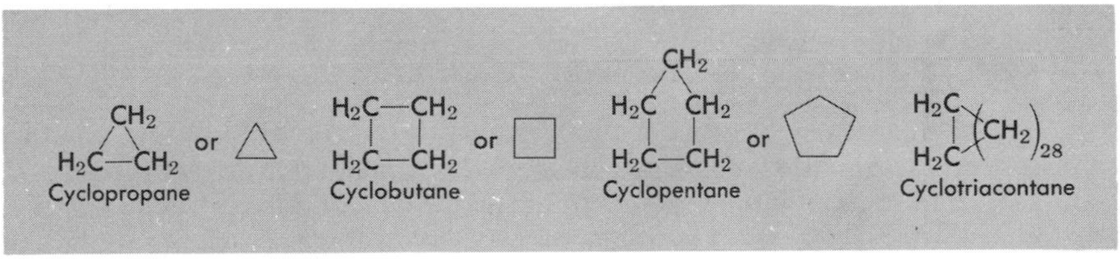

Fig. 3-10. Cyclic hydrocarbons.

formulas of the monocyclic alkanes correspond to the general formula C_nH_{2n}. Many types of cyclic alkanes have been prepared, some quite complex; examples are given in Fig. 3-11. Since the chemical properties of cyclic alkanes are very similar to those of linear alkanes, we shall not discuss them separately.

Fig. 3-11. Complex cyclic hydrocarbons.

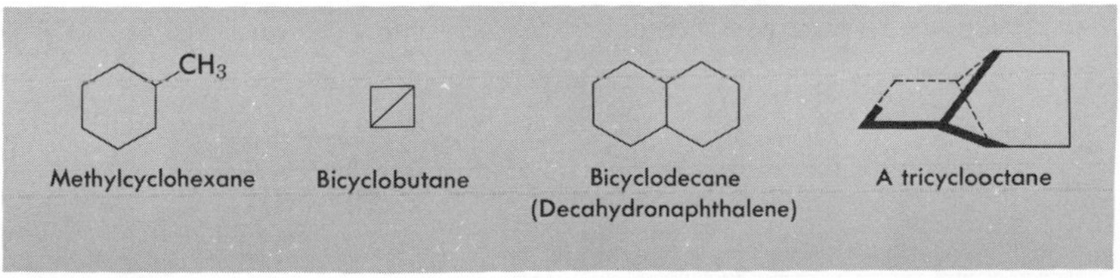

Preparation of the Alkanes

Many of the alkanes may be obtained by the fractional distillation of petroleum. Most complex hydrocarbons do not exist in nature, however, and they must be synthesized in the laboratory. One convenient method is based on the reduction of the corresponding halogen derivatives:

$$CH_3-\overset{\displaystyle H}{\underset{\displaystyle X}{\overset{|}{\underset{|}{C}}}}-CH_3 + 2\ (H\cdot) \longrightarrow CH_3CH_3CH_3 + HX$$

where R is an organic radical and X is a halogen atom. The most common reducing agents are sodium metal in liquid ammonia, zinc in acetic acid, and lithium aluminum hydride ($LiAlH_4$). The latter reagent, which was introduced to organic chemistry in 1947, is one of the most valuable of all reducing agents. Several other instances of its use are cited in Chapters 5 and 6.

A second synthetic method is the **Wurtz** reaction, in which an alkyl halide is treated with sodium metal: $2CH_3-Br + 2\ Na \longrightarrow CH_3-CH_3 + 2NaBr$.

Reactions of the Alkanes

The alkanes are relatively stable compounds and the variety of reactions they undergo is limited; some of the more common reactions are given below:

$$2\ C_2H_6 + 7\ O_2 \longrightarrow 6\ H_2O + 4\ CO_2$$

$$CH_4 + Cl_2 \longrightarrow HCl + CH_3Cl\ \text{(Chloromethane)}$$

$$\underset{\text{(Excess)}}{CH_4 + 4\ Cl_2} \longrightarrow 4\ HCl + CCl_4\ \text{(Tetrachloromethane, or carbon tetrachloride)}$$

$$C_2H_6 + Br_2 \longrightarrow HBr + CH_3CH_2Br\ \text{(Bromoethane)}$$

All hydrocarbons react with an excess of oxygen at high temperature to give carbon dioxide and water in a process called burning, or combustion. In addition to serving as a source of heat, this reaction is often used in chemical analysis since the empirical formula of a hydrocarbon can be calculated from the weights of carbon dioxide and water obtained on combustion (see Chapter 2).

Free-Radical Reactions

A majority of the reactions of the alkanes are **free-radical** reactions; this means that species with an odd number of electrons are formed as intermediates. Reactions of this type (for example, the chlorination of methane) are usually started by the symmetrical cleavage of an electron-pair bond:

Step 1 $\qquad\qquad\qquad :\overset{..}{\underset{..}{Cl}}:\overset{..}{\underset{..}{Cl}}: + \text{light} \longrightarrow 2\ :\overset{..}{\underset{..}{Cl}}\cdot$

The free radicals formed (chlorine atoms in this case) then react with other molecules to give new radicals:

Step 2a $\qquad :\overset{..}{\underset{..}{Cl}}\cdot + H-\overset{\displaystyle H}{\underset{\displaystyle H}{\overset{|}{\underset{|}{C}}}}-H \longrightarrow :\overset{..}{\underset{..}{Cl}}-H + \cdot\overset{\displaystyle H}{\underset{\displaystyle H}{\overset{|}{\underset{|}{C}}}}-H$

Step 2b
$$H-\overset{\overset{H}{|}}{\underset{\underset{H}{|}}{C}}\cdot + :\ddot{\underset{..}{Cl}}-\ddot{\underset{..}{Cl}}: \longrightarrow H-\overset{\overset{H}{|}}{\underset{\underset{H}{|}}{C}}-Cl + :\ddot{\underset{..}{Cl}}\cdot$$

It is evident that each time a chloromethane molecule is formed (Step 2b), a chlorine atom is also formed, and that this species can then enter into Step 2a again, and so on. In principle, we would need to add only 1 chlorine atom to an equimolar mixture of chlorine and methane to convert all of the reactants into chloromethane and hydrogen chloride (Steps 2a and b). That is, the over-all reaction (obtained by adding the equations of Steps 2a and b) would be $Cl_2 + CH_4 \longrightarrow HCl + CH_3Cl$, even though several different steps are required in the reaction. In practice, more than 1 chlorine atom is required, though, because of the annihilation of free radicals by combination:

Step 3a
$$2 :\ddot{\underset{..}{Cl}}\cdot \longrightarrow Cl-Cl$$

Step 3b
$$2 H-\overset{\overset{H}{|}}{\underset{\underset{H}{|}}{C}}\cdot \longrightarrow H-\overset{\overset{H}{|}}{\underset{\underset{H}{|}}{C}}-\overset{\overset{H}{|}}{\underset{\underset{H}{|}}{C}}-H$$

Nevertheless, 1 chlorine atom is usually sufficient to lead to the formation of several thousand chloromethane molecules, and only very small quantities of light are required to bring about the full reaction of chlorine with methane or with the other alkanes (often with explosive violence). Reactions of this type are called **radical-chain** reactions; Step 1 is usually referred to as the **initiation** step, steps 2a and b as the **propagation** steps, and steps 3a and b as the **termination** steps.

THE ALKENES

The alkenes (often called olefins or unsaturated hydrocarbons) are hydrocarbons containing 1 or more double bonds. They can be pictured as arising from the alkanes by the loss of 2 hydrogen atoms from adjacent carbons:

$$\underset{\text{Ethane}}{H\overset{\overset{H}{|}}{\underset{\underset{H}{|}}{C}}-\overset{\overset{H}{|}}{\underset{\underset{H}{|}}{C}}H} \longrightarrow 2H\cdot + \left[H\overset{\cdot}{\underset{\underset{H}{|}}{C}}-\overset{\cdot}{\underset{\underset{H}{|}}{C}}H\right] \longrightarrow \underset{\text{Ethene}}{HC=CH} + H_2$$

Typical alkenes are given in Fig. 3-12. The alkenes are named by the substitution of the suffix **ene** for the alkane suffix **ane** (the simplest alkene is usually referred to as ethylene, however). In complex alkenes, in addition, a number is assigned to the first carbon atom of the double bond to indicate its position in the hydrocarbon chain (Fig. 3-12).

The alkenes are quite common in nature; for example, the compounds responsible for the colors of tomatoes, carrots, boiled lobsters, and autumn leaves form a group of related polyolefins called **carotenes.** The carotenes are important intermediates in photosynthesis, in the biosynthesis of vitamin A, and in other cellular processes. The structure of the most common carotene is given in Fig. 3-13.

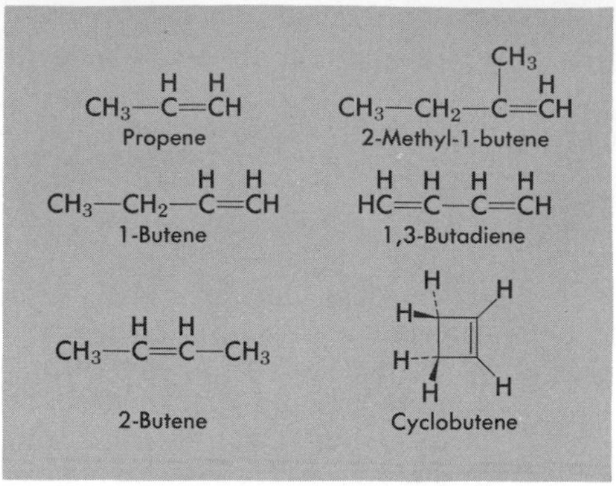

$$CH_3-\overset{\displaystyle H}{C}=\overset{\displaystyle H}{CH}$$
Propene

$$CH_3-CH_2-\overset{\displaystyle CH_3}{\underset{\displaystyle }{C}}=\overset{\displaystyle H}{CH}$$
2-Methyl-1-butene

$$CH_3-CH_2-\overset{\displaystyle H}{C}=\overset{\displaystyle H}{CH}$$
1-Butene

$$HC=\overset{\displaystyle H}{C}-\overset{\displaystyle H}{C}=\overset{\displaystyle H}{CH}$$
1,3-Butadiene

$$CH_3-\overset{\displaystyle H}{C}=\overset{\displaystyle H}{C}-CH_3$$
2-Butene

Cyclobutene

Fig. 3-12. Representative alkenes.

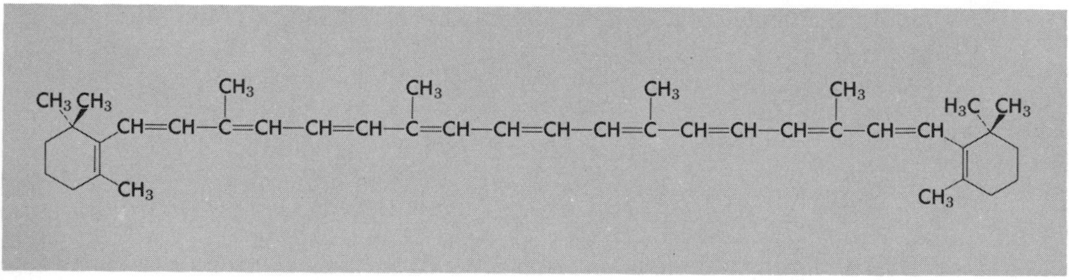

Fig. 3-13. β-Carotene.

The Structure of the Alkenes

The alkenes are far more reactive than the alkanes, a fact which can be explained in terms of the structure of the double bond. It was pointed out in the first chapter that the carbon atoms in methane are sp^3 hybridized. According to one group of theoretical chemists, the double bond is formed by the overlap of two sp^3 orbitals from each of two carbon atoms (Fig. 3-14). The bonds joining the carbon atoms in this way are called bent, or banana, bonds.

Fig. 3-14. The double bond in ethylene formed from two sp^3 hybridized carbon atoms.

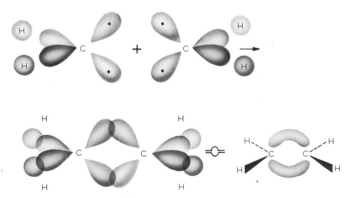

According to a second group of theoretical chemists, the double bond is constructed of two sp^2 hybridized carbon atoms, thus:

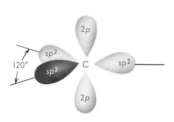

The three sp^2 orbitals in this atom are in 1 plane and separated by 120°, whereas the $2p$ orbital is perpendicular to this plane (Fig. 3-15). Two of the sp^2 bonds form bonds to the hydrogen atoms and the third forms a σ bond to the second carbon atom (Fig. 3-16). The remaining $2p$ orbitals can then overlap to form a new molecular orbital called a π orbital (Fig. 3-17).

Both physical pictures of the double bond lead to similar predictions, but the π-orbital picture of the double bond is the most widely accepted and we shall use it throughout the remainder of this volume. The π electrons are more exposed than σ electrons and this provides an explanation of why the alkenes are more reactive than the alkanes.

Fig. 3-15. An sp^2 hybridized carbon atom.

The 4 hydrogen atoms in ethylene (and the carbon atoms attached to the double bond in the higher alkenes) lie in one plane and the π electrons are perpendicular to that plane. To rotate 1 carbon atom of ethylene by 90°, it would be necessary to break the π bond to form two p orbitals in the new species (Fig. 3-18). This would require a large amount of energy and consequently groups attached to a double bond are locked in place. There is no rotation about a double bond at room temperature, in contrast to the essentially free rotation about single bonds. This analysis accounts for the existence of 2 stable isomeric 2-butenes (Fig. 3-19A). In the *trans* isomer, the 2 methyl groups are on opposite sides

Fig. 3-16. The formation of single bonds by two sp^2 carbon atoms.

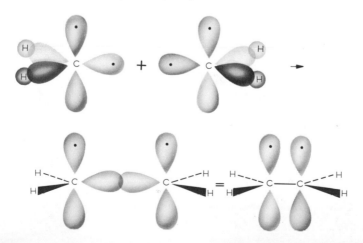

H
H
C
C
H
H
π
π
H
H
C
C
H
H

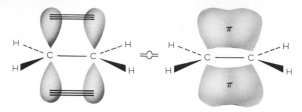

Fig. 3-17. The π orbital of ethylene.

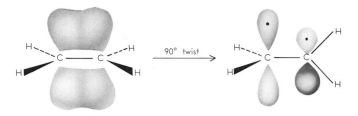

H
H
C
C
H
H
90° twist
H
H
C
C
H
H

Fig. 3-18. The twisting of a double bond by 90°.

of the carbon-carbon double bond, whereas in the *cis* isomer, they are on the same side of the double bond. This type of isomerism is called **geometric isomerism;** it occurs whenever 2 groups can be rigidly attached to different sides of a molecule. Two further examples are given in Figs. 3-19B and C (for convenience, double bonds are usually represented by 2 dashes).

Preparation of the Alkenes

The alkenes are synthesized most often by the elimination of a hydrohalic acid or water molecule from the appropriately substituted alkane.

Fig. 3-19. *Cis* and *trans* isomers.

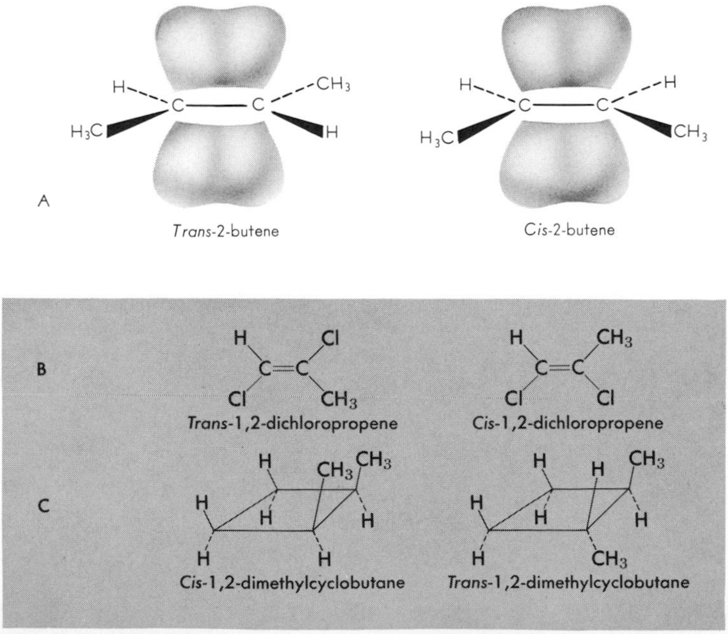

A
Trans-2-butene
Cis-2-butene
B
Trans-1,2-dichloropropene
Cis-1,2-dichloropropene
C
Cis-1,2-dimethylcyclobutane
Trans-1,2-dimethylcyclobutane

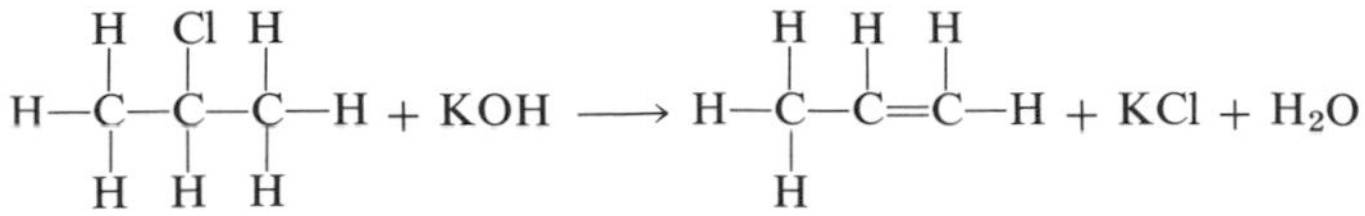

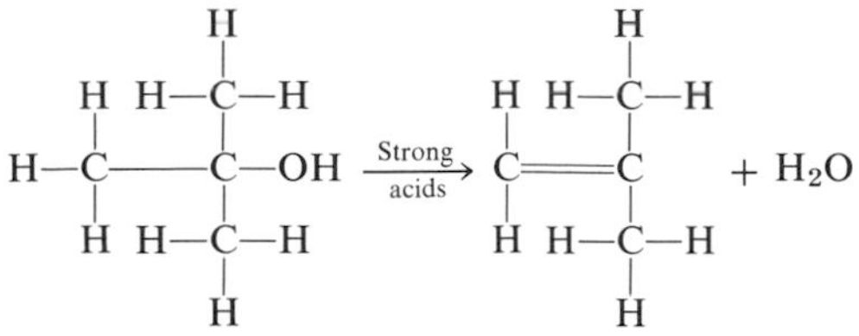

$$\underset{\underset{H}{|}}{\overset{\overset{H}{|}}{H-C}}-\underset{\underset{H}{|}}{\overset{\overset{Cl}{|}}{C}}-\underset{\underset{H}{|}}{\overset{\overset{H}{|}}{C}}-H \;+\; KOH \;\longrightarrow\; \underset{\underset{H}{|}}{\overset{\overset{H}{|}}{H-C}}-\overset{\overset{H}{|}}{C}=\overset{\overset{H}{|}}{C}-H \;+\; KCl \;+\; H_2O$$

$$\underset{\underset{H}{|}}{\overset{\overset{H-C-H}{|}}{H-C}}\quad\underset{\underset{H}{|}}{\overset{\overset{H-C-H}{|}}{C}}-OH \;\xrightarrow[\text{acids}]{\text{Strong}}\; C=C \;+\; H_2O$$

The latter reaction has been studied extensively and its mechanism has been well established. By **reaction mechanism,** we mean a detailed account of a reaction in terms of the sequence and manner in which the bonds are made and broken. We have already examined one reaction mechanism, the chlorination of the alkanes (a free-radical chain reaction). The 2 reactions listed above in which alkenes are formed are called **elimination** reactions. They are also **ionic** reactions; that is, reactions in which ions are formed as intermediates. The mechanism of the acid-catalyzed elimination reaction is given in Fig. 3-20.

In our representations of reaction mechanisms (Fig. 3-20 and others), curved arrows indicate the direction of movement of electrons. In the first step (Fig. 3-20), the reaction of the hydroxy compound with sulfuric acid yields a protonated species very similar structurally to the hydronium ion. In the second step, the C—O bond is broken. This ionization reaction is made possible by the protonation. The hydroxy compound itself does not ionize since this process would involve the separation of a negative ion (OH⁻) from a positive ion and this charge separation requires too much energy. In step 2, ionization yields the neutral species, H_2O, and a positively charged carbon

Fig. 3-20. The mechanism of the elimination of water from 2-methyl-2-hydroxypropane.

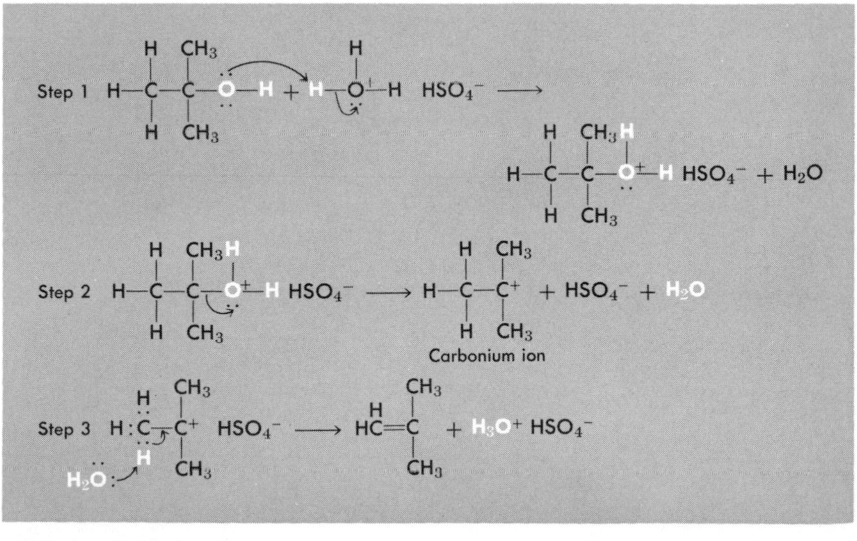

ion, called a **carbonium** ion, containing only 6 electrons in its valence shell. Carbonium ions are highly reactive species that tend to gain the stable octet of electrons (neon electron structure) by "pulling in" electrons from an adjacent carbon-hydrogen bond to give an olefin (Step 3, Fig. 3-20), or by reacting with a negative ion present in solution. For example, if the **dehydration** (elimination of water) is carried out in the presence of chloride ion, 2-methyl-2-chloropropane is formed in addition to the olefin.

$$CH_3-\underset{\underset{CH_3}{|}}{\overset{\overset{CH_3}{|}}{C}}-OH + H_2SO_4 + Na^+ \; :\ddot{\underset{..}{Cl}}:^- \longrightarrow \left[CH_3-\underset{\underset{CH_3}{|}}{\overset{\overset{CH_3}{|}}{C}}^+ \right] \xrightarrow[-H^+]{} H\overset{\overset{H}{|}}{C}=\overset{\overset{CH_3}{|}}{C}-CH_3$$

$$\xrightarrow[+Cl^-]{} CH_3-\underset{\underset{CH_3}{|}}{\overset{\overset{CH_3}{|}}{C}}-\ddot{\underset{..}{Cl}}:$$

In contrast to this multistep reaction, the elimination of hydrohalic acids with bases is a concerted, or 1-step, reaction; that is, a reaction in which no intermediates are formed.

The hydroxide ion plucks off a proton in this reaction, and in light of our definition of acids and bases, we would say that it is acting here as a typical base.

The study of reaction mechanisms has shown that the very large number of organic reactions known today can be organized and correlated by a relatively small number of mechanisms. A knowledge of one reaction then permits the extrapolation of the information to other reactions of this type, and often to totally new reactions. Therefore the mechanisms of important reactions will be outlined in each of the following sections, and a summary of the basic mechanisms will be given in Chapter 4.

Reactions of the Alkenes

The chemical reactions of the alkenes are characterized by addition to the double bond; that is, by reactions in which the double bond is lost and derivatives of the alkanes are formed. Several examples follow; if a catalyst is required, it is indicated above the arrow in the equation.

$$CH_3-\overset{\overset{H}{|}}{C}=\overset{\overset{H}{|}}{C}H + HCl \longrightarrow CH_3-\underset{\underset{Cl}{|}}{\overset{\overset{H}{|}}{C}}-CH_3$$

$$CH_3-\overset{\overset{H}{|}}{C}=\overset{\overset{H}{|}}{C}-CH_3 + H_2 \xrightarrow{Pt} CH_3CH_2CH_2CH_3$$

$$CH_3-\overset{\overset{CH_3}{|}}{\underset{\underset{H}{|}}{C}}=CH + H_2O \xrightarrow{H_2SO_4} CH_3-\underset{\underset{CH_3}{|}}{\overset{\overset{CH_3}{|}}{C}}-OH$$

The last reaction above is the reverse of the dehydration reaction outlined in the last section, and the mechanism of the reaction is—in a time sequence —the reverse of the dehydration mechanism:

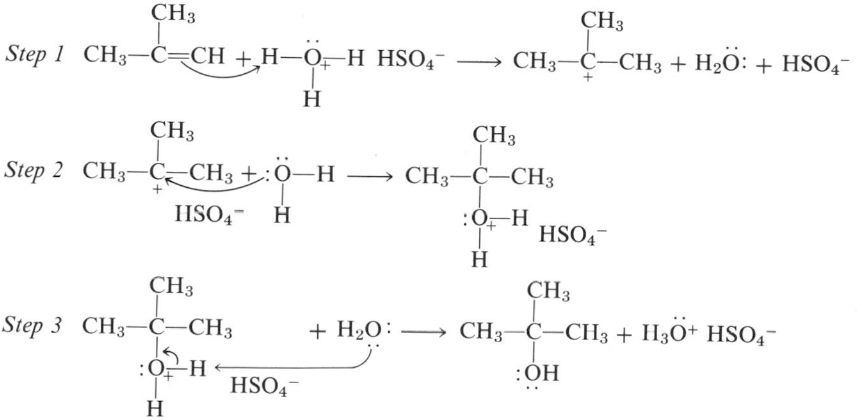

Step 1 $CH_3-\underset{\underset{CH_3}{|}}{C}=CH +H-\overset{..}{\underset{\underset{H}{|}}{O}}-H\ HSO_4^- \longrightarrow CH_3-\underset{\underset{CH_3}{|}}{\overset{+}{C}}-CH_3 + H_2\overset{..}{O}: + HSO_4^-$

Step 2 $CH_3-\underset{\underset{HSO_4^-}{}}{\overset{\underset{CH_3}{|}}{\overset{+}{C}}}-CH_3 +:\overset{..}{\underset{\underset{H}{|}}{O}}-H \longrightarrow CH_3-\underset{\underset{:\overset{..}{O}-H}{|}}{\overset{\underset{CH_3}{|}}{C}}-CH_3$
$\overset{+}{\underset{\underset{H}{|}}{}}\ HSO_4^-$

Step 3 $CH_3-\underset{\underset{:\overset{+}{O}-H}{|}}{\overset{\underset{CH_3}{|}}{C}}-CH_3\underset{\underset{H}{|}}{}$ $\underset{HSO_4^-}{} + H_2O: \longrightarrow CH_3-\underset{\underset{:\overset{..}{O}H}{|}}{\overset{\underset{CH_3}{|}}{C}}-CH_3 + H_3\overset{..}{O}{}^+\ HSO_4^-$

The hydration-dehydration reactions are reversible:

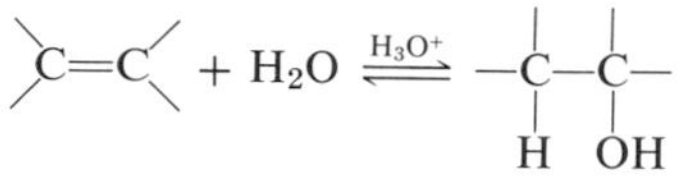

$$\underset{}{>}C=C\underset{}{<} + H_2O \underset{}{\overset{H_3O^+}{\rightleftharpoons}} -\underset{\underset{H}{|}}{C}-\underset{\underset{OH}{|}}{C}-$$

and strictly speaking, we should consider the amounts of alkene and hydroxyalkane present at equilibrium. However, large amounts of water favor the hydration reaction whereas high concentrations of acid (for example, concentrated sulfuric acid) and high temperatures favor the dehydration reaction. Depending on the conditions, it is quite possible to obtain 70 to 100 per cent of the hydroxyalkanes, or 70 to 100 per cent yields of the alkenes at equilibrium.

The reactions of alkenes with the hydrohalic acids proceed by a similar mechanism.

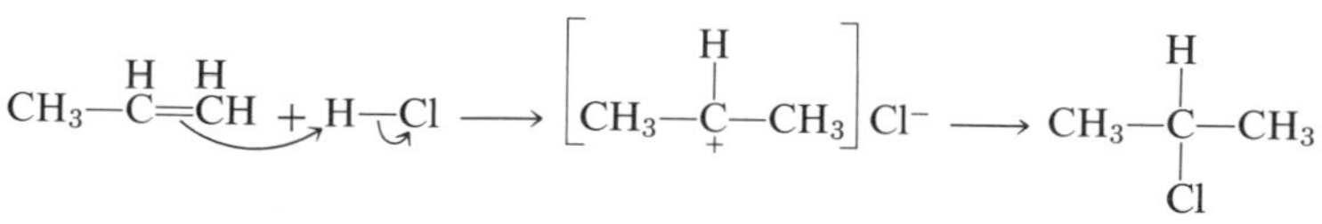

$$CH_3-\overset{H}{\underset{}{C}}=\overset{H}{\underset{}{C}}H +H-Cl \longrightarrow \left[CH_3-\overset{H}{\underset{}{\overset{+}{C}}}-CH_3\right]Cl^- \longrightarrow CH_3-\overset{H}{\underset{\underset{Cl}{|}}{C}}-CH_3$$

The product of this reaction is exclusively 2-chloropropane. The reason why no 1-chloropropane is formed or why no 2-methyl-1-propanol was formed in the previous example will be discussed in the section on aromatic compounds.

ELECTROPHILES AND NUCLEOPHILES.   The majority of alkene addition reactions are acid-catalyzed, or they involve the addition of acids; in each case, the first step is the attack of a proton or positive ion—the **electrophile,** or electron-seeking reagent—on the π electrons of the double bond; reactions of this type are called **electrophilic** reactions. As we shall see in the next chapter, many reactions involve bases and negative ions—**nucleophiles,** or electron donors—in the initial step; reactions of this type are called **nucleophilic** reactions. Consideration of the nature of such reactions led

G. N. Lewis, an American chemist, to propose a definition of acids and bases more general than the Brønsted definitions. According to Lewis, acids are electron acceptors and bases are electron donors; that is, in the following example, the carbonium ion is a **Lewis acid** and ammonia is a **Lewis base:**

$$\underset{\underset{\displaystyle H}{|}}{\overset{\underset{\displaystyle H}{|}}{H-N}} : \; + \; CH_3-\underset{\underset{\displaystyle CH_3}{|}}{\overset{\overset{\displaystyle CH_3}{|}}{C^+}} \longrightarrow H-\underset{\underset{\displaystyle H}{|}}{\overset{\overset{\displaystyle H}{|}}{N^{\pm}}}-\underset{\underset{\displaystyle CH_3}{|}}{\overset{\overset{\displaystyle CH_3}{|}}{C}}-CH_3$$

The analogy of this reaction to the neutralization of ammonia by hydrochloric acid is obvious:

$$\underset{\underset{\displaystyle H}{|}}{\overset{\overset{\displaystyle H}{|}}{H-N}} : \; + \; H_3O^+Cl^- \longrightarrow H-\underset{\underset{\displaystyle H}{|}}{\overset{\overset{\displaystyle H}{|}}{N^{\pm}}}-H \; \; Cl^- + H_2O$$

POLYMERIZATION.   The formation of giant molecules by the addition of one molecule to another is called **polymerization.** When ethylene is heated with certain compounds (R—R) which dissociate to give free radicals, polymerization occurs by a free-radical chain reaction similar to that involved in the chlorination of the alkanes.

Initiation $R-R \longrightarrow 2 \; R\cdot$

Propagation
$$\begin{bmatrix} R\cdot + CH_2{=}CH_2 \longrightarrow R-CH_2-CH_2\cdot \\ R-CH_2-CH_2\cdot + CH_2{=}CH_2 \longrightarrow R-CH_2-CH_2-CH_2-CH_2\cdot \\ R-CH_2-CH_2-CH_2-CH_2\cdot + CH_2{=}CH_2 \longrightarrow R-(CH_2)_n\cdot \end{bmatrix}$$

Termination
$$\begin{bmatrix} R-(CH_2)_n\cdot + R\cdot \longrightarrow R-(CH_2)_n-R \\ 2 \; R-(CH_2)_n\cdot \longrightarrow R-(CH_2)_{2n}-R \end{bmatrix}$$

The polymer formed in this way, called polyethylene, is of considerable commercial importance. Since n is a very large number (1000 or larger), the polymer molecule is essentially a very-long-chain alkane. Polymers are occasionally found in nature; natural rubber and gutta-percha are examples of naturally occurring polymers in which the repeat unit (or **monomer**) is 2-methylbutadiene (also called isoprene).

OZONOLYSIS.   One last reaction of alkenes deserves mention because it leads to the cleavage of the double bond, and as such is useful for the degradation of large alkenes. This reaction is called **ozonolysis.**

$$\underset{H_3C}{\overset{H_3C}{>}}C{=}C\underset{CH_3}{\overset{CH_3}{<}} + O_3 \longrightarrow \underset{CH_3}{\overset{CH_3}{>}}\underset{O-O}{\overset{O}{C}}\underset{CH_3}{\overset{CH_3}{<}} \xrightarrow[Z_n]{H_2O} 2 \; CH_3-\overset{\overset{\displaystyle O}{||}}{C}-CH_3$$

Ozone   An ozonide   Acetone

THE ALKYNES

The alkynes (often called acetylenes) are hydrocarbons containing one or more triple bonds. Their names are obtained by substitution of the suffix **yne** for the alkane suffix **ane;** the simplest member (ethyne) is usually called acetylene, however. Representative members of this class of compounds are given below.

$$H-C\equiv C-H \qquad CH_3-C\equiv C-CH_3$$
$$\text{Acetylene} \qquad\qquad \text{2-Butyne}$$

$$CH_3-C\equiv C-H \qquad H-C\equiv C-C\equiv C-H$$
$$\text{Propyne} \qquad\qquad \text{Butadiyne}$$

The structure of the alkynes is derived from still another hybridization of carbon.

Electron distribution in an excited carbon atom $\left[\begin{array}{cccc} ⑆ & ① & ① & ① \\ 2s & 2p & 2p & 2p \end{array}\right. \longrightarrow \begin{array}{cc|cc} ① & ① & + ① & ① \\ \text{Two } sp & & 2p & 2p \\ \text{hybrid} & & & \\ \text{orbitals} & & & \end{array}\left]\right.$ Electron distribution in an sp hybridized carbon atom

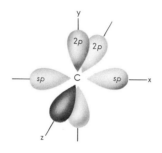

Fig. 3-21. An sp hybridized carbon atom.

The bond angle between sp orbitals is 180° and the remaining p orbitals are found at 90° to one another <u>and</u> to the sp axis (Fig. 3-21). In the acelylene molecule, one sp orbital is used to form the bond to hydrogen, the other is used to form a σ bond to the second carbon atom, and the p orbitals are used to form 2 π orbitals (Fig. 3-22).

There is further overlapping between the π bonds, with the result that the 4 lobes of the π orbitals form new orbitals that are cylindrical and symmetric about the C—C bond axis (Fig. 3-23). The molecular orbital pictures are inconvenient to use, however, so the triple bond is usually indicated by 3 dashes representing the 3 electron pairs of the bond. Because of the sp hybridization, acetylene is a linear molecule and the 4 carbon atoms in 2-butyne and butadiyne, for example, fall on a single line, the line of the bond axes.

As might be expected from the structures of the double and triple bonds, the syntheses and chemical reactions of the alkynes are quite similar to those of the alkenes.

$$CH_3-C\equiv C-H + HBr \longrightarrow CH_3-CBr_2-CH_3$$

$$CH_3-C\equiv C-CH_3 + 2\,Br_2 \longrightarrow CH_3-CBr_2-CBr_2-CH_3$$

$$CH_3CBr_2CH_3 + 2\,KOH \longrightarrow CH_3-C\equiv C-H + 2\,K^+Br^-$$

Acetylene itself, however, is usually made by a unique method, the hydrolysis of calcium carbide: $CaC_2 + 2\,H_2O \longrightarrow H-C\equiv C-H + Ca(OH)_2$.

A number of interesting acetylenes have been isolated recently from various wild flowers, principally from the *Compositae*. A surprising example, trideca-1-ene-3,5,7,-9,11-pentayne, is given on page 62 with some attempt to indicate the rod-like shape of the molecule.

Fig. 3-22. The π electron overlap of two sp hybridized carbon atoms.

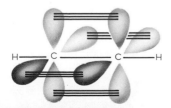

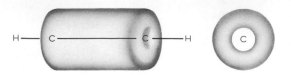

Fig. 3-23. Cylindrical π electron cloud of the acetylene molecule.

$$H-C\equiv C-H \qquad C$$

$$\underset{H}{\overset{H}{\underset{\displaystyle H}{}}}\hspace{-1em}C-C\equiv C-C\equiv C-C\equiv C-C\equiv C-C\equiv C-\underset{\displaystyle \underset{H}{\overset{\displaystyle C}{}}}{C}\overset{H}{\underset{H}{}}$$

Trideca-1-ene-3,5,7,9,11-pentayne

AROMATIC HYDROCARBONS

Aromatic hydrocarbons are unsaturated hydrocarbons that resemble benzene (C_6H_6) in behavior. The name of this class of compounds was assigned in the nineteenth century from the observation that many members had fragrant odors. The simplest member of the series, benzene, is a cyclic molecule containing a 6-membered ring and 3 double bonds.

This structure was first proposed by the German chemist August Kekulé in 1865, and it successfully accounted for the chemistry of benzene known at that time. It soon became apparent, however, that the structure was inadequate since it suggested that benzene was simply a cyclic olefin, whereas the chemical reactions of benzene proved to be quite different from those of the olefins. Refinements in the structure of benzene, which successfully account for its properties have been made in light of modern structural theory, and these will be outlined in a later section; for the time being, we shall continue to use a simple hexagon as the symbol for benzene. Examples of various aromatic hydrocarbons are given in Fig. 3-24 along with their systematic names (the hydrogens attached to the ring are usually omitted from the graphic formulas of aromatic molecules).

The monocyclic aromatic hydrocarbons are usually named as derivatives of benzene whereas the higher members are named as derivatives of a particular ring structure (Fig. 3-24B). It is of some interest that 10-methyl-1, 2-benzanthracene (Fig. 3-24B) and related compounds are **carcinogenic;** that is, they are able to initiate the formation of cancerous growths in animal tissues.

Although they are not hydrocarbons, the heterocyclic compounds should be mentioned at this point since in chemical reactivity they are very similar to the aromatic hydrocarbons. The **heterocyclics** are cyclic unsaturated compounds that contain 1 or more atoms of the elements in the right-hand portion of the periodic table. Examples of heterocyclic compounds are given in Fig. 3-25.

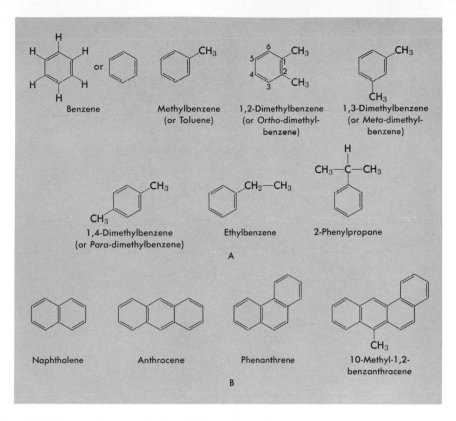

Fig. 3-24. (A) Benzene and its alkyl derivatives. (B) Polycyclic aromatic compounds.

Reactions of Aromatic Compounds

The characteristic reactions of aromatic compounds are substitutions; that is, reactions in which some group is substituted for a hydrogen atom on the ring. Examples are given below.

These substitution reactions of benzene are in marked contrast to the addition reactions of the alkenes and alkynes. The alkene isomers of benzene,

63

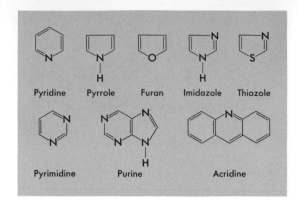

Fig. 3-25. Heterocyclic compounds.

1,3-hexadiene-5-yne (H—C≡C—CH=CH—CH=CH₂), for example, react typically by addition; furthermore, they are far less stable than benzene. These differences in properties are satisfactorily accounted for by a theory developed during the early part of this century, the theory of resonance. The resonance theory has proved to be of great value in the interpretation of the stability of compounds, the nature of the chemical reactions undergone, and the orientation, or direction of chemical attack; we shall now examine this theory.

Resonance

Molecules containing only single bonds are satisfactorily represented by formulas in which a dash is used to symbolize an electron-pair bond, as in methane:

$$H:\overset{\cdot\cdot}{\underset{\cdot\cdot}{C}}:H \;=\; H-\overset{\displaystyle H}{\underset{\displaystyle H}{C}}-H$$

The electrons in bonds of this type are largely localized between the atoms forming the bond. This is essentially true also for molecules containing one double or triple bond, and also for those containing several such bonds if the multiple bonds are separated by a saturated carbon atom as in 1,4-pentadiene:

$$\underset{H}{\overset{H}{>}}C=\overset{H}{\underset{}{C}}-\overset{H}{\underset{H}{C}}-\overset{H}{\underset{}{C}}=C\overset{H}{\underset{H}{<}}$$

The symbolism breaks down, however, for molecules that contain 2 or more multiple bonds attached directly to one another as in butadiene and benzene, and for molecules or ions that contain atoms with unshared electrons attached directly to a double bond. The π electrons in molecules or ions of this type are not localized; they are spread out over all the atoms involved in the multiple bonding and the atoms bearing unshared electrons. For example, we can readily write a structure for the carbonate ion ($CO_3^=$) in which each atom has an octet of electrons:

$$\underset{^-:\overset{\cdot\cdot}{O}\cdot\quad\cdot\overset{\cdot\cdot}{O}:^-}{\overset{:\overset{\cdot\cdot}{O}:}{\overset{\|}{C}}}$$

Two oxygen atoms are connected to carbon by σ bonds, and the third is connected by both σ and π bonds. There is no reason why 1 oxygen atom should differ from the other 2, so we must consider 2 more structures:

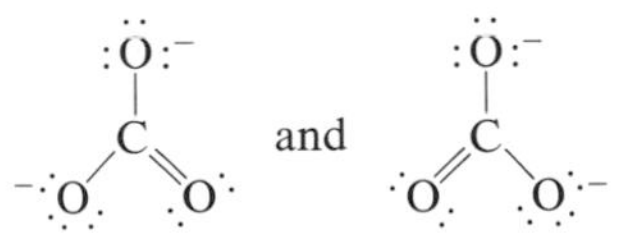

Is it possible that all the oxygen atoms are bonded to carbon in the same way? X-ray diffraction studies, in fact, show that this is the case; the 3 C—O bond lengths in the carbonate ion are identical.

Compounds or ions of this type, then, cannot be represented satisfactorily by a single valence bond structure; they are represented instead by a series of structures connected by double-headed arrows.

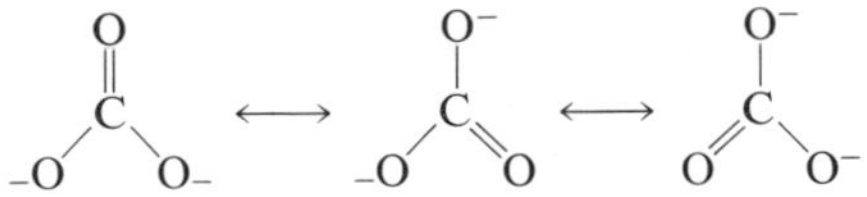

The "true structure" of the compound is an average of the structures drawn. Molecules or ions of this type are called **resonance hybrids,** and the individual structures that can be drawn are called **contributing** structures.

The representation of resonance hybrids in this way is an attempt to show that the unshared electrons in the $CO_3^=$, for example, are not localized on 2 of the oxygen atoms and that the π electrons are not localized between the carbon atom and 1 oxygen atom (as shown in any contributing structure), but that these electrons are delocalized, or spread out, over all the atoms with available p orbitals. A second way to represent the resonance hybrids involves the use of dotted lines to indicate the π-p system over which the electrons are delocalized:

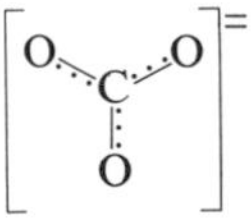

This type of formula more clearly indicates the symmetry of the system.

Similarly, if a proton is removed from a propene molecule,

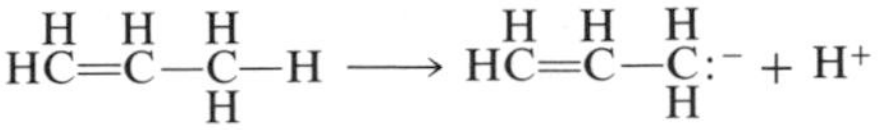

the electron pair is not localized on one carbon atom, but is delocalized over the π network:

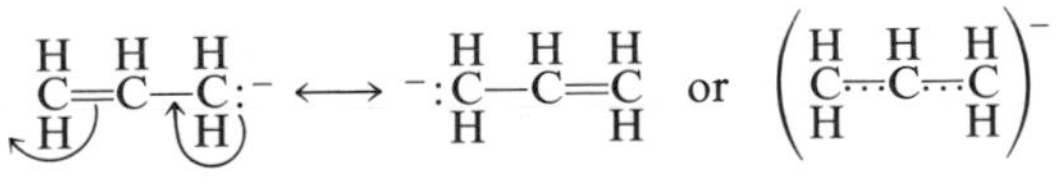

This delocalization can be represented by the interaction of the π and p orbitals involved, as in Fig. 3-26.

THE RESONANCE OF BENZENE. The resonance concept is required for an understanding of the structures of aromatic compounds. Benzene, for example, is not represented well by a single formula:

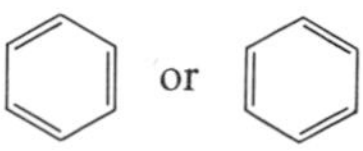

These formulas stand for "cyclohexatriene," a molecule that should show the reactions of an alkene. Neither formula represents benzene, then, which as

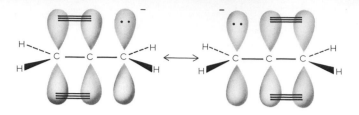

Fig. 3-26. Delocalization of electrons in the negative ion of propene.

we have seen from its chemical reactions is not an alkene. Instead, we represent benzene by a pair of resonance contributors, or by a single structure with

dotted lines to represent the π electrons: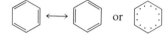

In this way we imply delocalization of the π electrons.

The delocalization of electrons in benzene can be illustrated more clearly through the use of molecular orbitals. The 6 carbon atoms of benzene are sp^2 hybrids, and a 6-membered ring may be formed by the use of two sp^2 orbitals from each atom to form bonds to two neighboring carbon atoms; the remaining sp^2 orbital is used to form a bond to hydrogen.

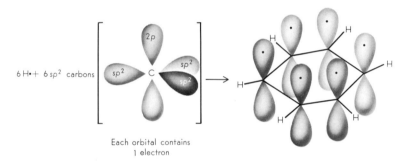

If adjacent p orbitals are now allowed to form ordinary 2-atom π orbitals, the resulting 2 equivalent structures (Figs. 3-27A and B) would correspond to our resonance contributors. However, a molecular orbital can be constructed in which overlap occurs between all of the p orbitals, allowing complete delocalization of the π electrons (Fig. 3-27C). This orbital contains 2 of the π electrons of benzene; the other 4 are placed in 2 other similar orbitals. This physical picture of the molecule satisfactorily accounts for the facts that are known about the structure of benzene. The benzene molecule is planar and highly symmetrical; the 6 bonds to hydrogen are identical in length, the 6 carbon-carbon bonds are identical in length, and all the bond angles are the same (120°). It is the closed ring of π electrons that accounts for the special properties of benzene.

The benzene molecule contains a closed ring of 6 π electrons. Organic chemists have studied many other monocyclic structures with π electrons, and it is interesting to note that only those compounds with a closed ring of 4 n + 2 π electrons proved to have aromatic properties (the n in 4 n + 2 can be any integer). This rule predicts that aromatic compounds can be prepared with what might be called "magic" numbers of 2, 6, 10, 14, 18, etc. π electrons, corresponding to values of n of 0, 1, 2, 3, 4, etc. Benzene corresponds to a magic number of 6, and recently, compounds have been made corresponding to magic numbers of 2, 6, and 18.

The number of isomers of the substituted benzenes is also in accord with the resonance theory of benzene. If the electrons were not delocalized in the aromatic ring, we would expect 2 isomers of 1,2-dimethylbenzene:

one with a double bond connecting carbon atoms 1 and 2, and the other with a single bond connecting those atoms. But the resonance picture suggests that 1,2-dimethylbenzene should exist in a single form.

Fig. 3-27. Resonance in benzene. (From C. R. Noller, *J. Chem. Ed.*, 27, 505, 1950.)

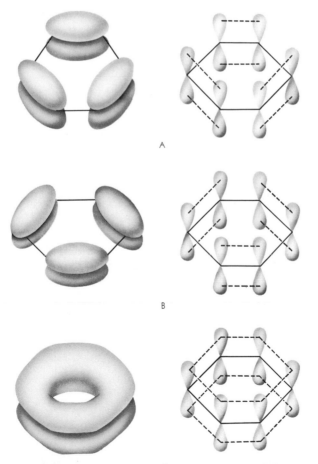

Many careful attempts have been made to determine the homogeneity of this compound and related 1,2-disubstituted benzenes, and in every case, the resonance theory has been upheld; that is, only 1 form of these compounds has been found.

RESONANCE ENERGY. A resonance hybrid is more stable (that is, it contains less energy) than the contributing structures. This difference is the **resonance energy** of the compound. The resonance energy may be approximated by measuring the energy released during a chemical reaction. For example, the reaction of cyclohexene with hydrogen over a nickel catalyst yields cyclohexane, and 28,000 calories of energy are released in the form of heat (ΔH).

$$\bigcirc + H_2 \xrightarrow{\text{Ni}} \bigcirc \qquad \Delta H = -28,000 \text{ calories}$$

This value of ΔH is also found for the hydrogenation of ethylene, propene, and other alkenes with only 1 double bond. Furthermore, the hydrogenation of 1,4-cyclohexadiene liberates 56,000 calories:

$$\bigcirc + 2 H_2 \xrightarrow{\text{Ni}} \bigcirc \qquad \Delta H = -56,000 \text{ calories}$$

That is, the same amount of energy is released during the hydrogenation of each double bond. We now assume that our hypothetical resonance contributor to benzene (which we will call "cyclohexatriene," no delocalization of π electrons being permitted) would yield 3(28,000) = 84,000 calories on hydrogenation.

$$+ 3 H_2 \xrightarrow{\text{Ni}} \bigcirc \qquad \Delta H = -84,000 \text{ calories}$$

Fig. 3-28. The resonance energy of benzene.

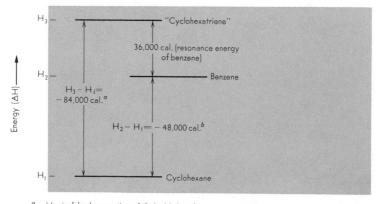

^{a} = Heat of hydrogenation of 3 double bonds
^{b} = Heat of hydrogenation of benzene

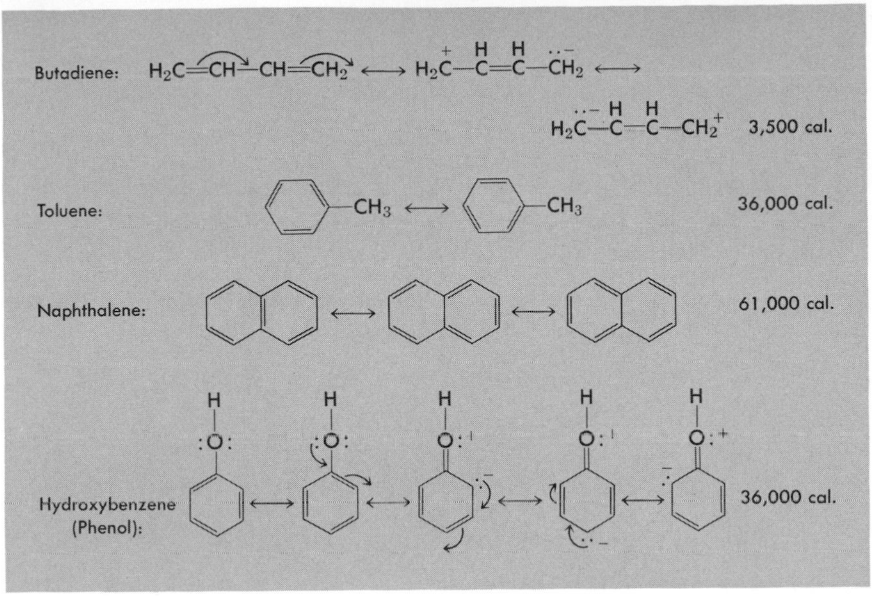

Fig. 3-29. Resonance energy and principal resonance contributors for selected compounds.

The hydrogenation of benzene, however, actually yields 48,000 calories, or 36,000 calories less than the cyclohexatriene value. This means that benzene contains 36,000 calories less energy than "cyclohexatriene," or in effect, that it is more stable by 36,000 calories. This difference in energy (36,000 calories) is the resonance energy of benzene (also called the delocalization energy). The relationships just outlined are illustrated in Fig. 3-28.

Several analogs of benzene and a few other resonance-stabilized molecules are given in Fig. 3-29 along with the principal resonance contributors, and values of the resonance energy. (The curved arrows signify the movement of electron pairs and they lead to the molecules on the nearest right.) Very often only one resonance contributor is used to represent an aromatic compound, as in Fig. 3-24A; this is done purely for convenience, and in such cases the structure stands for the resonance-stabilized molecule.

The resonance contributors shown for phenol in Fig. 3-29 illustrate that unshared p electrons on atoms attached directly to a double bond or aromatic system are also delocalized over the π electron network. The charges indicated on these resonance contributors are called **formal charges;** they represent the difference in the number of electrons "possessed" by the bonded atom and the number in the valence shell of the free atom. In nitromethane,

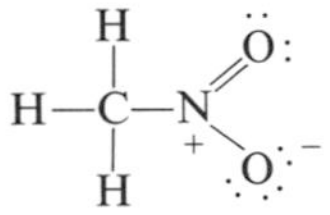

the singly bonded oxygen atom contains 3 pairs of unshared electrons (6 e) and it shares one electron pair with nitrogen ($\frac{1}{2}$ of 2 = 1 e). This bonded oxygen atom, therefore, possesses 7 electrons, whereas the valence shell of an isolated oxygen atom contains 6 electrons ($\cdot \ddot{O} \cdot$). The formal charge indicated on the oxygen atom in nitromethane (-1) gives this difference in the number of electrons $(7 - 6 = 1$ e$)$. The formal charge on the nitrogen atom is arrived at in a similar fashion.

RESONANCE ENERGY AND THE ELECTROPHILIC SUBSTITUTION OF AROMATIC COMPOUNDS. The concept of resonance accounts for the fact that substitution is the characteristic reaction of aromatic hydrocarbons rather than addition. Most of the reactions of aromatic compounds are electrophilic substitution reactions; that is, reactions in which positively charged ions, or electrophiles, attack the ring. Thus, the mechanism for bromination of benzene catalyzed by ferric bromide is:

$$FeBr_3 + Br_2 \longrightarrow FeBr_4^- + Br^+$$

Since the transition metal compounds are Lewis acids, they tend to form complex ions with the halide and other negatively charged ions. The other species formed in this reaction, the Br^+ ion, attacks the π electron system to give an adduct with 3 principal resonance contributors; these contributors show that the positive charge is not localized on the second carbon atom, but that it resides in addition on carbon atoms 4 and 6. The loss of a proton by this carbonium ion gives the fully aromatic, resonance-stabilized bromobenzene as the product. If instead a bromide ion were to add to the carbonium ion, the product would be a simple cyclohexadiene with very little resonance energy. It is the regaining of a resonance-stabilized system by the loss of a proton that leads to substitution in the aromatic series. In summary, then, resonance-stabilized alkenes or aromatic compounds react by electrophilic substitution reactions, whereas alkenes with little or no resonance energy react by electrophilic addition reactions. Other electrophiles that are capable of substitution reactions with aromatic compounds are NO_2^+ (from nitric acid: $HONO_2 + H^+ \longrightarrow H_2O + NO_2^+$), carbonium ions (from $RCl + AlCl_3 \longrightarrow R^+ + AlCl_4^-$ or $ROH + H_2SO_4$, or alkenes +

acids), and $R-\overset{\overset{O}{\|}}{C}{}^+$ (from carboxylic acids + H^+) (see page 63 for examples).

Orientation in Aromatic Substitution

The nitration of toluene under mild conditions yields a mixture of *ortho* and *para* nitrotoluenes:

whereas the nitration of nitrobenzene yields principally *meta* dinitrobenzene:

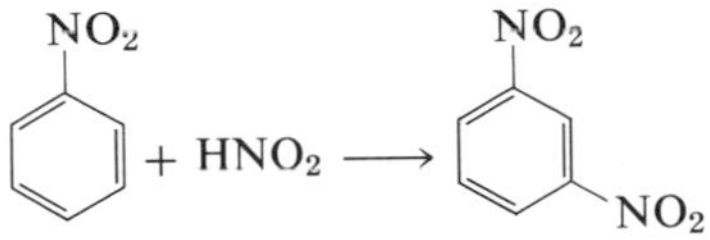

This difference in orientation is determined by the nature of the substituent (or group) on the benzene ring. How the substituent influences the orientation in reactions of this type is related to the explanation of why the addition of hydrogen chloride to propene yields 2-chloropropane and not the 1-chloro isomer (see p. 59).

$$CH_3-\overset{H}{C}=\overset{H}{CH} + HCl \longrightarrow \begin{array}{l} \not\longrightarrow CH_3CH_2CH_2Cl \\ \longrightarrow CH_3CHClCH_3 \end{array}$$

We shall discuss the question of orientation in aliphatic systems first.

ORIENTATION IN CARBONIUM ION REACTIONS. The carbon atom to which the chlorine becomes bonded is, in reality, determined by the type of carbonium ion formed in the first stage of the reaction, the first stage being the attack of a proton on the π electrons.

$$CH_3-\overset{H}{C}=\overset{H}{CH} + H^+ \longrightarrow \begin{array}{l} \not\longrightarrow CH_3CH_2CH_2{}^+ \\ \longrightarrow CH_3\underset{+}{C}HCH_3 \xrightarrow{Cl^-} CH_3CHClCH_3 \end{array}$$

The carbonium ions formed in reactions of this type are, invariably, the most highly substituted ones. We distinguish 3 types of carbonium ions by the number of alkyl groups attached to the electron-deficient carbon atom:

Primary carbonium ions: $H\overset{H}{\underset{H}{C}}{}^+$, $H\overset{H}{\underset{H}{C}}-\overset{H}{\underset{H}{C}}{}^+$, etc.

Secondary carbonium ions: $H\overset{H}{\underset{H}{C}}-\overset{H}{\underset{+}{C}}-\overset{H}{\underset{H}{C}}H$, etc.

Tertiary carbonium ions: etc.

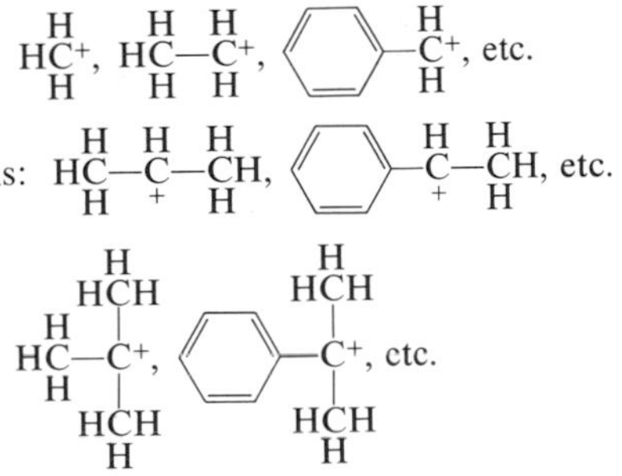

Alkyl groups are electron-releasing groups (relative to hydrogen) and therefore alkyl groups stabilize (or lower the energy) of carbonium ions. The stability order of carbonium ions is: tertiary > secondary > primary; the ease of forming these carbonium ions also decreases in this order. To return to the addition of hydrogen chloride to propene, the secondary propyl carbonium ion is more stable than the primary, and therefore the secondary propyl carbonium ion is formed from the addition of the proton to propene. The addition of chloride ion, leading to 2-chloropropane, then terminates the reaction. For similar reasons, the reaction of benzene with propene (catalyzed by sulfuric acid) leads to 2-phenylpropane and not 1-phenylpropane.

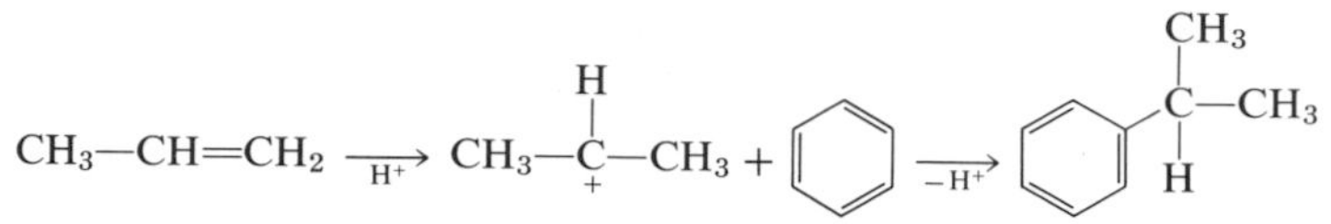

$$CH_3-CH=CH_2 \xrightarrow[H^+]{} CH_3-\overset{H}{\underset{+}{C}}-CH_3 + \bigcirc \xrightarrow[-H^+]{} \text{(benzene ring with } \overset{CH_3}{\underset{H}{C}}-CH_3 \text{)}$$

ELECTRON-RELEASING GROUPS AND THE *ortho-para* SUBSTITUTION OF ARO-MATIC COMPOUNDS. When attached to carbonium ions or to double bonds, most atoms and groups containing only single bonds are electron-releasing groups. This is illustrated with the aid of the resonance contributors for 3 derivatives of benzene in Fig. 3-30. Notice that the electron-releasing groups place a partial negative charge on the *ortho* and *para* positions of the ring, but *not* on the meta positions. This delocalization of electrons is especially important for groups bearing unshared electrons. The attack of an electrophilic species on a ring containing an electron-releasing substituent occurs preferentially in the *ortho* and *para* positions, because the positive charge on the ring in these cases can be partially neutralized by the electron release of the substituent; in other words, the charge is delocalized over the ring and also over the substituent (Fig. 3-31A).

A similar set of four resonance contributors can be written for substitution in the *para* position. Substitution in the *meta* position, however, leads to an intermediate in which the positive charge on the ring cannot be delocalized over the substituent (Fig. 3-31B). Consequently, very few molecules react by *meta* nitration because of the high activation energy of this path. The result of this type of resonance interaction is *ortho-para* substitution in nitration and in other electrophilic substitution reactions of benzene rings containing electron-releasing substituents.

ELECTRON-ATTRACTING GROUPS AND THE *meta* SUBSTITUTION OF AROMATIC COMPOUNDS. The second major type of substituent is the electron-attracting variety. In general, substituents of this type contain multiple bonds to oxygen or nitrogen, elements which are more electronegative than carbon. Examples illustrating the resonance interaction of substituents of this type are given in Fig. 3-32. Notice that these groups place partial positive charges on the *ortho* and *para* positions. This results in a lower electron density on the benzene ring, and in electrophilic substitution at a slower rate than in rings containing electron-supplying groups; furthermore, since the electron density is greater in the *meta* position, these groups lead to principally *meta* substitu-

Fig. 3-30. Resonance interaction of electron-releasing groups.

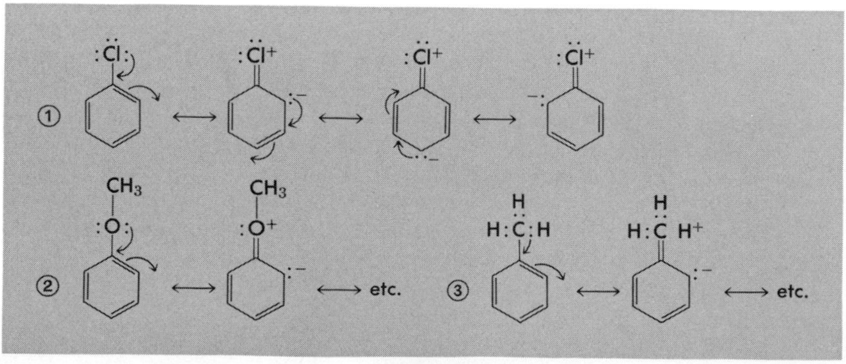

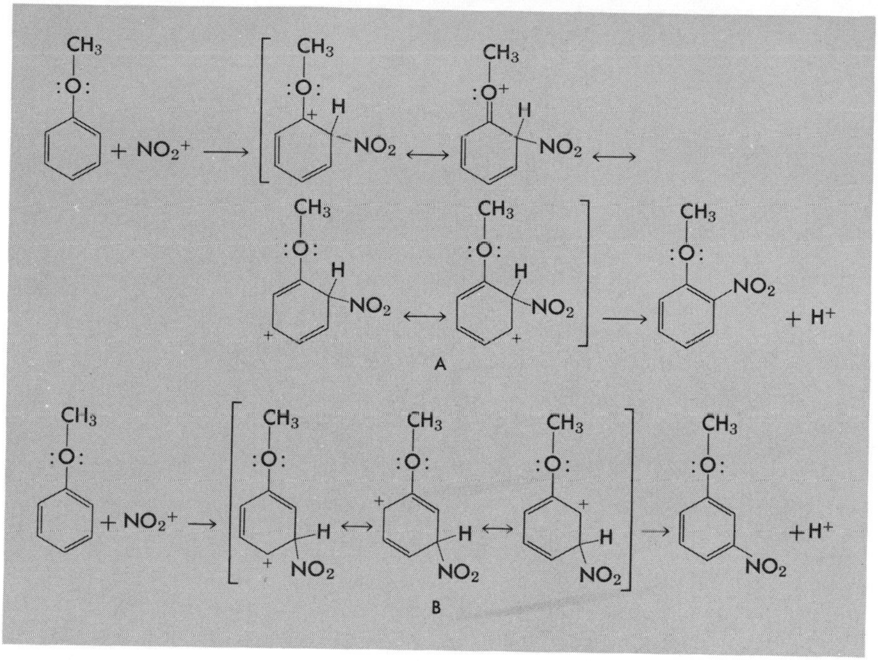

Fig. 3-31. (A) Electron delocalization during the electrophilic substitution of an aromatic ring *ortho* to an electron-releasing substituent. (B) Electron delocalization during the electrophilic substitution of an aromatic ring in the *meta* position.

tion. Specifically, electrophilic attack at the *ortho* and *para* positions is a relatively high-energy process since resonance involving the positive charge generated by the attack of the electrophile (NO_2^+, for example) places positive charges on adjacent atoms in one of the resonance contributors (Fig. 3-33A). The repulsion of like charges makes this resonance contributor an improbable one. This means that, effectively, delocalization occurs over only

Fig. 3-32. Resonance contributors of benzene rings bearing electron-attracting substituents.

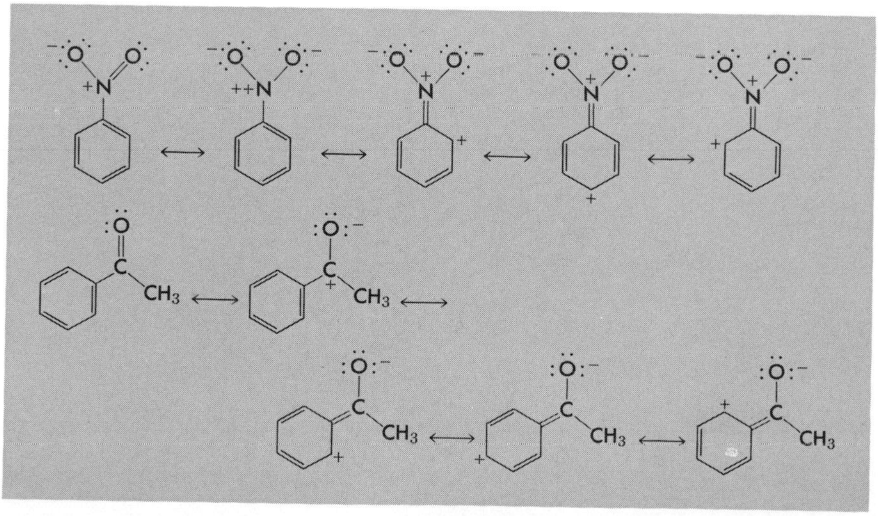

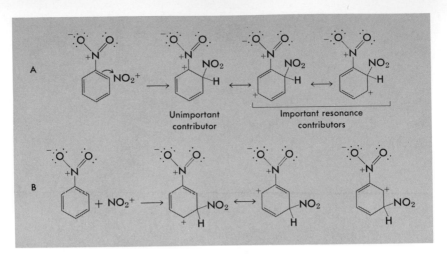

Fig. 3-33. (A) *Ortho* attack on a benzene ring containing an electron-attracting substituent. (B) *Meta* attack.

two positions of the ring (Fig. 3-33A). In contrast, attack in the *meta* position leads to delocalization over 3 positions of the ring (Fig. 3-33B), and in none of the resonance contributors are like charges placed on adjacent atoms.

The classification of substituents into electron-releasing and electron-attracting groups is fundamental to the study of the reactions a compound will undergo, the rates of such reactions, and the reaction mechanisms involved. We shall have occasion to apply the principles outlined in this chapter to some concrete examples in the remainder of this volume.

Organic Compounds Containing Oxygen

Compounds containing only carbon, hydrogen, and oxygen are extremely important in organic chemistry. In a structural sense, many of the simple oxygen-containing compounds may be considered as derivatives of the hydrocarbons in which some functional group containing oxygen is attached to a chain or a ring of the hydrocarbon. In this chapter, we shall cover the principal groups of oxygen derivatives in the order of the oxidation level of their functional groups.

ALCOHOLS

The alcohols (R—O—H) are alkyl derivatives of water, or in view of the definition above, hydroxy derivatives of the hydrocarbons. The systematic names of the alcohols are derived by the substitution of the suffix **ol** for the suffix **ane** of the corresponding hydrocarbons; the hydroxy derivatives of benzene, however, are usually referred to as phenols. Examples of alcohols and phenols along with their systematic names, and in certain cases their common names, are given in Fig. 4-1.

The alcohols are widely distributed in nature, although they are very often found in the bound state (in the form of esters, acetals, or other derivatives). Ethyl alcohol usually

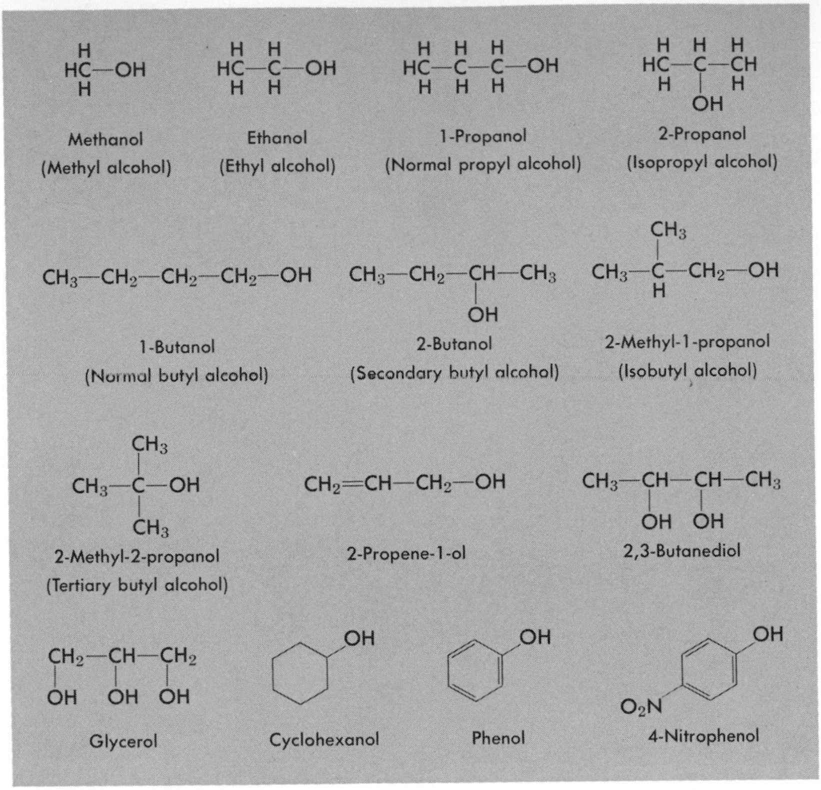

Methanol
(Methyl alcohol)

Ethanol
(Ethyl alcohol)

1-Propanol
(Normal propyl alcohol)

2-Propanol
(Isopropyl alcohol)

$CH_3-CH_2-CH_2-CH_2-OH$

1-Butanol
(Normal butyl alcohol)

$CH_3-CH_2-CH-CH_3$ with OH

2-Butanol
(Secondary butyl alcohol)

CH_3-C-CH_2-OH with CH_3 and H

2-Methyl-1-propanol
(Isobutyl alcohol)

CH_3-C-OH with CH_3 above and CH_3 below

2-Methyl-2-propanol
(Tertiary butyl alcohol)

$CH_2=CH-CH_2-OH$

2-Propene-1-ol

$CH_3-CH-CH-CH_3$ with OH OH

2,3-Butanediol

$CH_2-CH-CH_2$ with OH OH OH

Glycerol

OH (cyclohexane)

Cyclohexanol

OH (benzene)

Phenol

OH (benzene) with O_2N

4-Nitrophenol

Fig 4-1. Common alcohols and phenols.

occurs in the free state, however, and as such it is the active principle in beer, wine, and other "alcoholic" beverages; it is commonly prepared by the fermentation of the sugars present in grains, fruits, vegetables, etc. Many of the naturally occurring alcohols have complex structures, as exemplified by Vitamin A, which is essential for the growth of mammals. Note the relationship of the structure of Vitamin A to that of β-carotene (Fig. 3-13):

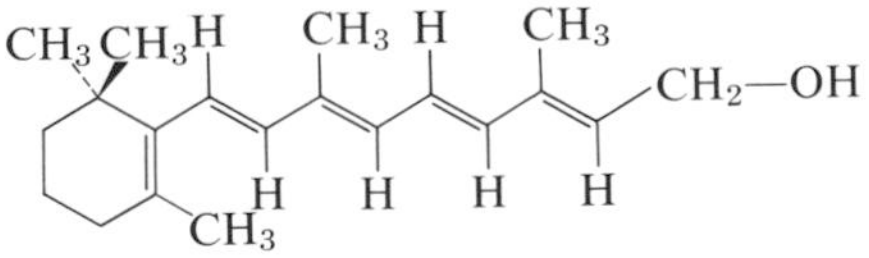

Vitamin A

Properties of the Alcohols

Methanol, ethanol, and the propanols are soluble in water in all proportions, and their physical and chemical properties resemble those of water. The alcohols of higher molecular weight are either only partly soluble or insoluble in water because they have long hydrocarbon chains and the ratio of carbons to the solubilizing OH group is high (hydrocarbons are insoluble in water). In physical properties, therefore, the higher alcohols resemble the alkanes; the OH groups of these alcohols still dominate the <u>chemical</u> reactivity, however.

The boiling points of water and the alcohols are abnormally high relative to the boiling points of the hydrocarbons, ethers, and related compounds of similar molecular weight (Table 4-1). Studies of the alcohols by means of

Table 4-1

BOILING POINTS OF PAIRS OF COMPOUNDS
WITH APPROXIMATELY THE SAME MOLECULAR WEIGHT

Compound	Molecular Weight	Boiling Point (° C)
CH_4	16	−161
H_2O	18	100
CH_3CH_3	30	−89
CH_3OH	32	65
CH_3—O—CH_3	46	−24
CH_3—CH_2—OH	46	78

their absorption of infrared light have provided an explanation of this fact. The —OH bond is highly polar because of the great electronegativity of of oxygen: $R—\overset{..}{\underset{..}{O}}—H \longleftrightarrow R—\overset{..}{\underset{..}{O}}:^- H^+$ (or $R—\overset{\delta^-}{O}—\overset{\delta^+}{H}$). Since a proton is very small, an adjacent molecule can approach to within a very short distance of it; the electrostatic force of attraction between oppositely charged atoms is appreciable at this short distance, and the molecules tend to form aggregates of various sizes in solution:

$$\underset{R}{\overset{\delta^-}{:\overset{..}{O}}}—\overset{\delta^+}{H}\text{------}\underset{R}{\overset{\delta^-}{:\overset{..}{O}}}—\overset{\delta^+}{H} \quad \text{and} \quad \underset{R}{O}—H\text{---}\left(\underset{R}{-O}—H\right)_n\text{---------}\underset{R}{O}—H$$

The forces holding the molecules together are called **hydrogen bonds;** they are about 5 per cent as strong as the average C—C, C—N, and C—O covalent bonds. The high boiling points arise from the extra energy required to break up these aggregates to allow individual molecules to enter the vapor phase. Hydrogen bonds are formed between compounds that are weak acids and weak bases; this limits the phenomenon essentially to compounds containing NH, OH, and SH bonds. If one of the components were a strong acid or a strong base, complete proton transfer would occur, as for example in the reaction of water with strong acids to form the hydronium ion (H_3O^+), or the reaction of acids with ammonia to give the ammonium ion (NH_4^+).

Preparation of the Alcohols

The alcohols are prepared by the reaction of Grignard reagents (see p. 88) with aldehydes, ketones, and esters, by the addition of water to alkenes (see p. 59), and also by the **hydrolysis** (decomposition with water) of the halogen derivatives of the alkanes (RX): $RX + H_2O \longrightarrow ROH + HX$. A similar reaction occurs with hydroxide ion: $RX + OH^- \longrightarrow ROH + X^-$.

These substitution reactions proceed by one of two mechanisms, depending on the stability of the carbonium ion derived from the halide, RX. If the carbonium ion is relatively stable, a 2-step reaction occurs in hydrolysis:

$$\text{Step 1} \qquad \underset{\underset{CH_3}{|}}{\overset{\overset{CH_3}{|}}{CH_3-C-Br}} \longrightarrow \underset{\underset{CH_3}{|}}{\overset{\overset{CH_3}{|}}{CH_3-C^+}} + Br^-$$

Slow

$$\text{Step 2} \qquad \underset{\underset{CH_3}{|}}{\overset{\overset{CH_3}{|}}{CH_3-C^+}} + 2\,H_2O \longrightarrow \underset{\underset{CH_3}{|}}{\overset{\overset{CH_3}{|}}{CH_3-C-O-H}} + H_3O^+$$

Fast

The first step is a slow ionization, giving the tertiary butyl carbonium ion and a bromide ion, and the second step is the reaction of the carbonium ion with the nucleophile water, giving the alcohol. Similarly:

$$CH_2{=}CH{-}CH_2{-}Br \xrightarrow[-Br^-]{H_2O} \quad \begin{bmatrix} \overset{H \quad H \quad H}{C{=}C{-}C^+} \\ \overset{|}{H} \qquad \overset{|}{H} \\ \\ \overset{H \quad H \quad H}{{}^+C{-}C{=}C} \\ \overset{|}{H} \qquad \overset{|}{H} \end{bmatrix} \xrightarrow[-H^+]{H_2O} CH_2{=}CH{-}CH_2OH$$

The carbonium ion formed here is a particularly stable one because of the resonance interaction (delocalization of the positive charge; see Fig. 3-26 for the resonance of the corresponding negative ion).

The second type of hydrolysis occurs with alkyl halides, such as the primary alkyl bromides, that have high-energy carbonium ions. Compounds of this type show little tendency to ionize in pure water. However, they react quite rapidly with hydroxide ions by a concerted process; that is, by a process in which bond-making (C—O bond-formation) and bond-breaking (C—Cl bond-rupture) occur simultaneously.

$$H-\overset{..}{\underset{..}{O}}{:}^- \qquad \underset{\underset{H}{\overset{H}{\big|}}}{\overset{H}{\underset{\quad}{\big\backslash}}}C{-}\overset{..}{\underset{..}{Cl}}{:} \longrightarrow H-\overset{..}{\underset{..}{O}}{-}CH_3 + Cl^-$$

Alcohol formation also occurs with the nucleophile water, but the rate is considerably lower. The hydroxide ion is a stronger base than water, and it is also a stronger nucleophile. Strictly speaking, basicity is a measure of the ability to abstract protons—for example, in acid-base reactions,

$$H-\overset{..}{\underset{..}{O}}{:}^- \qquad H{-}\overset{..}{\underset{..}{O}}{-}N{=}\overset{..}{O}{:} \rightleftharpoons H_2O + {}^-{:}\overset{..}{\underset{..}{O}}{-}N{=}\overset{..}{O}{:}$$

and nucleophilicity is a measure of the rate of attack on a carbon atom (in substitution reactions). However, as long as we are comparing reactions by the same atom in the base and in the nucleophile (an oxygen atom in this case), a strong base is also a good nucleophile; an increase in the electron density on oxygen increases both the base strength and the nucleophilicity. This parallelism breaks down when different atoms are being compared; for instance, SH⁻ is a better nucleophile than OH⁻, but it is a weaker base.

Many nucleophiles and inorganic ions other than hydroxide ion react with the alkyl halides:

$$K^+I^- + CH_3Cl \longrightarrow CH_3I + K^+Cl^-$$

$$Na^+SH^- + CH_2CH_2Cl \longrightarrow \underset{\text{Ethanethiol}}{CH_2CH_2SH} + Na^+Cl^-$$

$$Na^+ : C \equiv N :^- + CH_3CH_2Br \longrightarrow \underset{\text{Ethyl cyanide}}{CH_3CH_2C \equiv N :} + Na^+Br^-$$

$$: NH_3 + CH_3CH_2CH_2Br \longrightarrow CH_3CH_2CH_2NH_3^+Br^-$$

$$\xrightarrow[\text{NaOH}]{} \underset{\text{Propylamine}}{CH_3CH_2CH_2\overset{..}{N}H_2} + Na^+Br^- + H_2O$$

Reactions of this type are very important for the synthesis of organic compounds; they are called **nucleophilic substitution reactions** in view of the involvement of nucleophiles and the substitution nature of the reaction.

The reaction of a strong base with an alkyl halide leads to concurrent substitution and elimination reactions (see section on alkenes, Chapter 3).

$$\underset{\substack{H\ H\ H}}{\overset{\substack{H\ H\ H}}{HC-C-C}}-Cl + Na^+OH^- \longrightarrow \begin{cases} CH_3-CH=CH_2 + Na^+Cl^- + H_2O \\ \\ CH_3-CH_2-CH_2-OH + Na^+Cl^- \end{cases}$$

A number of variables influence the ratio of elimination to substitution, but one of the most important is the degree of branching of the alkyl halides. Highly branched alkyl halides such as tertiary butyl chloride give largely the alkene (2-methyl-2-propene in this case), whereas the primary alkyl halides give largely the alcohol.

Reactions of the Alcohols

Because of the structural relationship of the alcohols to water and the inertness of hydrocarbon chains, most of the reactions of the alcohols are similar to those of water. The alcohols react with alkali metals to give salts, for example: $2\,ROH + 2\,Na \longrightarrow 2\,RO^-Na^+ + H_2$. These are named by the substitution of the suffix **oxide** for the alcohol suffix **anol** and the addition of the name of the positive ion. Examples are sodium methoxide, $CH_3O^-Na^+$, and sodium ethoxide, $CH_3CH_2O^-Na^+$ (collectively, these salts are referred to as **alkoxides**).

The alcohols are about as weakly acidic as water ($ROH + H_2O \rightleftharpoons H_3O^+ + RO^-$; $K = 10^{-13}$ to 10^{-18}), whereas the phenols are considerably more acidic:

$$\text{C}_6\text{H}_5-OH + H_2O \rightleftharpoons H_3O^+ + \text{C}_6\text{H}_5-O^-; \quad K = 10^{-10}$$

Because of this higher acidity, phenols will dissolve in water solutions of sodium hydroxide, whereas the high-molecular-weight alcohols are not dissolved by aqueous base.

$$\text{C}_6\text{H}_5-OH + K^+OH^- \longrightarrow H_2O + \text{C}_6\text{H}_5-O^-K^+$$

Mixtures of phenols and alcohols can be readily separated, therefore, with a dilute solution of sodium hydroxide. The phenol enters the aqueous phase as the sodium salt whereas the alcohol remains as a separate layer that can be removed. The water layer is then acidified to regenerate the phenol.

The higher acidity of phenol is attributed to the resonance of the phenoxide ion:

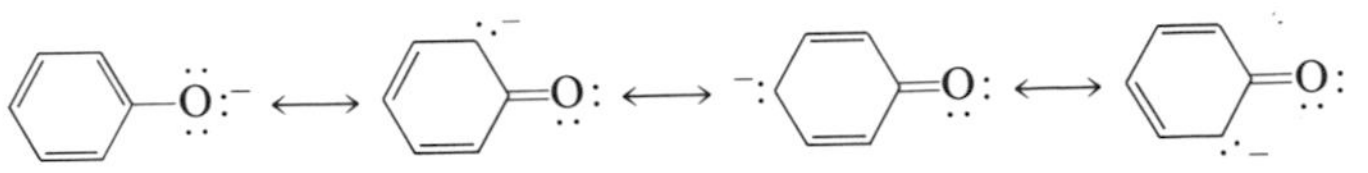

The negative charge is not localized on the oxygen atom, as it is in the alkoxide ions, $R-O^-$, but it is delocalized over the aromatic ring. This results in a low electron density on oxygen, a low basicity of the negative ion, and a high phenoxide concentration at equilibrium. A more detailed explanation of the relationship of acidity to the structure of acids will be given in a later section on the acid strengths of the carboxylic acids.

OXIDATION. Primary* alcohols are oxidized by sodium dichromate to give compounds called aldehydes:

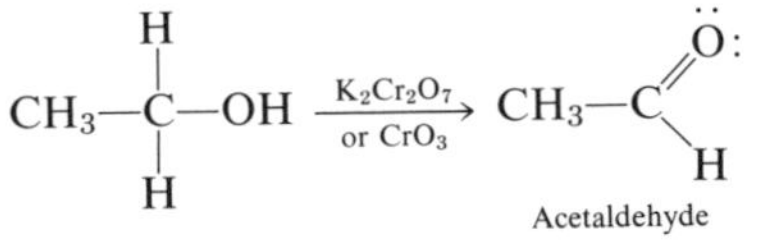

and secondary* alcohols yield compounds of a similar type called ketones:

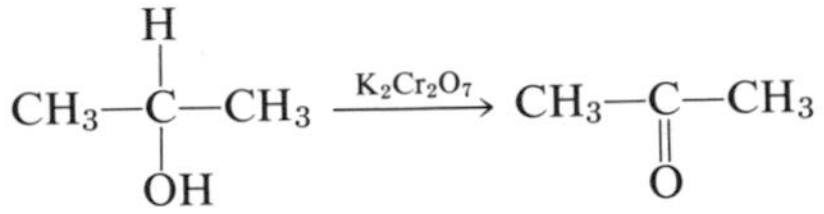

Tertiary* alcohols, in contrast, are stable to these oxidizing agents under normal conditions.

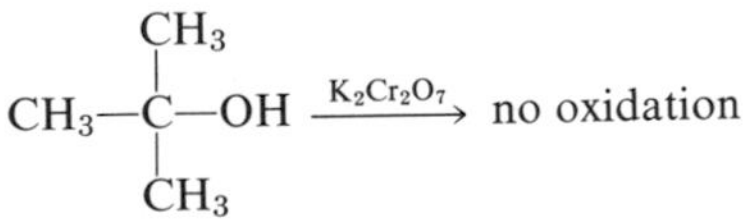

The oxidation of primary alcohols with an excess of $K_2Cr_2O_7$ or with $KMnO_4$ proceeds to a further stage to give the corresponding carboxylic acid: $R-CH_2-CH_2-OH \xrightarrow{KMnO_4} R-CH_2-CO_2H$. These oxidation reactions are made use of in the degradation of complex compounds. The formation of aldehyde or acid groups on oxidation would suggest, for example, that the compound contained primary alcohol groups, whereas the formation of ketone functions would indicate the presence of secondary alcohol groups.

The chemistry of the aldehydes, ketones, and acids will be outlined in the following sections of this chapter.

---

* See p. 71 for the meaning of the terms primary, secondary. and tertiary.

ESTERIFICATION.   One of the most valuable of the alcohol reactions is the formation from inorganic and organic acids of compounds known as esters:

$$2\ CH_3CH_2OH + H_2SO_4 \xrightarrow{25°} CH_3CH_2-O-\overset{\displaystyle O}{\underset{\displaystyle O}{\overset{|}{\underset{|}{S}}}}-O-CH_2CH_3 + 2\ H_2O$$

Ethyl sulfate

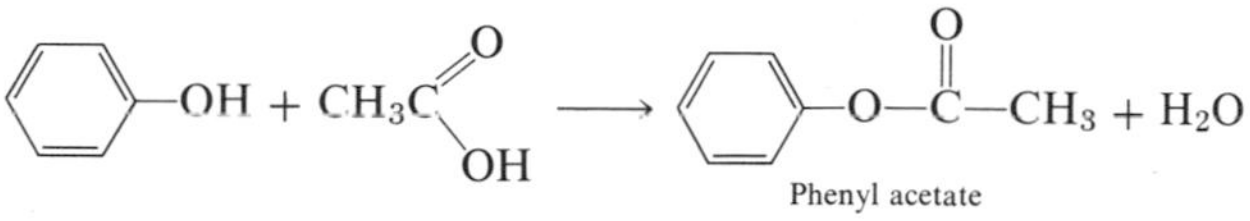

Phenyl acetate

$$CH_2-CH-CH_2 + 3\ HONO_2 \longrightarrow CH_2-CH-CH_2\ \ +\ 3\ H_2O$$

$$\underset{OH}{|}\ \ \underset{OH}{|}\ \ \underset{OH}{|} \qquad \underset{ONO_2}{|}\ \underset{ONO_2}{|}\ \underset{ONO_2}{|}$$

Glyceryl trinitrate
(Nitroglycerine)

The esters are named as if they were salts (from the name of the organic radical and the name of the negative ion of the acid) although in reality they are covalently bonded compounds. The chemistry of these compounds will be discussed in greater detail in a later section of this chapter.

DEHYDRATION.   Another typical reaction of the alcohols involves their dehydration with strong acids. This is a general method for the synthesis of alkenes (see p. 57 for more details about this reaction).

$$CH_3CH_2OH \xrightarrow[100°]{H_2SO_4} CH_2{=}CH_2 + H_2O$$

High temperatures alone may also be used to dehydrate alcohols.

$$CH_3\underset{\underset{OH}{|}}{CH}CH_3 \xrightarrow{200-300°} CH_3CH{=}CH_2 + H_2O$$

ETHERS

Ethers (ROR) are derivatives of water in which both of the hydrogen atoms are replaced by alkyl or aryl* groups. They are named in two different ways: either by the attachment of the names of the alkyl radicals to the generic name ether, or by the system in which they are treated as alkoxide derivatives of the hydrocarbons. Most of the *cyclic* ethers have common names, however. Examples are given in Fig. 4-2.

The ethers are widely distributed in nature, and a few—vanillin, for example, the principle flavoring agent of vanilla (shown below)—are of commercial importance. The lower-molecular-weight ethers are used principally as solvents, although diethyl ether is widely used in addition as an anesthetic.

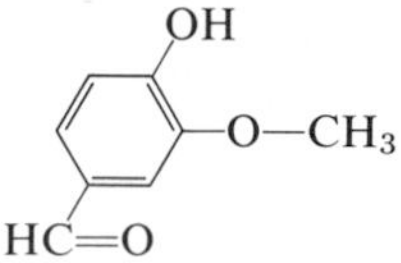

Vanillin

* A radical derived from an aromatic hydrocarbon.

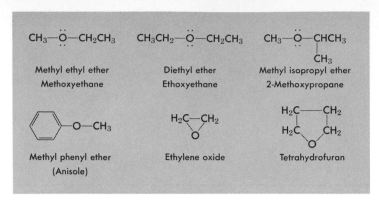

Fig. 4-2. Common ethers.

The ethers are conveniently prepared by the reaction of alkoxide ions with alkyl halides:

$$CH_3-\overset{..}{\underset{..}{O}}:\overset{\frown}{\longrightarrow}CH_3-\overset{\frown}{\underset{..}{Cl}}: \longrightarrow CH_3-O-CH_3 + Na^+Cl^-$$
$$Na^+$$

This is a typical nucleophilic displacement reaction of an alkyl halide, and it is restricted, essentially to primary and secondary alkyl halides (see section on the preparation of alcohols from alkyl halides).

As one might expect from the structure, pure ethers are not hydrogen-bonded, and as a result, their boiling points are similar to those of the related alkanes. The ethers are weak Lewis bases, however, and they do form hydrogen bonds with alcohols, $CH_3-\overset{..}{O}:------H-\overset{..}{\underset{..}{O}}-CH_3$; salts with
$$\underset{CH_3}{|}$$
strong protic acids, $CH_3-\overset{..}{O^\pm}-H\ Cl^-$; and salts with Lewis acids,
$$\underset{CH_3}{|}$$

$$CH_3CH_2OCH_2CH_3 + \underset{F\quad F}{\overset{F}{\underset{|}{B}}} \longrightarrow CH_3CH_2-\overset{..}{\underset{CH_3CH_2}{O}}-\overset{F}{\underset{F}{\overset{|}{B}^\pm}}-F$$

(BF$_3$ contains a boron atom with 6 electrons in its valence shell). Because of the basic properties of ethers, they may be cleaved by strong acids:

$$\text{⬡}-\overset{..}{\underset{..}{O}}-CH_3 + HI \longrightarrow \text{⬡}-\overset{..}{\underset{H}{O^\pm}}CH_3 \longrightarrow \text{⬡}-\overset{..}{\underset{..}{O}}-H + CH_3I$$
$$\quad\quad\quad\quad :\overset{..}{\underset{..}{I}}:^-$$

Since methoxy groups are common in compounds found in nature, the treatment of these compounds with hydrogen iodide and the isolation of the methyl iodide formed is very useful in studies aimed at determining their structures.

In contrast to this behavior with acids, ethers are very stable to bases, and unstable alcohols are often converted into ethers to protect the molecules from decomposition in certain reactions that would normally destroy the free alcohol (such as oxidation in basic solutions).

ALDEHYDES AND KETONES

Aldehydes and **ketones** are alkyl and aryl derivatives of the simplest organic compound containing doubly bonded oxygen, formaldehyde (CH_2O;

$$:\overset{\cdot\cdot}{\underset{\parallel}{O}}$$

H—C—H). The aldehydes (RCHO) are monoalkyl derivatives and the ketones (RCOR) are dialkyl derivatives of formaldehyde. The aldehydes are named systematically by the substitution of the suffix **al** for the suffix **e** of the hydrocarbon molecule with the same chain length, and the ketones, by the substitution of the suffix **one** for this ending (although in certain cases, the **e** is retained). For the structures of some simple aldehydes and ketones and their names (systematic and common), see Fig. 4-3.

The aldehyde and ketone functional groups are common in natural products; three examples are given below:

$$CH_3(CH_2)_{12}CHO \qquad CH_3-\underset{}{C}=CH-CH_2-CH_2-\underset{H}{\overset{CH_3}{C}}-CH_2CHO$$

Tetradecanal   Citronellal

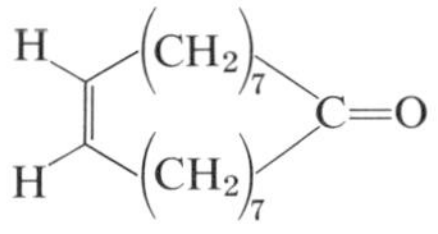

$$\underset{H}{\overset{H}{>}}\underset{(CH_2)_7}{\overset{(CH_2)_7}{<}}C=O$$

Civetone

Tetradecanal is required for light production in the luminous bacterium *Achromobacter fischeri,* citronellal is used by ants as a chemical alarm signal, and civetone is a perfume ingredient obtained from the scent glands of the civet cat.

Preparation of Aldehydes and Ketones

The most general reaction for the preparation of aldehydes and ketones is the oxidation of alcohols with sodium dichromate or chromic oxide (see sec-

Fig. 4-3. Representative aldehydes and ketones.

$$CH_3\underset{H}{\overset{}{C}}=O \qquad CH_3-\underset{H}{\overset{CH_3}{C}}-CH_2-\underset{H}{\overset{}{C}}=O \qquad CH_2=CH-\overset{O}{\overset{\parallel}{C}}-CH_3$$

Ethanal   3-Methylbutanal   3-Butene-2-one
(Acetaldehyde)   (3-Methylbutyraldehyde)

$$CH_3-\overset{O}{\overset{\parallel}{C}}-CH_3$$

2-Propanone   1,3-Cyclopentanedione   Benzaldehyde
(Acetone)

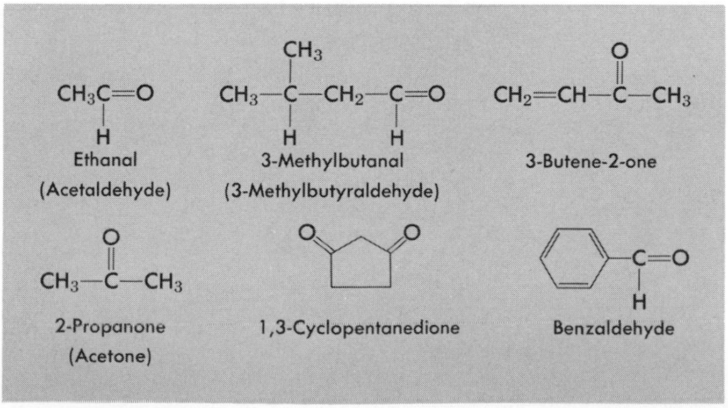

tion on alcohols). The aromatic ketones are often prepared, in addition, by the **Friedel-Crafts** reaction, the reaction of an aromatic compound with a halogen derivative catalyzed usually by aluminum chloride:

$$\underset{\substack{\| \\ O}}{R-C-Cl} + AlCl_3 \longrightarrow \underset{\substack{\| \\ O}}{R-C^+AlCl_4^-}$$

This is another example of electrophilic substitution.

Reactions of Aldehydes and Ketones

The doubly bonded carbon-oxygen group, called the **carbonyl group,** has a structure similar to that of the carbon-carbon double bond (Fig. 4-4). The 2 R groups and the 2 unshared electron pairs on the oxygen atom are in 1 plane and the π electrons are perpendicular to that plane. The bond is a polar one because of the greater electronegativity of the oxygen atom; this is shown by means of the principle resonance contributors of the carbonyl group.

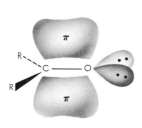

Fig. 4-4. Structure of the carbonyl group.

TAUTOMERISM. Electrons on the α carbon (the carbon atom adjacent to the carbonyl group) can be delocalized over the carbonyl group:

Negative ions of this type are far more stable than negative ions derived from hydrocarbons that are not resonance-stabilized, for example, the anion derived from methane, $H-\overset{\overset{\displaystyle H}{|}}{\underset{\underset{\displaystyle H}{|}}{C}}:^-$. As a result, aldehydes and ketones are far more acidic than the hydrocarbons.

The ion formed in this way from aldehydes and ketones is called an **enolate ion.** The acidification of enolate ions yields the parent carbonyl compound, but very often, in addition, an isomeric compound.

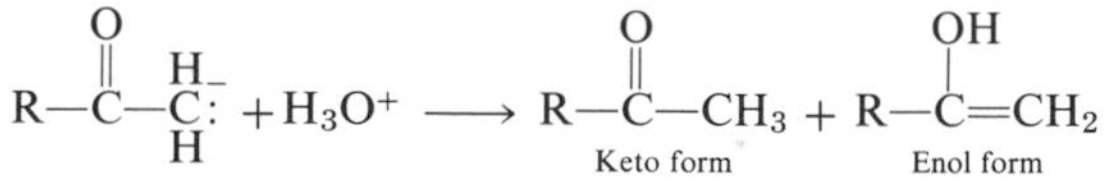

$$R-\overset{\overset{O}{\|}}{C}-\overset{\overset{H_-}{|}}{\underset{\underset{H}{|}}{C}}: + H_3O^+ \longrightarrow R-\overset{\overset{O}{\|}}{C}-CH_3 + R-\overset{\overset{OH}{|}}{C}=CH_2$$

Keto form   Enol form

The isomeric compound is called an **enol** (**en** for the double bond and **ol** for the hydroxy group). With time, these enol forms of most aldehydes and ketones change back into the normal carbonyl, or keto, forms; that is, the enol form is usually less stable than the keto form.

The formation of enols may also be catalyzed by acids:

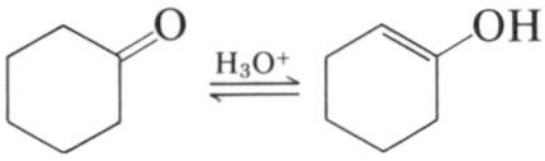

The general phenomenon of 2 isomeric species in equilibrium is called **tautomerism.** The equilibrium amount of the enol form in the tautomerism of simple aldehydes and ketones (acetone) is usually less than 1 per cent at room temperature. The equilibrium amount of the enol form can approach 100 per cent, however, in the case of diketones in which the enol form is stabilized by hydrogen-bonding (as in acetylacetone).

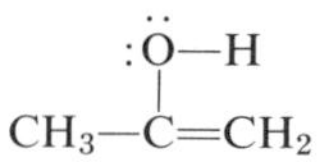

Enol of acetone 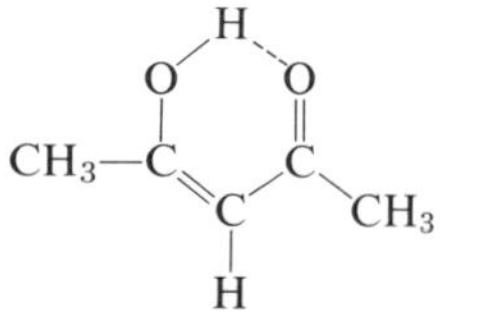   Acetylacetone

REACTIONS OF THE α CARBON ATOM.   Enols and enolate ions are highly reactive species that lead to substitution on the α position. The base- and acid-catalyzed brominations of acetone are examples (Fig. 4-5). In both types of bromination, the first step is a typical acid-base reaction, and the last step is a nucleophilic displacement on bromine of bromide ion.

Reactions of the Carbonyl Group

ACETALS AND KETALS.   Compounds containing carbonyl groups react not only at the α carbon atom, but also at the carbonyl group; reactions of the latter type involve, typically, the addition of some molecule across the multiple bond, just as the reactions of alkenes are characterized by addition across the carbon-carbon double bond. In water solutions of carbonyl compounds, for example, a low concentration of the **hydrate** (an addition compound of water) is formed:

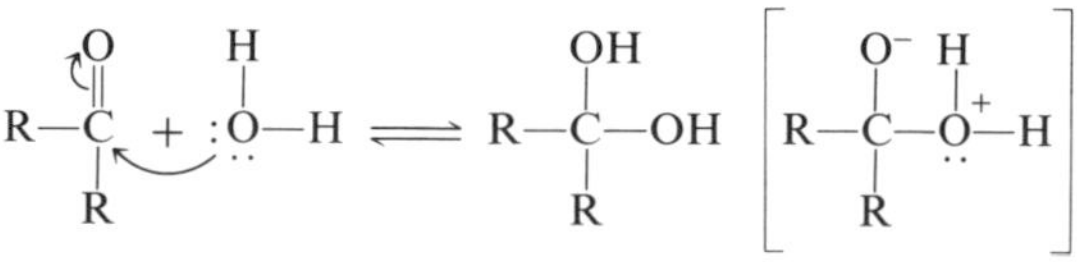

"X"

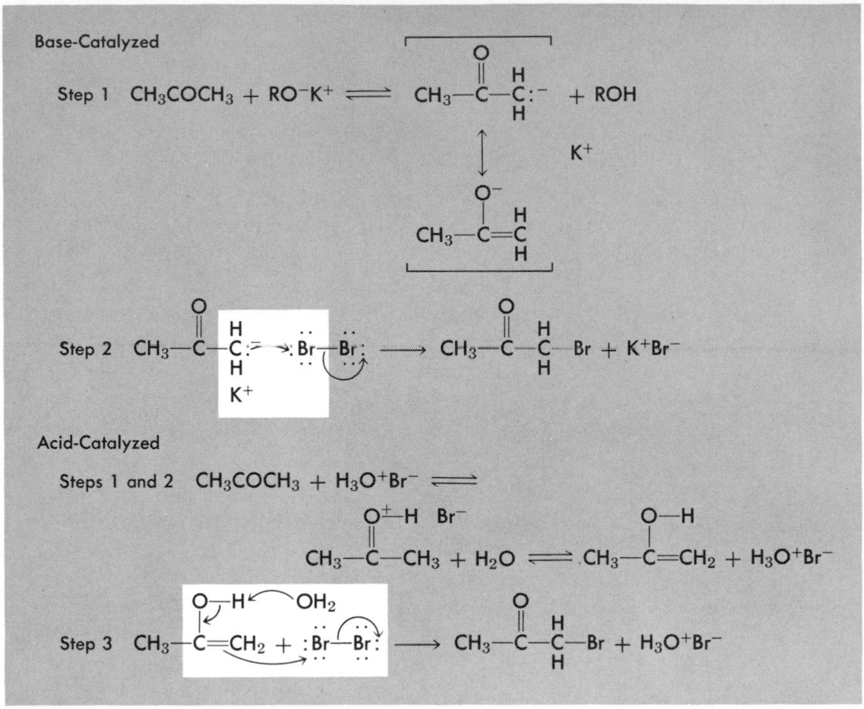

Base-Catalyzed

Step 1 $CH_3COCH_3 + RO^-K^+ \rightleftharpoons$ $CH_3-\overset{\overset{\displaystyle O}{\|}}{C}-\overset{\overset{\displaystyle H}{|}}{\underset{\underset{\displaystyle H}{|}}{C}}:^- + ROH$

$\Big\downarrow$ K^+

$CH_3-\overset{\overset{\displaystyle O^-}{|}}{C}=\overset{\overset{\displaystyle H}{|}}{\underset{\underset{\displaystyle H}{|}}{C}}$

Step 2 $CH_3-\overset{\overset{\displaystyle O}{\|}}{C}-\overset{\overset{\displaystyle H}{|}}{\underset{\underset{\displaystyle K^+}{}}{\underset{\underset{\displaystyle H}{|}}{C}}:\; \rightharpoondown :\ddot{B}r\!\!-\!\!\ddot{B}r\!: \longrightarrow CH_3-\overset{\overset{\displaystyle O}{\|}}{C}-\overset{\overset{\displaystyle H}{|}}{\underset{\underset{\displaystyle H}{|}}{C}}-Br + K^+Br^-$

Acid-Catalyzed

Steps 1 and 2 $CH_3COCH_3 + H_3O^+Br^- \rightleftharpoons$

$CH_3-\overset{\overset{\displaystyle O^{\pm}\!-\!H}{\|}}{C}-CH_3 + H_2O \rightleftharpoons CH_3-\overset{\overset{\displaystyle O-H}{|}}{C}=CH_2 + H_3O^+Br^-$

Step 3 $CH_3-\overset{\overset{\displaystyle O-H}{|}}{C}=CH_2 + :\ddot{B}r\!\!-\!\!\ddot{B}r\!: \longrightarrow CH_3-\overset{\overset{\displaystyle O}{\|}}{C}-\overset{\overset{\displaystyle H}{|}}{\underset{\underset{\displaystyle H}{|}}{C}}-Br + H_3O^+Br^-$

Fig. 4-5. The base- and acid-catalyzed brominations of acetone.

The first product formed during the addition reaction is actually species "X"; proton transfers are rapid, however, and often intermediates that can be converted to products solely by proton transfers are omitted from chemical equations.

In alcoholic solutions of aldehydes, a related adduct called a **hemiacetal** is formed:

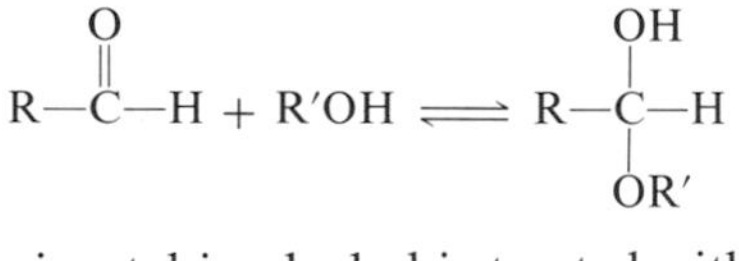

$$R-\overset{\overset{\displaystyle O}{\|}}{C}-H + R'OH \rightleftharpoons R-\overset{\overset{\displaystyle OH}{|}}{\underset{\underset{\displaystyle OR'}{|}}{C}}-H$$

If a solution of the hemiacetal in alcohol is treated with acids, another alcohol molecule participates, and a double ether called an **acetal** is formed:

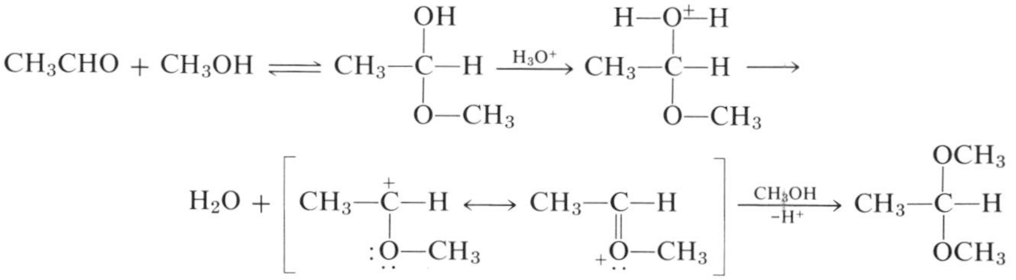

$$CH_3CHO + CH_3OH \rightleftharpoons CH_3-\overset{\overset{\displaystyle OH}{|}}{\underset{\underset{\displaystyle O-CH_3}{|}}{C}}-H \xrightarrow{H_3O^+} CH_3-\overset{\overset{\displaystyle H-O^{\pm}\!-\!H}{|}}{\underset{\underset{\displaystyle O-CH_3}{|}}{C}}-H \longrightarrow$$

$$H_2O + \left[CH_3-\overset{+}{\underset{\underset{\displaystyle :\ddot{O}-CH_3}{|}}{C}}-H \longleftrightarrow CH_3-\overset{\overset{\displaystyle }{}}{\underset{\underset{\displaystyle +\ddot{O}-CH_3}{\|}}{C}}-H \right] \xrightarrow[-H^+]{CH_3OH} CH_3-\overset{\overset{\displaystyle OCH_3}{|}}{\underset{\underset{\displaystyle OCH_3}{|}}{C}}-H$$

Acetaldehyde dimethyl acetal

This reaction proceeds through a carbonium ion, which is particulary stable because of the resonance interaction of the unshared electron pair on oxygen.

86

The attack of an alcohol molecule acting as a nucleophile on this ion leads to the acetal. The corresponding product from a ketone is called a **ketal.**

Ketals and acetals do not have the chemical properties of carbonyl compounds; instead, they behave as typical ethers. They are stable to bases, but they are cleaved by acids, and in aqueous acid solution they are readily reconverted into the corresponding carbonyl compounds.

THE ALDOL REACTION.   A related reaction known as the *aldol* condensation involves 2 molecules of a carbonyl compound:

$$CH_3CHO + OH^- \rightleftharpoons {}^-:CH_2CHO + H_2O$$

$$CH_3-\overset{\overset{O}{\parallel}}{C}-H + {}^-:\overset{\overset{H}{|}}{\underset{\underset{H}{|}}{C}}-CHO \longrightarrow$$

$$CH_3-\overset{\overset{O^-}{|}}{\underset{\underset{H}{|}}{C}}-CH_2-CHO \xrightarrow{H_2O} CH_3-\overset{\overset{OH}{|}}{\underset{\underset{H}{|}}{C}}-CH_2-CHO + OH^-$$
Aldol

The first step in this reaction is the formation of an enolate ion, and the second is the addition of the ion to the carbonyl group of a second molecule. The products of the aldol condensation are β-hydroxy aldehydes or ketones; if these compounds are treated with catalytic amounts of acids, an elimination reaction occurs to yield an α, β-unsaturated derivative, which, in the example cited, is known as crotonaldehyde (2-butenal).

$$CH_3-\overset{\overset{OH}{|}}{\underset{\underset{H}{|}}{C}}-CH_2-CHO \xrightarrow{H_3O^+} CH_3-CH=CH-CHO + H_2O$$
2-Butenal

The driving force for the elimination reaction is the formation of a set of double bonds which is resonance-stabilized:

$$CH_3-\overset{H}{\underset{}{C}}=\overset{H}{\underset{}{C}}-\overset{\overset{:\ddot{O}}{\parallel}}{C}-H \longleftrightarrow CH_3-\overset{H}{\underset{}{C}}=\overset{H}{\underset{+}{C}}-\overset{\overset{:\ddot{O}:^-}{|}}{C}-H \longleftrightarrow CH_3-\overset{H}{\underset{+}{C}}-\overset{H}{\underset{}{C}}=\overset{\overset{:\ddot{O}:^-}{|}}{C}-H$$

Double bonds joined in this way are called **conjugated** double bonds. Because of the resonance-stabilization of conjugated systems, compounds with nonconjugated double bonds can usually be isomerized into the conjugated forms through the catalytic action of acids or bases:

$$CH_2=CH-CH_2-\overset{\overset{O}{\parallel}}{C}-H + OH^- \longrightarrow$$

$$CH_2=CH-\overset{\overset{H}{|}}{\underset{}{C}}-\overset{\overset{O}{\parallel}}{\underset{}{C}}-H$$
$$\updownarrow \quad O$$
$${}^-:CH_2-\overset{H}{\underset{}{C}}=\overset{H}{\underset{}{C}}-\overset{\overset{O}{\parallel}}{C}-H$$
$$+ H_2O \longrightarrow$$

$$CH_3CH=CH-\overset{\overset{O}{\parallel}}{C}-H + OH^-$$

THE REACTION OF GRIGNARD REAGENTS WITH CARBONYL COMPOUNDS. Grignard reagents are organomagnesium compounds prepared by the action of metallic magnesium on the halogen derivatives of the hydrocarbons.

$$CH_3I + Mg \longrightarrow CH_3-Mg-I$$

$$CH_3CHBrCH_3 + Mg \longrightarrow CH_3-\overset{\displaystyle H}{\underset{\displaystyle CH_3}{\overset{|}{\underset{|}{C}}}}-Mg-Br$$

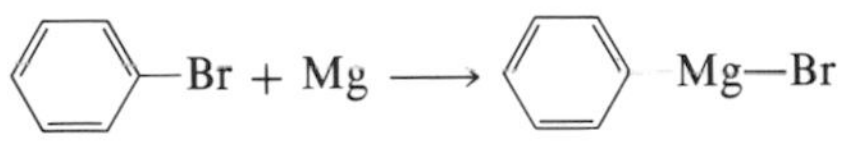

The carbon-metal bond is partially ionic, $R-Mg-X \longleftrightarrow R:^{-+}Mg-X$, and the carbon atom bonded to magnesium has some of the properties of a negative ion.

The reaction of Grignard reagents with carbonyl compounds is one of the best methods available for the synthesis of alcohols. The reaction involves the addition of the Grignard reagent to the C=O double bond (Fig. 4-6). A salt of the alcohol is formed as an intermediate in the reaction, but this derivative is readily hydrolyzed by dilute acids to yield the free alcohol. Primary, secondary, and tertiary alcohols may be prepared by this method (Fig. 4-6).

NUCLEOPHILIC ADDITION TO THE CARBONYL GROUP. The addition reactions of the carbonyl group that we have outlined in this chapter differ from the addition reactions of the olefins. Because of the polarization of the carbonyl

Fig. 4-6. The reaction of Grignard reagents with aldehydes and ketones.

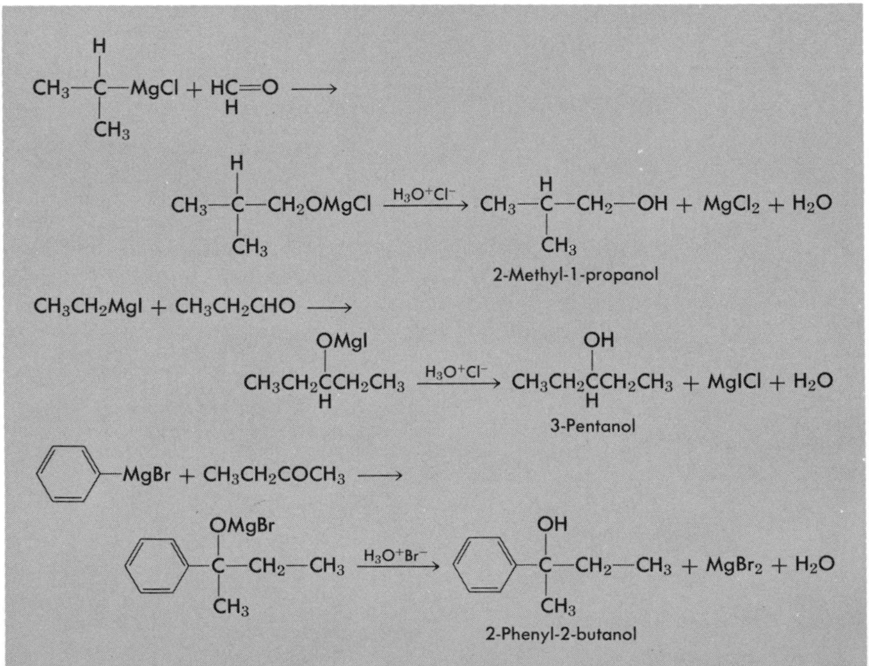

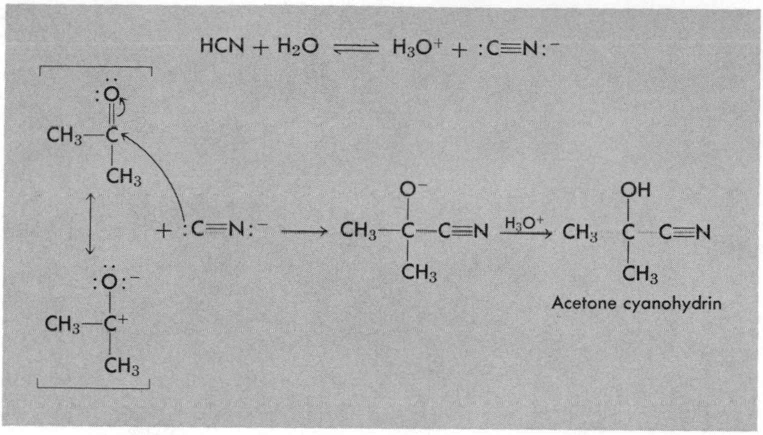

Fig. 4-7. A nucleophilic addition reaction of acetone.

group, species bearing unshared electrons (nucleophiles) can attack the bond directly (Fig. 4-7), whereas in general, the alkenes do not react directly with nucleophiles. The addition reactions of carbonyl compounds may thus be classified as **nucleophilic addition reactions.**

We have now covered the major classes of organic reaction mechanisms; for reference purposes, a concise summary of these mechanisms is given in Table 4-2.

Table 4-2

A SUMMARY OF THE MAJOR CLASSES OF ORGANIC REACTIONS

Reactions	Catalyzed by or Involving:	Types of Compounds Undergoing These Reactions	Pages in Text Involving This Material
I. Free-radical reactions		Alkanes, and alkane groups in other compounds	52–53
II. Ionic reactions			
(A) Substitution reactions			
(1) Electrophilic	Acids	Aromatic compounds	72–74
(2) Nucleophilic	Bases	Alkyl halides and related derivatives	78–79
(B) Addition reactions			
(1) Electrophilic	Acids or electrophiles	Alkenes	59, 71
(2) Nucleophilic	Bases or nucleophiles	Carbonyl compounds (and compounds containing C=N, and C≡N groups)	85–89
(C) Elimination reactions			
(1) Electrophilic	Acids	Alcohols	57
(2) Nucleophilic	Bases	Alkyl halides and related derivatives	58

DERIVATIVES OF ALDEHYDES AND KETONES.   In many nucleophilic addition reactions of carbonyl compounds, the intermediate addition compound cannot be isolated since the adduct readily loses a molecule of water. Reactions

89

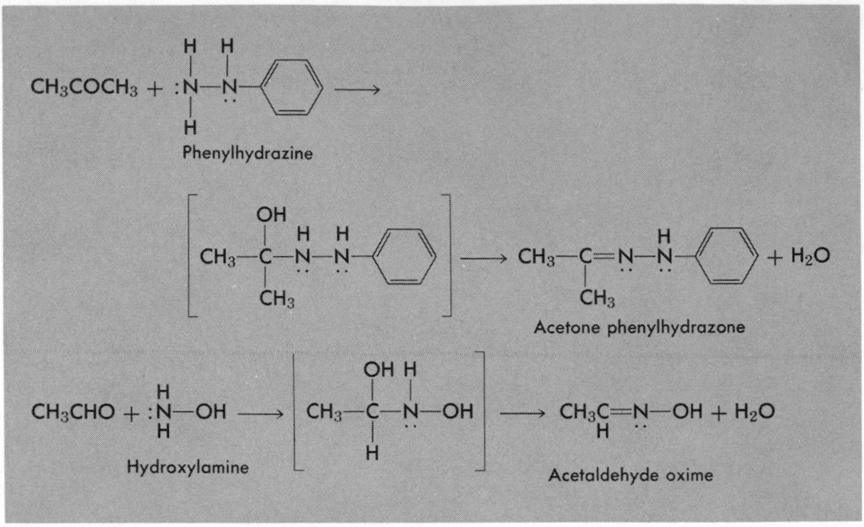

Fig. 4-8. The preparation of derivatives of aldehydes and ketones.

of this type involving hydrazine, hydroxylamine, phenylhydrazine, and related compounds are important since the derivatives ultimately formed (Fig. 4-8) are usually crystalline, whereas common aldehydes and ketones are liquids. The melting point of a derivative of this type may serve to identify a carbonyl compound isolated from some reaction mixture or natural source, since the melting points of the derivatives of most common carbonyl compounds are on record. The compound 2,4-dinitrophenylhydrazine is especially important in this respect in that its derivatives are readily obtained in the crystalline state and they have high melting points.

REDUCTION OF ALDEHYDES AND KETONES. Most carbonyl compounds are reduced to the corresponding alcohols by hydrogen in the presence of platinum and nickel catalysts, and also by lithium aluminum hydride:

$$\underset{\text{3-Pentanone}}{CH_3CH_2\overset{\overset{\displaystyle O}{\|}}{C}CH_2CH_3} \xrightarrow[\text{or } H_2 + \text{Pt or Ni}]{\text{LiAlH}_4} \underset{\text{3-Pentanol}}{CH_3CH_2\overset{\overset{\displaystyle OH}{|}}{\underset{\underset{\displaystyle H}{|}}{C}}CH_2CH_3}$$

The reduction of aldehydes and ketones with almalgamated zinc and hydrochloric acid, on the other hand, proceeds all the way to the hydrocarbon:

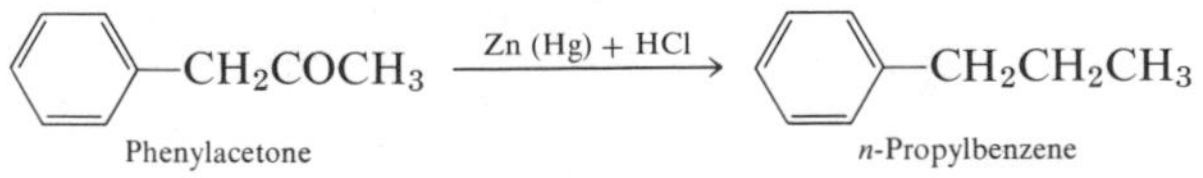

Phenylacetone $\qquad$ *n*-Propylbenzene

The latter reaction is known as the **Clemmenson** reduction.

CARBOXYLIC ACIDS

Carboxylic acids (RCO_2H) are hydrocarbon derivatives in which one of the end carbon atoms is in a maximum state of oxidation.

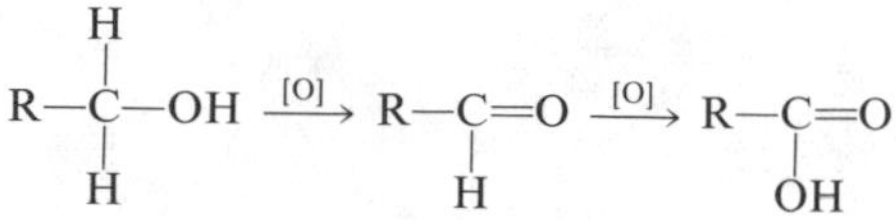

$$\underset{\underset{H}{|}}{\overset{\overset{H}{|}}{R-C-OH}} \xrightarrow{[O]} \underset{\underset{H}{|}}{R-C=O} \xrightarrow{[O]} \underset{\underset{OH}{|}}{R-C=O}$$

The $-CO_2H$ group is called a carboxyl group, and it is constructed of 1 carbonyl group and 1 hydroxyl group. The carbon atom is sp^2 hybridized, and therefore the 2 oxygen atoms, the carbon atom of the carbonyl group, and the α-carbon atom are in 1 plane (the OH bond can also be in this plane since there is free rotation about the bond joining it to the carbonyl group).

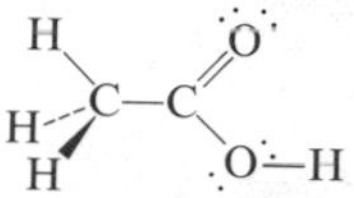

The carboxylic acids are easy to isolate from natural sources and quite a number of them have been known since the days of alchemy. Many of the acids were named in a nonsystematic way at that time, and a few of these names are still in use. Systematic names have been devised for the carboxylic acids, however; these are obtained by substitution of the suffix **oic** for the ending *e* of the hydrocarbon of the same chain length, and the addition of the word "acid." In a second system, the CO_2H group is treated as a substituent and the acid is named simply by the addition of the words "carboxylic acid" to the hydrocarbon name. Various common acids are listed in Fig. 4-9 (the common, or trivial, names are given in parentheses).

A large number of acids with 2, 3, or more carboxylic acid groups (di-, tri-, and polycarboxylic acids, respectively) occur in nature, where they are often responsible for the sourness of various unripened fruits; representative examples are given in Fig. 4-10. These polycarboxylic acids are easily

Fig. 4-9. Common monocarboxylic acids.

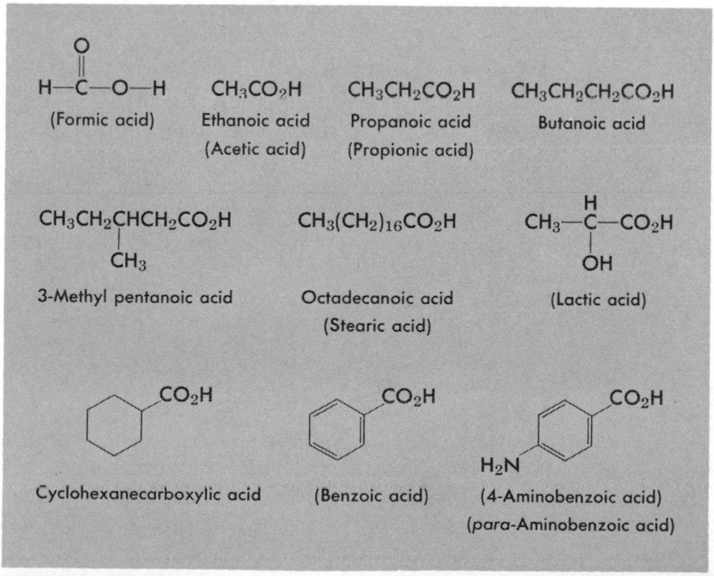

$H-\overset{\overset{O}{\|}}{C}-O-H$
(Formic acid)

CH_3CO_2H
Ethanoic acid
(Acetic acid)

$CH_3CH_2CO_2H$
Propanoic acid
(Propionic acid)

$CH_3CH_2CH_2CO_2H$
Butanoic acid

$CH_3CH_2\underset{\underset{CH_3}{|}}{CH}CH_2CO_2H$
3-Methyl pentanoic acid

$CH_3(CH_2)_{16}CO_2H$
Octadecanoic acid
(Stearic acid)

$CH_3-\underset{\underset{OH}{|}}{\overset{\overset{H}{|}}{C}}-CO_2H$
(Lactic acid)

Cyclohexanecarboxylic acid

(Benzoic acid)

(4-Aminobenzoic acid)
(*para*-Aminobenzoic acid)

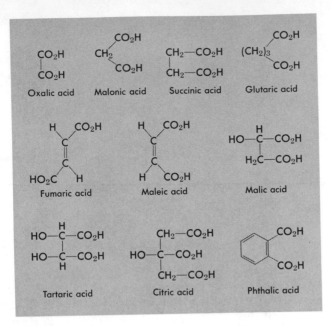

Fig. 4-10. Common polycarboxylic acids.

isolated from plant extracts; most of the aliphatic ones are also present in the human body where they are involved as intermediates in the conversion of more complex compounds into carbon dioxide (the citric acid cycle).

Acid Strength

The carboxylic acids are weak acids and their ionization constants may be readily calculated from the concentrations of the various species present at equilibrium:

$$R-\overset{\overset{\displaystyle O}{\|}}{C}-OH + H_2O \rightleftharpoons H_3O^+ + R-CO_2^-$$

$$K = \frac{[H_3O^+][RCO_2^-]}{[RCO_2H]}; K \text{ ranges from } 10^{-1} \text{ to } 10^{-6} \text{ depending on R}$$

The ionization constants are a measure of acid strength; the larger the constant, the stronger the acid.

The carboxylic acids, although they are weak, are far more acidic than the alcohols: $R-O-H + H_2O \rightleftharpoons H_3O^+ + R-O^-$. The greater acidity of the carboxylic acids is attributed largely to the resonance-stabilization of the carboxylate ion:

$$R-C\overset{\ddot{O}:}{\underset{:\ddot{O}:^-}{}} \longleftrightarrow R-C\overset{:\ddot{O}:^-}{\underset{:\ddot{O}:}{}}$$

In the carboxylate ion, the negative charge is delocalized over 2 oxygen atoms, whereas in the alkoxide ion, the charge resides on a single oxygen atom. The alkoxide ion has a higher electron density on oxygen, and therefore it is

92

a stronger base. This relationship of electron density to base strength is also seen in a series of alkyl-substituted amines; alkyl groups are electron-releasing groups and the base strength is a function of the number of alkyl groups attached to nitrogen.

$$\text{Base strength: } CH_3{-}\overset{H}{\underset{\cdot\cdot}{N}}{-}CH_3 \;>\; CH_3{-}\overset{H}{\underset{\cdot\cdot}{N}}H \;>\; H\overset{H}{\underset{}{N}}H$$

Continuing with the explanation for the low acidity of alcohols relative to the carboxylic acids, it follows that the stronger the negative ion is as a base, the faster it reacts with hydronium ion. This results in a lower concentration of H_3O^+ and a higher concentration of the neutral species at equilibrium (and a lower value of the ionization constant). That is, $K < K'$ for the following equilibria:

$$ROH + H_2O \underset{K}{\overset{\longrightarrow}{\longleftarrow}} H_3O^+ + RO^-$$

$$RCO_2H + H_2O \underset{K'}{\rightleftharpoons} H_3O^+ + RCO_2^-$$

This interpretation of the relative acidities of the carboxylic acids and alcohols suggests that electron-releasing groups should decrease the acidity of the carboxylic acids and that electron-attracting groups should increase the acidity. This is precisely the effect that is found. The ionization constants for several series of acids are given in Table 4-3.

The acidities of the acids vary over a wide range. The aliphatic acids listed are all derivatives of acetic acid, and therefore the differences in acidity must be due to the substituents on the α carbon atom. Alkyl groups are electron-releasing groups, as will be recalled from the accounts of

Table 4-3

IONIZATION CONSTANTS OF CARBOXYLIC ACIDS

A. Aliphatic Acids

Acid	Formula	K	
Propionic acid	$CH_3CH_2CO_2H$	1.4×10^{-5}	
Acetic acid	CH_3CO_2H	1.8×10^{-5}	
Iodoacetic acid	ICH_2CO_2H	7.5×10^{-4}	Acid strength
Chloroacetic acid	$ClCH_2CO_2H$	1.6×10^{-3}	
Trichloroacetic acid	Cl_3CCO_2H	2.0×10^{-1}	

B. Substituted Benzoic Acids

$$p \longrightarrow \underset{\substack{\nearrow \quad \nwarrow \\ m \qquad o}}{\bigcirc}{-}CO_2H$$

Substituent	K	Substituent	K	Substituent	K
p-NH$_2$	1.2×10^{-5}	m-NH$_2$	1.6×10^{-5}	o-NH$_2$	1×10^{-5}
p-CH$_3$	4.2×10^{-5}	m-CH$_3$	5.4×10^{-5}	o-CH$_3$	1.2×10^{-4}
p-H	6.3×10^{-5}	m-H	6.3×10^{-5}	o-H	6.3×10^{-5}
p-NO$_2$	3.8×10^{-4}	m-NO$_2$	3.2×10^{-4}	o-NO$_2$	6.7×10^{-3}

the stability order of carbonium ions (tertiary > secondary > primary) and of the direction in which water and the acids add to double bonds (Chapter 3). Consistent with the direction of these effects and with the interpretation of acid strengths given in our comparison of alcohols and carboxylic acids, the substitution of a methyl group for an α hydrogen in acetic acid results in a decrease of the ionization constant from 1.8×10^{-5} to 1.4×10^{-5} (Table 4-3).

The halogens are electron-attracting substituents, on the other hand, and we see from Table 4-3 that chloroacetic acid is about 90 times as strong as acetic acid and that trichloroacetic acid is about 125 times as strong as monochloroacetic acid. The position of iodoacetic acid on our scale indicates a parallelism between the electronegativity of the halogen (which decreases with atomic number in the periodic table) and the effect of the halogens in increasing the strength of the substituted acetic acids.

We must also consider the effect of substituents on the rate of the forward reaction in the ionization of carboxylic acids:

$$R-\overset{\overset{\textstyle O}{\parallel}}{C}-O-H + :OH_2 \rightleftharpoons H_3O^+ + R-CO_2^-$$

Electron-attracting substituents should increase this rate since they should facilitate the separation of the developing positive charge on the proton and the negative charge on the oxygen. This effect happens to be in the same direction as the effect of electron-attracting substituents on the carboxylate ion; that is, both explanations lead to the conclusion that electron-attracting substituents should increase the strength of acids. The effect of substituents on neutral species is less, in general, than the effect on charged species, and for convenience, we often focus attention on only the negative ion in acid-base equilibrium.

THE INDUCTIVE EFFECT.   The release and withdrawal of electrons by the substituent in the aliphatic acids is transmitted through the saturated α carbon atom of the acid; that is, through the σ bonds. The alteration of the electron density at the reaction site in this way is called the **inductive effect** and it is usually symbolized by an arrow indicating the direction of the electron displacement:

$$\overset{\overset{\textstyle H}{|}}{\underset{\underset{\textstyle H}{|}}{H C}}\longrightarrow CH_2 \longrightarrow CO_2H \qquad Cl \longleftarrow CH_2 \longleftarrow CO_2H$$

The inductive effect of a substituent (left) and the resonance effect (right):

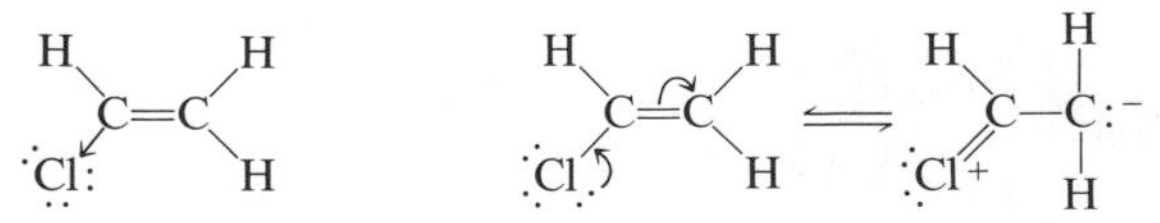

are the principal ways in which the electronic structure of a compound may be altered by a substituent. In some cases, the effects are in opposite direction (as in the example of chloroethylene cited above), whereas in others, the effects are in the same direction (as in the methyl derivative of ethylene). In general, when the effects are in opposite directions, the resonance effect outweighs the inductive effect.

The effect of substituents on the acidity of benzoic acid is illustrated by the ionization constants in Table 4-3; the effects are similar to those discussed in the section on the aliphatic acids in that electron-attracting substituents lead to large values of K, whereas electron-releasing substituents lead to small values of K. Substitution in the *ortho* position is anomalous, however. We do not yet know for certain why this is so, but it is thought to involve the steric interaction of the carboxyl group and the substituent which is very close to it in space. It should be noted that those substituents which decrease the acid strength of benzoic acid activate the aromatic ring and lead to *ortho-para* electrophilic substitution, whereas those substituents that increase the acid strength deactivate the ring and lead to *meta* electrophilic substitution (see Chapter 3).

Preparation of Carboxylic Acids

The carboxylic acids may be prepared by the oxidation of primary alcohols and aldehydes, RCH_2OH or $RCHO$ $\xrightarrow{KMnO_4}$ RCO_2H, and also by the addition of Grignard reagents to carbon dioxide:

$$R:^-MgCl^+ + \;\ddot{O}{=}C{=}\ddot{O}: \longrightarrow \left[R{-}\overset{\overset{\textstyle O}{\|}}{C}{-}\ddot{O}:^-MgCl^+ \right] \xrightarrow{HCl} R{-}CO_2H + MgCl_2$$

A third useful method involves the acid hydrolysis of an alkyl cyanide, prepared in turn by the displacement reaction of cyanide ion on an alkyl halide (bromide or iodide preferably):

$$R{-}Br + Na^+:C{\equiv}N:^- \longrightarrow Na^+Br^- + R{-}C{\equiv}N:$$

$$\xrightarrow[HCl]{H_2O} R{-}CO_2H + NH_4^+Cl^-$$

Reactions of Carboxylic Acids

Most of the reactions of carboxylic acids involve the nucleophilic addition of some reagent to the carbonyl group, followed by an elimination reaction to regenerate the carbonyl group:

$$R{-}\overset{\overset{\textstyle O}{\|}}{C}{-}OH + XY \longrightarrow R{-}\overset{\overset{\textstyle OX}{|}}{\underset{\underset{\textstyle Y}{|}}{C}}{-}OH \longrightarrow R{-}\overset{\overset{\textstyle O}{\|}}{C}{-}Y + XOH$$

The formation of esters from carboxylic acids and alcohols is an example:

$$CH_3{-}\overset{\overset{\textstyle O}{\|}}{C}{-}OH + CH_3CH_2OH \rightleftharpoons CH_3{-}\overset{\overset{\textstyle OH}{|}}{\underset{\underset{\textstyle OCH_2CH_3}{|}}{C}}{-}OH \rightleftharpoons CH_3{-}\overset{\overset{\textstyle O}{\|}}{C}{-}O{-}CH_2CH_3 + H_2O$$

Ethyl acetate

The concentration of ester at equilibrium is low if equal amounts of the reactants are used; high yields are obtained only if the water is removed during the course of the reaction, or if one of the reactants is present in excess. This reaction is also catalyzed by strong acids and a simple procedure for the preparation of esters involves the treatment of a mixture of the carboxylic acid and an excess of the alcohol with a small amount of concentrated sulfuric acid.

The addition-elimination mechanism outlined for this reaction has been confirmed through the use of the oxygen-18 isotope. When an alcohol labelled with oxygen-18 is condensed with a carboxylic acid, ordinary water and an ester containing all the oxygen-18 are obtained:

$$
\underset{\text{O}}{\overset{\text{O}}{R-\overset{\|}{C}-OH}} + R'-O^{18}H \longrightarrow R-\overset{OH}{\underset{OH}{\overset{|}{\underset{|}{C}}}}-O^{18}R' \longrightarrow R-\overset{O}{\overset{\|}{C}}-O^{18}R' + H_2O
$$

The following hypothetical reaction course is, therefore, eliminated from consideration by the oxygen-18 results:

$$
R-\overset{O}{\overset{\|}{C}}-O-\boxed{H + H-O^{18}}R' \not\longrightarrow R-\overset{O}{\overset{\|}{C}}-O-R' + H_2O^{18}
$$

ACID CHLORIDES.   Acid chlorides (RCOCl) are highly reactive derivatives of the carboxylic acids. They are generally prepared by the reaction of the acids with thionyl chloride ($SOCl_2$):

$$
CH_3-\overset{O}{\overset{\|}{C}}-\overset{..}{\underset{..}{O}}-H + :\overset{:\overset{..}{O}:}{\underset{..}{Cl}}-S-Cl: \rightarrow HCl + CH_3-\overset{O}{\overset{\|}{C}}-O-S: \rightarrow CH_3-\overset{O}{\overset{\|}{C}}-Cl + SO_2
$$

Acetyl chloride

Acid chlorides react quantitatively with water to regenerate the acids:

$$
R-\overset{O}{\overset{\|}{C}}-Cl + H_2O \longrightarrow R-\overset{OH}{\underset{OH}{\overset{|}{\underset{|}{C}}}}-Cl \longrightarrow R-\overset{O}{\overset{\|}{C}}-O-H + HCl
$$

and they react in a similar fashion with alcohols to form the corresponding esters:

$$
R-\overset{O}{\overset{\|}{C}}-Cl + R'OH \longrightarrow R-\overset{OH}{\underset{O-R'}{\overset{|}{\underset{|}{C}}}}-Cl \longrightarrow R-\overset{O}{\overset{\|}{C}}-OR' + HCl
$$

In the laboratory, most of the derivatives of the carboxylic acids are prepared, in fact, by way of the acid chlorides.

ACID ANHYDRIDES.   Acid anhydrides are compounds that yield acids on reaction with water. The inorganic anhydrides SO_3, N_2O_5, and P_2O_5 yield H_2SO_4, HNO_3, and H_3PO_4 on hydrolysis, for example. The acid chlorides may be viewed as mixed anhydrides of a carboxylic acid and hydrogen chloride since the two acids are formed during hydrolysis (see previous section). The carboxylic acids form a series of mixed anhydrides, examples of which are given below:

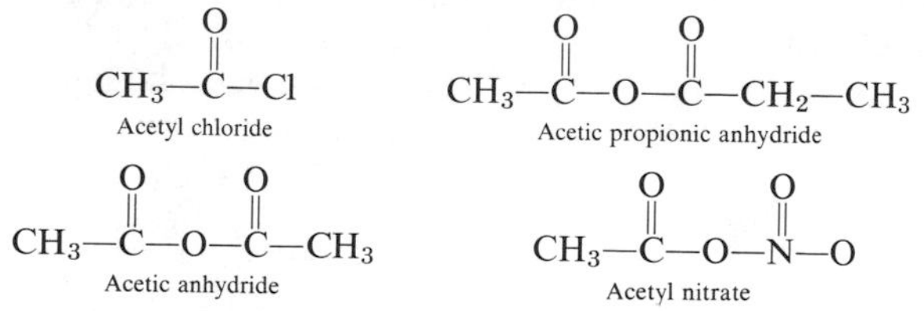

$$CH_3-\overset{\overset{\displaystyle O}{\|}}{C}-Cl$$
Acetyl chloride

$$CH_3-\overset{\overset{\displaystyle O}{\|}}{C}-O-\overset{\overset{\displaystyle O}{\|}}{C}-CH_2-CH_3$$
Acetic propionic anhydride

$$CH_3-\overset{\overset{\displaystyle O}{\|}}{C}-O-\overset{\overset{\displaystyle O}{\|}}{C}-CH_3$$
Acetic anhydride

$$CH_3-\overset{\overset{\displaystyle O}{\|}}{C}-O-\overset{\overset{\displaystyle O}{\|}}{N}-O$$
Acetyl nitrate

The carboxylic acid-carboxylic acid anhydrides are named by the addition of the word "anhydride" to the names of the acids involved. The anhydrides of inorganic acids are named essentially as salts with the organic radical (RCO) named through the substitution of the suffix **yl** for the **ic** ending of the acids; that is, the acetyl radical is CH_3CO. The last three anhydrides shown above are prepared by the reaction of acetyl chloride with a salt of the other acid, for example:

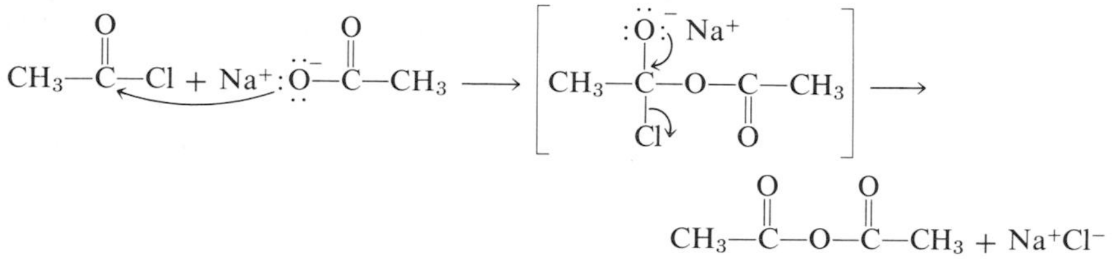

$$CH_3-\overset{\overset{\displaystyle O}{\|}}{C}-Cl + Na^+ : \overset{..}{\underset{..}{O}}-\overset{\overset{\displaystyle O}{\|}}{C}-CH_3 \longrightarrow \left[CH_3-\overset{\overset{\displaystyle :\overset{..}{O} : ^- Na^+}{|}}{\underset{\underset{\displaystyle Cl}{|}}{C}}-O-\overset{\overset{\displaystyle O}{\|}}{C}-CH_3 \right] \longrightarrow$$

$$CH_3-\overset{\overset{\displaystyle O}{\|}}{C}-O-\overset{\overset{\displaystyle O}{\|}}{C}-CH_3 + Na^+Cl^-$$

The acid anhydrides are far more reactive than the acids themselves. This is usually attributed to the inductive effect of the halide, acetate, nitrate groups, etc., attached to the carbonyl group:

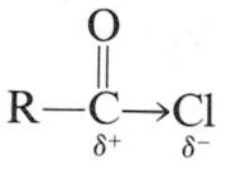

$$R-\overset{\overset{\displaystyle O}{\|}}{\underset{\delta^+}{C}}\rightarrow\underset{\delta^-}{Cl}$$

(see p. 126 for an elaboration of this explanation).

DERIVATIVES OF THE CARBOXYLIC ACIDS. A number of nitrogen-containing derivatives of the carboxylic acids can be prepared from the corresponding acid anhydrides (usually from the acid chlorides):

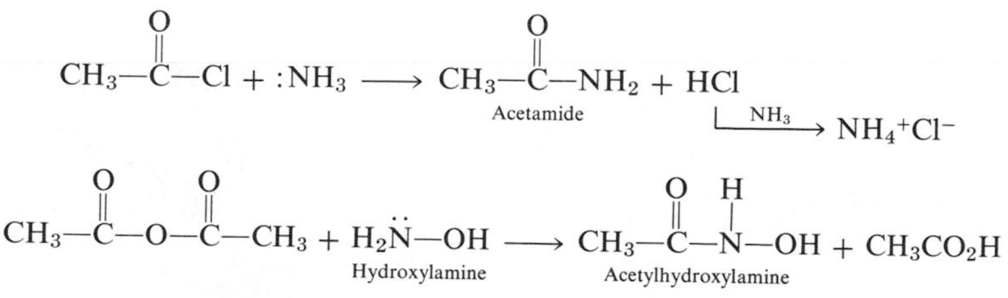

$$CH_3-\overset{\overset{\displaystyle O}{\|}}{C}-Cl + :NH_3 \longrightarrow CH_3-\overset{\overset{\displaystyle O}{\|}}{C}-NH_2 + HCl$$
Acetamide
$$\overset{NH_3}{\longrightarrow} NH_4^+Cl^-$$

$$CH_3-\overset{\overset{\displaystyle O}{\|}}{C}-O-\overset{\overset{\displaystyle O}{\|}}{C}-CH_3 + H_2\overset{..}{N}-OH \longrightarrow CH_3-\overset{\overset{\displaystyle O}{\|}}{C}-\overset{\overset{\displaystyle H}{|}}{N}-OH + CH_3CO_2H$$
Hydroxylamine   Acetylhydroxylamine

These derivatives are highly crystalline and they have characteristic melting points. Carboxylic acids are often converted into their amides or other nitrogen derivatives so that they can be purified readily and identified by means of their melting points. Derivatives of this type cannot be prepared directly from the carboxylic acids. A mixture of acetic acid and ammonia, for example, gives not acetamide, but ammonium acetate, the product of an acid-base reaction: $CH_3CO_2H + NH_3 \longrightarrow CH_3CO_2^- NH_4^+$.

Many of the reactions of carboxylic acids in biological systems involve mixed anhydrides with phosphoric acid such as

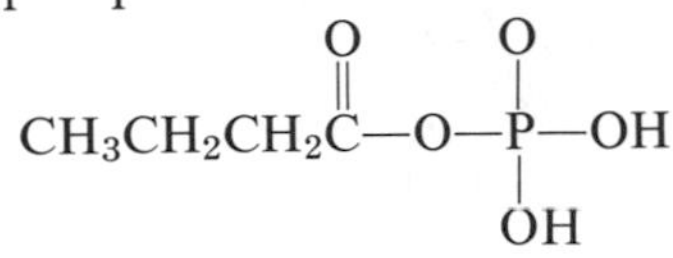

$$CH_3CH_2CH_2\overset{O}{\underset{}{\overset{\|}{C}}}-O-\overset{O}{\underset{\underset{OH}{|}}{\overset{\|}{P}}}-OH$$

Butanoyl phosphate

butanoyl phosphate, or certain sulfur derivatives $(CH_3\overset{O}{\overset{\|}{C}}-S-R)$ that also react rapidly at the carbonyl group. Since the free carboxylic acids do not react under these circumstances, these acid anhydrides and sulfur derivatives are often referred to as "activated" acids by biologists.

REDUCTION OF CARBOXYLIC ACIDS. The carboxyl group is reduced to the corresponding primary alcohol group by lithium aluminum hydride: $RCO_2H \xrightarrow{LiAlH_4} RCH_2OH$. This is the only commonly used reagent that is able to reduce the carboxyl group. This fact can be turned to advantage when selective reductions are desired; the reactions in Fig. 4-11 illustrate this point.

DECARBOXYLATION OF CARBOXYLIC ACIDS. Saturated, unsubstituted carboxylic acids are very stable compounds and they are decomposed only at high temperatures in the presence of a base.

$$CH_3-\overset{O}{\overset{\|}{C}}-O^-Na^+ \xrightarrow[300°]{NaOH} CH_4 + Na_2CO_3$$

Reactions of this type in which carboxylic acids yield carbon dioxide (or its derivatives) are called **decarboxylation** reactions. In contrast to the stability of the simple carboxylic acids, two types of substituted acids are particularly susceptible to decarboxylation.

Fig. 4-11. The selective reduction of various functional groups in a complex carboxylic acid.

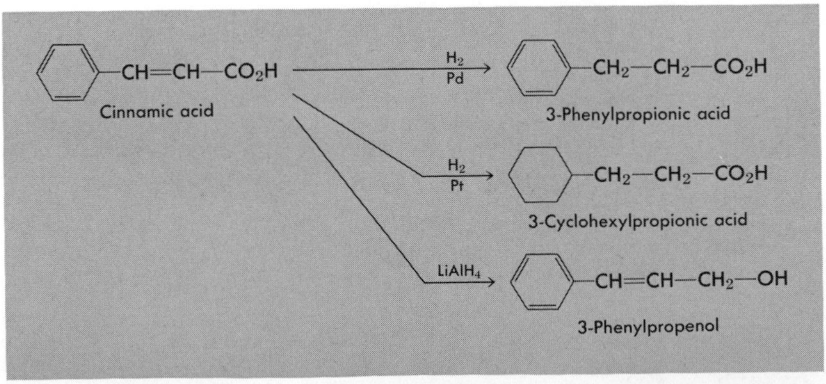

(1) 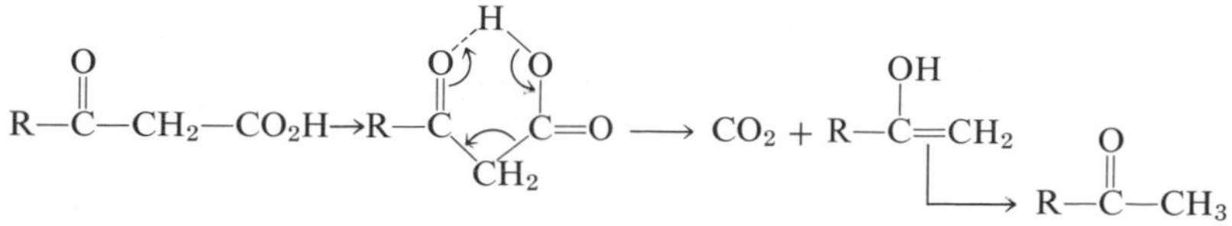 $\quad$ R—C(=O)—CH$_2$—CO$_2$H → [cyclic intermediate] ⟶ CO$_2$ + R—C(OH)=CH$_2$ ⟶ R—C(=O)—CH$_3$

(2) $\quad$ Cl$_3$C—C(=O)—O$^-$K$^+$ $\xrightarrow[\text{H}_2\text{O}]{\text{KOH}}$ K$_2$CO$_3$ + Cl$_3$C:$^-$ $\xrightarrow{\text{H}_2\text{O}}$ CHCl$_3$ + OH$^-$

Chloroform

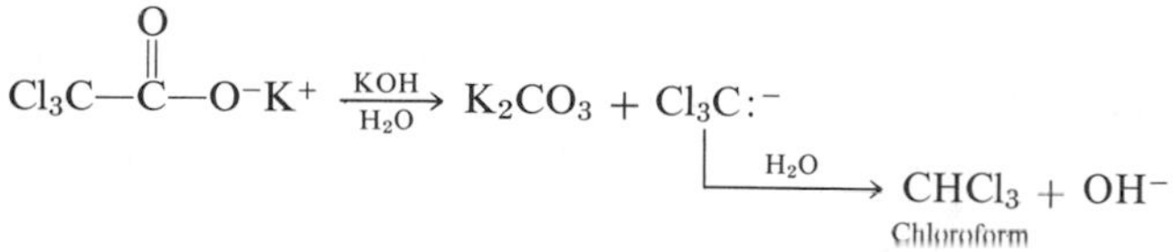

In the first example, the reaction is a concerted one and the enol of the product is formed as a reaction intermediate. Acids of this type, with a carbonyl group in the β position (called β-keto acids), decarboxylate rapidly, even at room temperature.

In the second example, the negative charge on carbon formed by the loss of CO$_2$ is stabilized by the inductive effect of the chlorine atoms: $\quad$ Cl←C:$^-$.

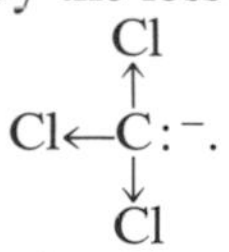

It is for this reason that the halogenated acetic acids decarboxylate far more readily than acetic acid itself.

ESTERS

Esters (R—C(=O)—O—R′) may be considered as alkyl derivatives of acids, or alternatively as acid derivatives of alcohols. They are usually named in the former sense, however; that is, the name of the radical R′ is given first, then a term is added for the acid portion (derived by dropping the acid ending, **ic acid,** and substituting the suffix **ate**). Selected examples of esters and their names are given in Fig. 4-12.

It is interesting to note that whereas the lower-molecular-weight carboxylic

Fig. 4-12. Esters of carboxylic acids.

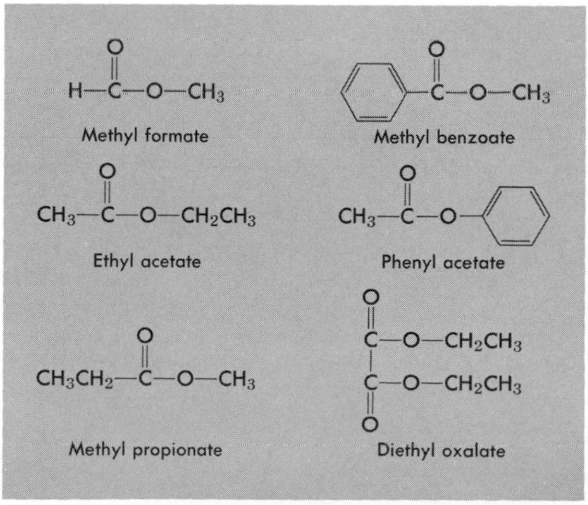

H—C(=O)—O—CH$_3$
Methyl formate

(C$_6$H$_5$)—C(=O)—O—CH$_3$
Methyl benzoate

CH$_3$—C(=O)—O—CH$_2$CH$_3$
Ethyl acetate

CH$_3$—C(=O)—O—(C$_6$H$_5$)
Phenyl acetate

CH$_3$CH$_2$—C(=O)—O—CH$_3$
Methyl propionate

C(=O)—O—CH$_2$CH$_3$ / C(=O)—O—CH$_2$CH$_3$
Diethyl oxalate

acids have odors that range from objectionable (propionic) to vile (butanoic and pentanoic), the corresponding esters have very pleasant odors that resemble the odors of ripe fruits. For example, methyl butanoate has a pineapple-like odor and isoamyl acetate smells like ripe bananas. Mixtures of the lower-molecular-weight esters are in fact responsible for the flavor and aroma of many flowers and fruits. A number of interesting esters have been isolated recently from insect sources. The compound illustrated below is secreted by the female gypsy moth (*Porthetria dispar*). It is an incredibly potent attractant, and with the aid of this "insect perfume," a single female can attract males from a distance of up to 3 miles!

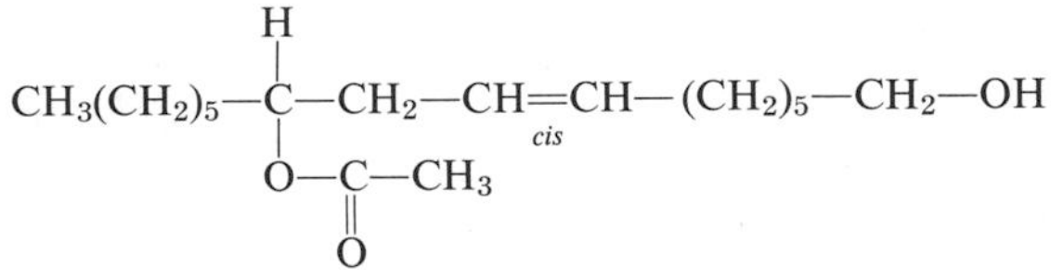

$$CH_3(CH_2)_5—\underset{\underset{\underset{O}{\overset{\|}{C}}}{\overset{|}{\underset{|}{O—C—CH_3}}}}{\overset{H}{\overset{|}{C}}}—CH_2—CH{=}CH—(CH_2)_5—CH_2—OH$$

cis

Preparation of the Esters

Esters may be prepared directly from carboxylic acids as outlined in the section on acids. They are usually prepared from the acid chlorides, however:

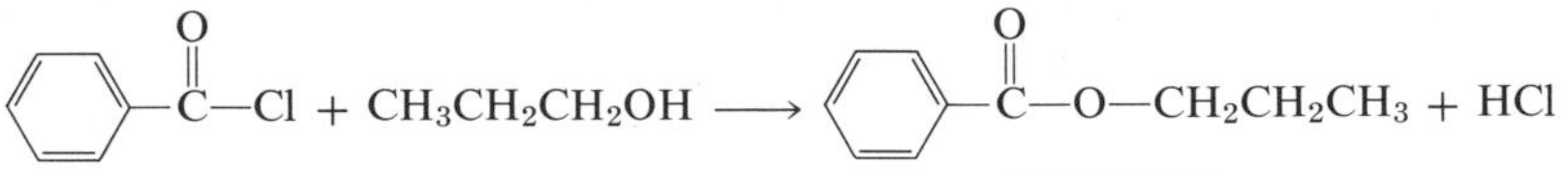

$$\langle\bigcirc\rangle-\overset{O}{\overset{\|}{C}}—Cl + CH_3CH_2CH_2OH \longrightarrow \langle\bigcirc\rangle-\overset{O}{\overset{\|}{C}}—O—CH_2CH_2CH_3 + HCl$$

Propyl benzoate

or from other esters by a process called **ester interchange:**

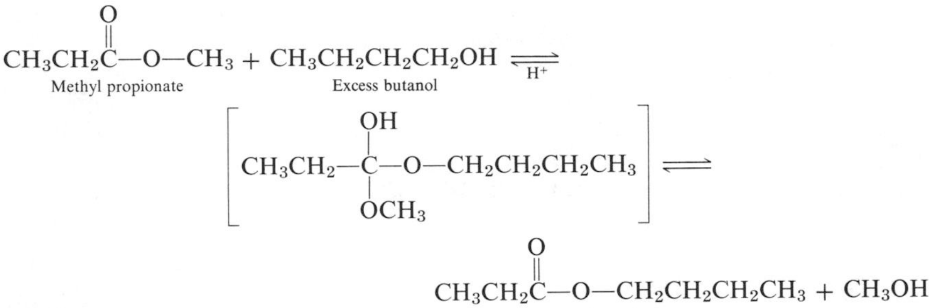

$$CH_3CH_2\overset{O}{\overset{\|}{C}}—O—CH_3 + CH_3CH_2CH_2CH_2OH \underset{H^+}{\rightleftharpoons}$$

Methyl propionate   Excess butanol

$$\left[CH_3CH_2—\overset{OH}{\underset{OCH_3}{\overset{|}{\underset{|}{C}}}}—O—CH_2CH_2CH_2CH_3 \right] \rightleftharpoons$$

$$CH_3CH_2\overset{O}{\overset{\|}{C}}—O—CH_2CH_2CH_2CH_3 + CH_3OH$$

Butyl propionate

In this process, an equilibrium is established between 2 alcohols and the corresponding esters. If an excess of one alcohol is used or if the other alcohol is removed by distillation, etc., a good yield of the interchange ester (here the butyl propionate) can be obtained.

Reactions of the Esters

Most of the reactions of esters involve nucleophilic addition to the carbonyl group. Most esters react with water, for example, to yield the acid and alcohol from which the ester was made:

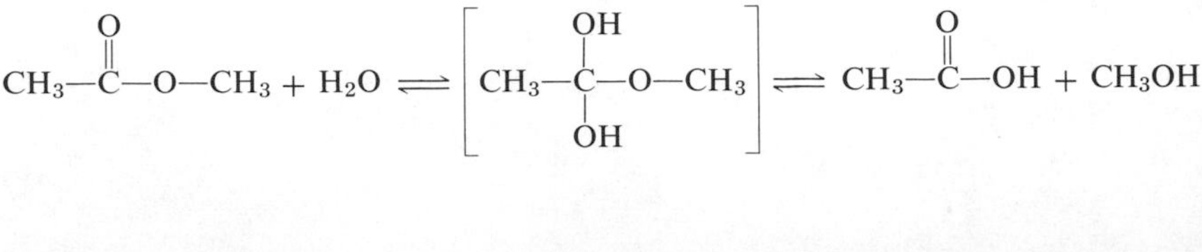

$$CH_3—\overset{O}{\overset{\|}{C}}—O—CH_3 + H_2O \rightleftharpoons \left[CH_3—\overset{OH}{\underset{OH}{\overset{|}{\underset{|}{C}}}}—O—CH_3 \right] \rightleftharpoons CH_3—\overset{O}{\overset{\|}{C}}—OH + CH_3OH$$

The reaction is catalyzed by acids and the use of a large excess of water insures that the equilibrium will be shifted to the right; that is, that hydrolysis will be complete.

THE STERIC EFFECT. Esters with several alkyl groups on the α-carbon atom react only very slowly with water. It is thought that this decrease in rate is due to the blocking of the approach of the water molecule to the carbonyl group by the bulky alkyl groups (Fig. 4-13). Interactions of this type are called **steric** effects. The base-catalyzed hydrolysis of esters of bulky alcohols, such as the acetate of tertiary butyl alcohol, are also abnormally slow, and the low rates are also attributed to the steric interaction of the nucleophile and the alkyl groups (this time on the alcohol portion). We have not stressed the role of steric effects in organic reactions up to this point; however, it should be pointed out that in certain systems, steric effects may outweigh both the inductive and resonance effects in determining the rate or course of a reaction.

SAPONIFICATION OF ESTERS. Most esters react with aqueous bases to give the free alcohols and salts of carboxylic acids; this process is called **saponification:**

$$CH_3-\overset{\overset{\text{O}}{\|}}{C}-O-CH_2CH_3 + Na^+OH^- \rightleftharpoons \left[CH_3-\overset{\overset{\text{O}^-Na^+}{|}}{\underset{\overset{|}{OH}}{C}}-O-CH_2CH_3 \right] \longrightarrow$$

$$CH_3CO_2H + Na^{+-}OCH_2CH_3 \longrightarrow CH_3CO_2^-Na^+ + CH_3CH_2OH$$

The reaction involves a nucleophilic attack of hydroxide ion on the carbonyl group to give the adduct, the regeneration of the carbonyl group to yield acetic

Fig. 4-13. Steric blocking of a nucleophile by the α-alkyl groups of a carboxylic ester. The sizes of the interacting species are approximate.

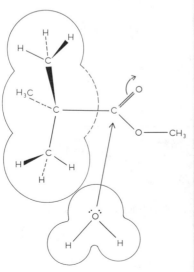
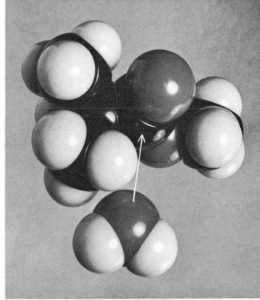

acid and an alkoxide ion, and an acid-base reaction to yield acetate ion and the free alcohol. The saponification reaction is irreversible, since carboxylate ions do not react with nucleophiles (because of the repulsion of like charges):

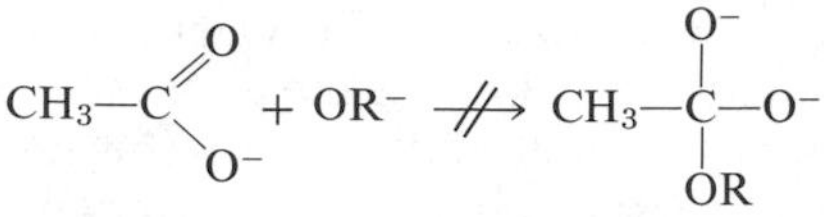

$$CH_3-C\overset{O}{\underset{O^-}{\Big\langle}} + OR^- \not\longrightarrow CH_3-\overset{O^-}{\underset{OR}{\overset{|}{C}}}-O^-$$

Saponification is therefore a quantitative method for the cleavage of esters. The sodium salts of the higher acids, prepared commercially by the saponification of fats, are **soaps:**

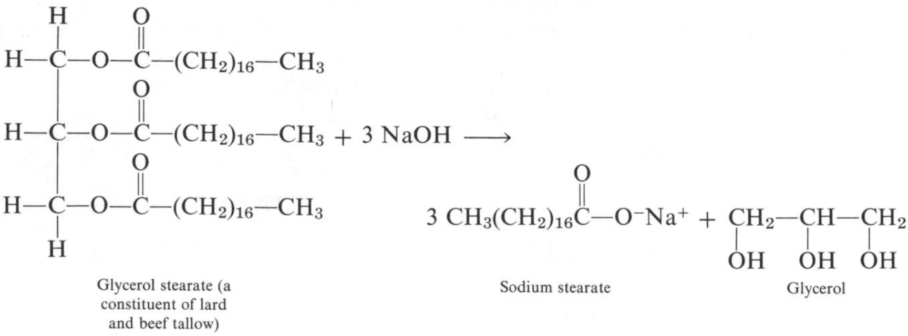

$$H-\overset{H}{\underset{}{\overset{|}{C}}}-O-\overset{O}{\overset{||}{C}}-(CH_2)_{16}-CH_3$$
$$H-\overset{}{\underset{}{\overset{|}{C}}}-O-\overset{O}{\overset{||}{C}}-(CH_2)_{16}-CH_3 + 3\ NaOH \longrightarrow$$
$$H-\overset{}{\underset{H}{\overset{|}{C}}}-O-\overset{O}{\overset{||}{C}}-(CH_2)_{16}-CH_3 \qquad 3\ CH_3(CH_2)_{16}\overset{O}{\overset{||}{C}}-O^-Na^+ + \underset{OH\ \ OH\ \ OH}{CH_2-CH-CH_2}$$

Glycerol stearate (a
constituent of lard
and beef tallow)   Sodium stearate   Glycerol

Sodium stearate, for example, is the principle active agent in common household soap.

Esters also react with many of the nucleophiles that attack acid anhydrides, and it is often more convenient to prepare carboxylic acid derivatives from the esters than from the anhydrides.

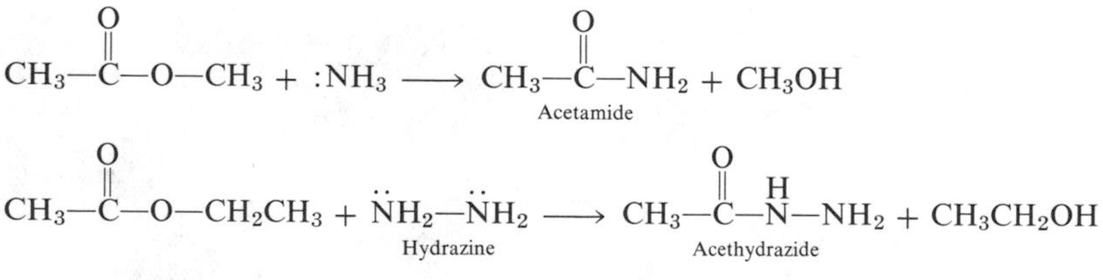

$$CH_3-\overset{O}{\overset{||}{C}}-O-CH_3 + :NH_3 \longrightarrow CH_3-\overset{O}{\overset{||}{C}}-NH_2 + CH_3OH$$

Acetamide

$$CH_3-\overset{O}{\overset{||}{C}}-O-CH_2CH_3 + \overset{..}{N}H_2-\overset{..}{N}H_2 \longrightarrow CH_3-\overset{O}{\overset{||}{C}}-\overset{H}{\overset{|}{N}}-NH_2 + CH_3CH_2OH$$

Hydrazine   Acethydrazide

Fig. 4-14. The reaction of esters with a Grignard reagent.

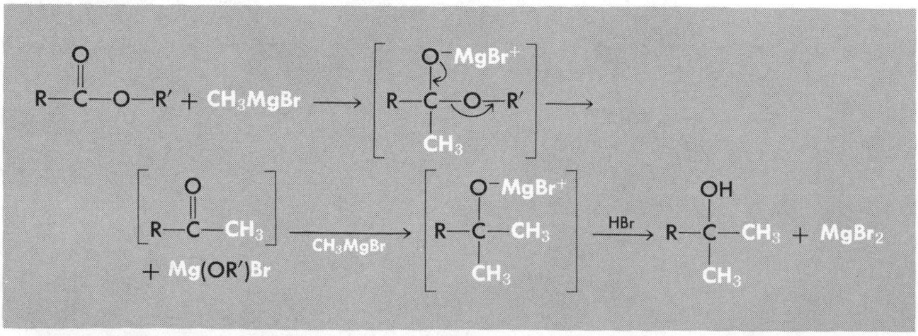

THE REACTION OF GRIGNARD REAGENTS WITH ESTERS.   The reaction of esters with Grignard reagents is important in that it represents one of the better ways to synthesize alcohols (Fig. 4-14). A magnesium derivative of the alcohol is the immediate product of the reaction; however, these compounds may be readily hydrolyzed to the alcohols.

The reaction in effect converts an ester into a symmetrical alcohol. If R is an alkyl group, the product is a tertiary alcohol in which 2 of the alkyl groups came from the Grignard reagent. The ketone is presumed to be an intermediate in this reaction, but since it reacts with the Grignard reagent at a faster rate than does the starting ester, it is rarely isolated from reactions of this type. If the ester used is a derivative of formic acid (R═H), on the other hand, the product is a secondary alcohol:

$$
\underset{\substack{\| \\ O}}{H-C-O-CH_3} + 2\ CH_3CH_2MgBr \longrightarrow CH_3-CH_2-\underset{\substack{| \\ H}}{\overset{\substack{OH \\ |}}{C}}-CH_2-CH_3
$$

Organic Compounds Containing Nitrogen, Sulfur, and Phosphorus

CHAPTER FIVE

COMPOUNDS OF NITROGEN

The organic compounds of oxygen are characterized largely by the acidic properties of the hydroxyl group on the one hand, and by the nucleophilic addition reactions of the carbonyl group on the other. The organic compounds of nitrogen also undergo reactions of this type, but these properties are often dominated by the basicity of the nitrogen atom. The chemistry is more varied also because of the greater range of oxidation states available to nitrogen; the values range from -3 for ammonia and the amines to $+3$ for the nitro derivatives. Since the amines play a central role in the chemistry of the nitrogen compounds, our first section is devoted to the chemistry of these compounds.

AMINES

Amines are derivatives of ammonia in which 1 or more of the hydrogen atoms are replaced by alkyl or aryl groups. If 1 hydrogen is replaced (RNH_2), the compound is called a **primary** amine; if 2 hydrogens are replaced (R_2NH), the compound is called a **secondary** amine; and if 3 hydrogens are replaced (R_3N), the compound is called a **tertiary** amine.

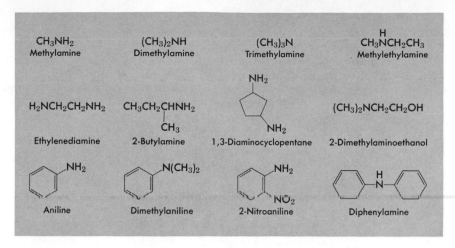

Fig. 5-1. Aliphatic and aromatic amines.

The amines are named as alkyl derivatives of ammonia in which the root term ammonia is contracted to **"amine"**—or the NH_2 group is treated as a substituent, in which case the prefixes **amino, methylamino,** etc., are used. Many of the aromatic amines are referred to by their common names, however. Examples of the amines are given in Fig. 5-1.

Ammonium ions are tetrahedrally symmetrical (Fig. 5-2), and the hybridization of the nitrogen atom is presumed to be sp^3; in these respects, the ammonium ion resembles methane. Ammonia and the amines have approximately the same shape as the ammonium ion, with the exception that an electron pair takes the place of one of the NH bonds; the hybridization of the nitrogen atom in these compounds may also be sp^3 (a somewhat different interpretation of the hybridization is given in Chapter 1). Molecules shaped like ammonia and the amines are said to have pyramidal symmetry.

Properties of the Amines

The amines are more basic and less acidic than the corresponding alcohols (as follows from the lower electronegativity of nitrogen relative to oxygen) and they are often used in reactions when weak bases are required. The basic ionization constants of the amines range from 10^{-3} to about 10^{-12}:

$$R_3N: + H-O-H \rightleftharpoons R_3\overset{+}{N}H \; OH^- \qquad K = \frac{[R_3\overset{+}{N}H][OH^-]}{[R_3N]}$$

The base strength of an amine is determined by the electron density on nitrogen, which in turn is determined by the nature of the substituent R. Since alkyl groups are electron-releasing groups, most alkylamines are stronger bases than ammonia itself. Electron-withdrawing groups decrease

Fig. 5-2. The geometry of the ammonium ion, ammonia, and trimethyl amine.

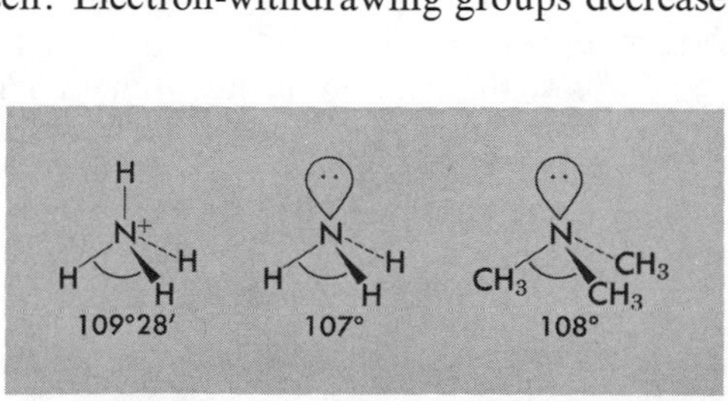

the base strength; for example, $CF_3CH_2NH_2$ is a relatively weak base because the inductive effect of the fluorine atoms decreases the electron density on nitrogen. Aromatic amines such as aniline are weaker bases than ammonia because of resonance interactions; the unshared electron pair is not localized on the nitrogen atom as it is in ammonia, but it is delocalized over the aromatic ring.

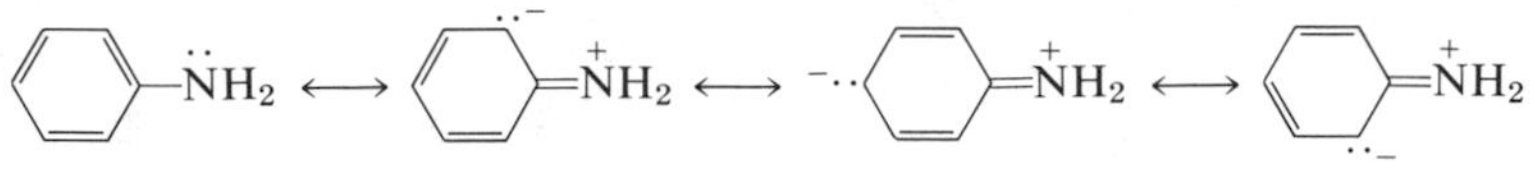

This resonance interaction is lacking in the ammonium salt,

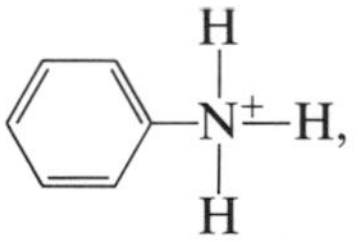

and consequently considerable resonance energy is lost when the amine is converted into the ion. For this reason, and because of the low electron density on nitrogen, aromatic amines tend to remain in the unprotonated form; that is to say, they are weak bases.

The resonance interaction of aromatic amines is reflected in the high reactivity of these compounds to electrophilic substitution and in the orientation observed. Aniline, for example, reacts extremely rapidly with bromine to give 2,4,6-tribromoaniline:

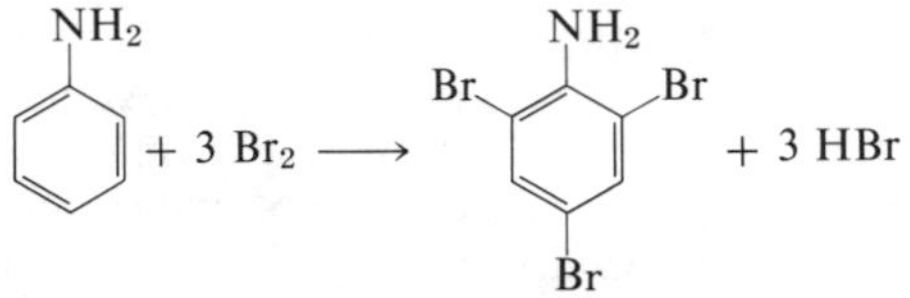

whereas toluene ($C_6H_5CH_3$) under the same reaction conditions gives no reaction whatsoever (p-bromotoluene is formed when the reaction is catalyzed by $FeBr_3$ and carried out at higher temperatures, however). The halogenated anilines are very insoluble in water and this reaction with bromine serves as a characteristic test for solutions of the aromatic amines. In strongly acidic solutions, aniline exists as the anilinium salt; under these conditions aniline does not react with bromine and when nitrated under forcing conditions it gives *meta*-nitroaniline rather than the *ortho* and *para* isomers (the positively charged NH_3^+ group which is formed is an electron-attracting group).

A list of ionization constants for various amines (Table 5-1) illustrates the effect of substituents on the base strength. In the aromatic amine series, electron-attracting groups clearly decrease the base strength and electron-donating groups increase the base strength. In the aliphatic series, the base strength is proportional to the number of alkyl groups attached to nitrogen up to a point. It will be observed that although methylamine is a stronger base than ammonia, and dimethylamine is a stronger base than methylamine, trimethylamine is weaker than dimethylamine. This weakening of the base strength has been observed in other highly substituted amines and it has been attributed to a steric effect of the bulky alkyl groups attached to the nitrogen.

It should be pointed out that the formation of hydroxide ions by amines

Table 5-1

BASE STRENGTHS OF AMINES

Amine	K	
Dimethylamine	6.0×10^{-4}	
Methylamine	5.1×10^{-4}	
Trimethylamine	6.3×10^{-5}	
Ammonia	1.8×10^{-5}	Base
4-Methylaniline	1.2×10^{-9}	strength
Aniline	4.2×10^{-10}	
4-Chloroaniline	1.5×10^{-10}	
4-Nitroaniline	1.0×10^{-13}	

in water is not necessary for these compounds to show acid-base reactions: $CH_3NH_2 + H_2O \rightleftharpoons CH_3NH_3^+OH^-$. The amines themselves are bases (Lewis bases by the definition given in Chapter 2). Ethylamine, for example, reacts with hydrogen chloride in an organic solvent to give ethylammonium chloride by a direct proton transfer:

$$CH_3CH_2\overset{H}{\underset{H}{N}}: \quad \longrightarrow H\overgroup{:Cl} \longrightarrow CH_3CH_2NH_3^+Cl^-.$$

Full proton transfer does not occur when a weaker acid such as ethanol is used, however:

$$CH_3CH_2\ddot{N}H_2 + CH_3CH_2OH \longrightarrow CH_3CH_2\overset{H}{\underset{H}{N}}:\text{-------}HOCH_2CH_3$$
$$\text{"X"}$$

As we have seen from our discussion of the properties of alcohols, the species "X" represents an ethanol molecule hydrogen-bonded to ethylamine. Since the amine is a stronger base than ethanol, this type of hydrogen bond is stronger than that occurring in pure ethanol:

$$CH_3CH_2\overset{..}{\underset{H}{O}}:\text{----------}H\overset{..}{O}CH_2CH_3.$$

Pure amines also form hydrogen bonds, $CH_3\overset{H}{\underset{H}{N}}:\text{-------}H\overset{..}{\underset{H}{N}}CH_3$, but since the amines are very weak acids, these hydrogen bonds are weak.

Preparation of the Amines

Most aliphatic amines may be prepared by the displacement of halide ions from alkyl halides by ammonia and the amines:

$$H-\overset{H}{\underset{H}{N}}: \quad \longrightarrow \overset{}{\underset{CH_3}{CH_2}}\overgroup{Br} \longrightarrow H-\overset{H}{\underset{H}{N^{\pm}}}-CH_2CH_3 \quad Br^- \xrightarrow{\text{NaOH}}$$

$$H-\overset{..}{\underset{H}{N}}-CH_2CH_3 + H_2O + Na^+Br^-$$

Ethylamine

A substituted ammonium salt is formed as an intermediate in the reaction but the free amine may be obtained from this salt by treatment with sodium hydroxide. A few examples are listed to illustrate the range and versatility of the reaction.

$$CH_3CH_2NH_2 + CH_3Br \longrightarrow CH_3CH_2-\overset{\overset{\displaystyle H}{|}}{\underset{\underset{\displaystyle H}{|}}{N^{\pm}}}-CH_3 \ Br^- \xrightarrow{NaOH} CH_3CH_2\overset{..}{\underset{\underset{\displaystyle H}{|}}{N}}CH_3$$

Methylethylamine

$$CH_3CH_2\overset{..}{\underset{\underset{\displaystyle H}{|}}{N}}CH_3 + \langle\bigcirc\rangle-CH_2Br \longrightarrow$$

$$CH_3CH_2-\overset{\overset{\displaystyle H}{|}}{\underset{\underset{\displaystyle CH_3}{|}}{N^{\pm}}}-CH_2\langle\bigcirc\rangle \xrightarrow{NaOH} CH_3CH_2-\overset{..}{\underset{\underset{\displaystyle CH_3}{|}}{N}}-CH_2\langle\bigcirc\rangle$$

Br⁻

Methylethylbenzylamine

$$CH_3CH_2-\overset{..}{\underset{\underset{\displaystyle CH_3}{|}}{N}}-CH_2\langle\bigcirc\rangle + CH_3Br \longrightarrow CH_3CH_2-\overset{\overset{\displaystyle CH_3}{|}}{\underset{\underset{\displaystyle CH_3}{|}}{N^{\pm}}}-CH_2\langle\bigcirc\rangle \ Br^-$$

Dimethylethylbenzylammonium
bromide

In the last example, a tertiary amine has been converted into a **quaternary** salt. The quaternary salts are neutral, fully ionic compounds that have the properties of typical inorganic salts. Most primary and secondary amines may be transformed directly into quaternary salts if an excess of an alkyl halide and sodium hydroxide is used, since the hydroxide converts the ammonium salts into the free amines, which are re-alkylated, and so on until the quaternary stage is reached.

$$CH_3CH_2NH_2 + \underset{excess}{CH_3Br} \xrightarrow{NaOH} CH_3CH_2-\overset{\overset{\displaystyle CH_3}{|}}{\underset{\underset{\displaystyle CH_3}{|}}{N^{\pm}}}-CH_3 \ Br^-$$

A few quaternary compounds are found in nature; the compound choline, for example, is found in muscle tissue:

$$(CH_3)_3\overset{+}{N}-CH_2CH_2OH \ \ OH^-$$

THE HOFMANN REARRANGEMENT. This reaction is one of the most reliable of the methods used for the preparation of primary amines. The following sequence is involved in the reaction, although technically the term "Hofmann rearrangement" refers to only the last step:

$$R-\overset{\overset{\displaystyle O}{\|}}{C}-OH \xrightarrow{SOCl_2} R-\overset{\overset{\displaystyle O}{\|}}{C}-Cl \xrightarrow{NH_3} R-\overset{\overset{\displaystyle O}{\|}}{C}-NH_2 \xrightarrow[\substack{NaOH \\ H_2O}]{Br_2} R-NH_2 + CO_2$$

The reaction, in essence, converts a carboxylic acid into an amine with the over-all loss of 1 carbon atom from the molecule. If the product is a primary amine (RCH_2NH_2), it can be oxidized with potassium permanganate to form a new carboxylic, $RCH_2NH_2 \xrightarrow{KMnO_4} RCO_2H$, and the sequence can be

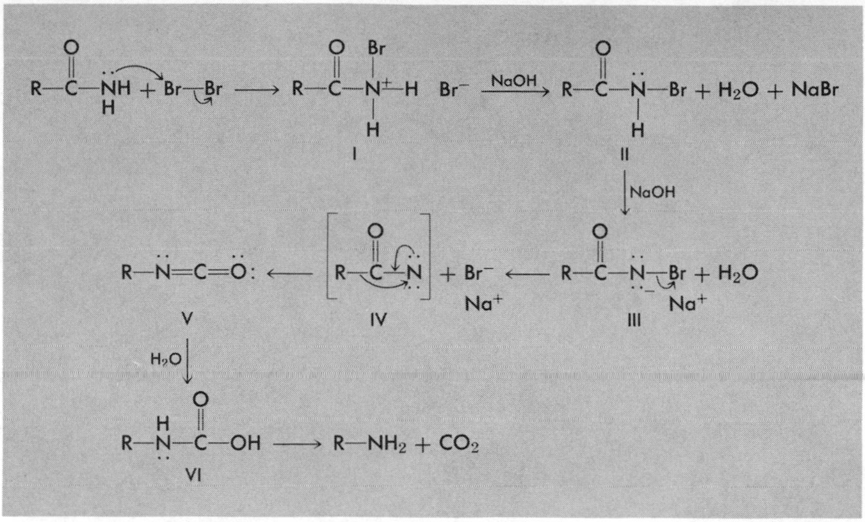

Fig. 5-3. The mechanism of the Hofmann rearrangement.

repeated. For this reason, the Hoffman rearrangement and the oxidation step are often used to degrade long-chain carboxylic acids, carbon atom by carbon atom.

The mechanism of this reaction involves several intermediates (Fig. 5-3). The first step is the nucleophilic displacement of bromide ion to give the substituted ammonium salt (I); this compound then reacts with base to give the free N-bromoamide (II). Because of the presence of two electron-withdrawing groups, this compound is an acid, and reaction with base gives the negative ion (III). The loss of a bromide ion then gives the highly reactive monovalent species (IV), which electronically resembles a carbonium ion. The alkyl group and its pair of electrons move to the electron-deficient nitrogen to give an intermediate (V) called an **isocyanate.** The addition of water across the carbon-nitrogen double bond yields a compound (VI) with a carboxyl group attached directly to nitrogen. These compounds are called **carbamic** acids and although their esters are stable, the carbamic acids themselves readily undergo decarboxylation to give the free amine. It can be seen that although the Hofmann rearrangement as a whole is complex, the individual steps are reasonably simple.

ISOCYANATES.   Isocyanates may be prepared directly by a number of reactions which permit the isolation of the pure compounds. A particularly direct method involves the displacement of halide ions from the alkyl halides by cyanate ion:

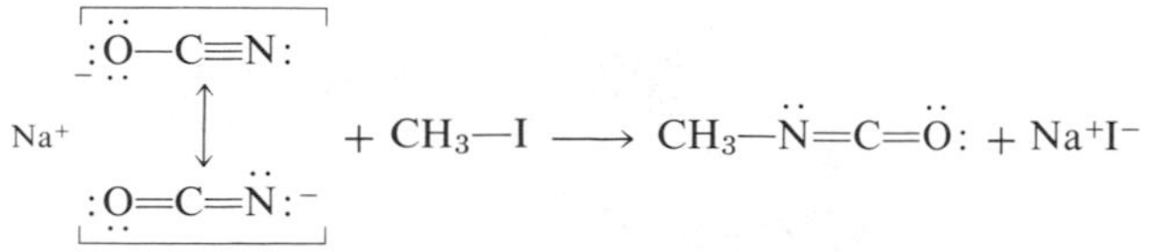

$$Na^+ \quad \begin{array}{c} :\ddot{O}-C\equiv N: \\ \updownarrow \\ :O=C=\ddot{N}:^- \end{array} \quad + CH_3-I \longrightarrow CH_3-\ddot{N}=C=\ddot{O}: + Na^+I^-$$

Sodium cyanate   Methyl isocyanate

A second method, which is especially valuable for the preparation of aromatic isocyanates, involves the reaction of phosgene (the acid chloride of carbonic acid) with primary amines:

$$\text{C}_6\text{H}_5\text{—NH}_2 + \text{Cl—C(=O)—Cl} \xrightarrow{-\text{HCl}} \left[\text{C}_6\text{H}_5\text{—N(H)—C(=O)—Cl} \right] \xrightarrow{-\text{HCl}} \text{C}_6\text{H}_5\text{—N=C=O}$$

Phosgene   Phenyl isocyanate

The isocyanates react with alcohols to give esters of carbamic acid in a similar fashion to their reaction with water (Fig. 5-3):

$$\text{CH}_3\text{—N=C=O:} + \text{CH}_3\text{OH} \longrightarrow \text{CH}_3\text{—N(H)—C(=O)—O—CH}_3$$

Methyl N-methylcarbamate

In addition, they react with ammonia or the amines to give derivatives of **urea** (a compound which may be considered to be the diamide of carbonic acid):

$$\text{CH}_3\ddot{\text{N}}=\ddot{\text{O}}: + :\text{NH}_3 \longrightarrow \text{CH}_3\text{—N(H)—C(=O)—NH}_2$$

N-Methylurea

The carbamates and ureas very often are crystalline, and the isocyanates are widely used to prepare solid derivatives of alcohols and amines.

PREPARATION OF AMINES BY REDUCTION. The catalytic reduction of nitro compounds is a useful method for the preparation of primary amines:

$$\text{R—NO}_2 \xrightarrow[\text{Pt}]{\text{H}_2} \text{R—NH}_2 + 2\text{H}_2\text{O}.$$ This method is particularly valuable in the synthesis of aromatic amines, since the nitro derivatives of the aromatic compounds are readily made by direct nitration:

1-Nitronaphthalene

The reduction may also be accomplished with chemical reducing agents, such as mixtures of iron or tin and hydrochloric acid. The reduction of nitriles and amides with lithium aluminum hydride is another versatile method for the synthesis of amines:

$$\text{CH}_3\text{—C}\equiv\text{N} \xrightarrow{\text{LiAlH}_4} \text{CH}_3\text{CH}_2\text{NH}_2$$

$$\text{CH}_3\text{—C(=O)—NH}_2 \xrightarrow{\text{LiAlH}_4} \text{CH}_3\text{CH}_2\text{NH}_2$$

$$\text{CH}_3\text{—C(=O)—N(CH}_3)_2 \xrightarrow{\text{LiAlH}_4} \text{CH}_3\text{CH}_2\text{N(CH}_3)_2$$

Reactions of the Amines

We have already mentioned the acid-base reactions of amines and also the reaction of amines with alkyl halides. The latter reaction is related to a useful method for the synthesis of olefins called the Hofmann elimination reaction.

THE HOFMANN ELIMINATION REACTION. Amines of all types react with an excess of methyl iodide in the presence of base to give a quaternary salt:

$$CH_3CH_2\overset{H}{N}CH_2CH_3 + 2CH_3I \xrightarrow{KOH} CH_3CH_2-\overset{CH_3}{\underset{CH_3}{\overset{|}{\underset{|}{N^\pm}}}}-CH_2CH_3 \quad I^-$$

These compounds react with silver hydroxide to give a precipitate of silver iodide and a solution of a quaternary hydroxide:

$$CH_3CH_2NR_3{}^+I^- + AgOH \longrightarrow CH_3CH_2NR_3{}^+OH^- + AgI$$

The quaternary hydroxides are strong bases, equal in strength to the alkali metal hydroxides, and when they are heated, an elimination reaction initiated by hydroxide ion occurs in which a tertiary amine, water, and an alkene are formed:

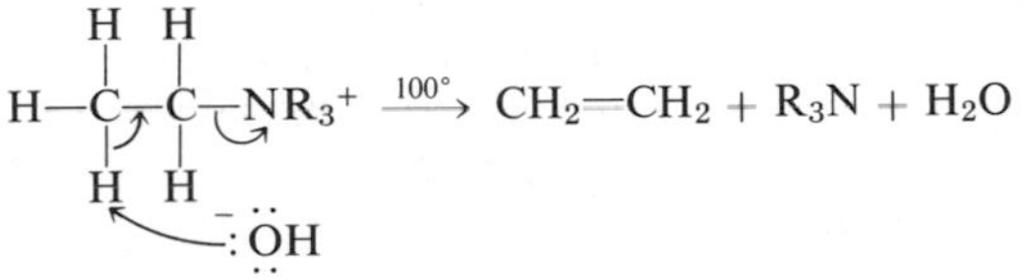

$$H-\overset{H}{\underset{H}{\overset{|}{\underset{|}{C}}}}-\overset{H}{\underset{H}{\overset{|}{\underset{|}{C}}}}-NR_3{}^+ \xrightarrow{100°} CH_2{=}CH_2 + R_3N + H_2O$$

$$\overset{\cdot\cdot}{:}\overset{-}{O}H$$

This reaction is a useful and general method for the synthesis of alkenes; the only structural requirement is that the amine must possess a β-hydrogen atom.

The Hofmann elimination reaction is often used to prove the structures of complex amines, as shown in the following sequence:

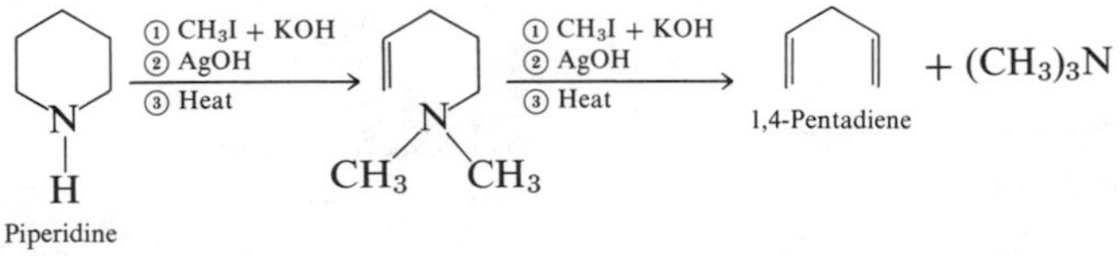

Piperidine

1,4-Pentadiene

The research chemist, at this point, might elect to oxidize the pentadiene to malonic acid ($HO_2CCH_2CO_2H$), a crystalline compound, which would then be compared with an authentic sample of the acid. From his knowledge of these reactions, and from the identification of malonic acid, the research chemist would know that the starting material was piperidine.

Diazonium Ions and Azo Dyes

Aromatic primary amines react with nitrous acid to give an ionic species called a diazonium salt:

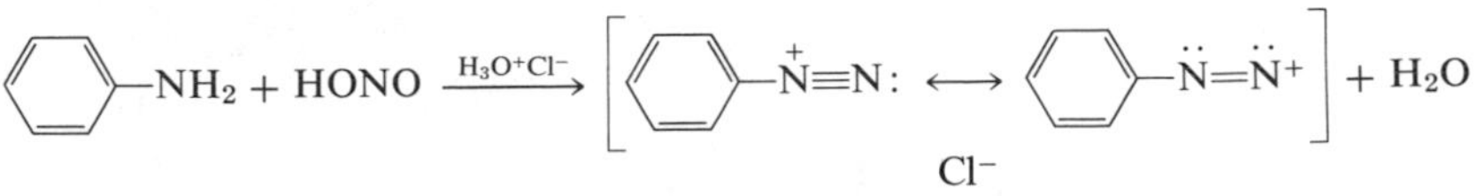

Benzenediazonium chloride

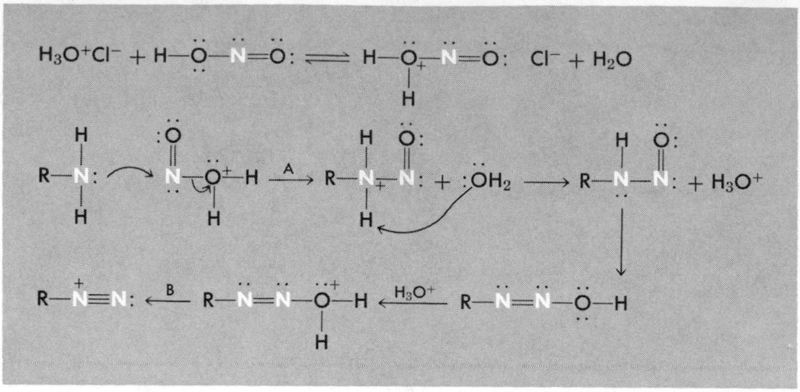

$$H_3O^+Cl^- + H-\overset{..}{\underset{..}{O}}-\overset{..}{N}=\overset{..}{\underset{..}{O}}: \;\rightleftharpoons\; H-\overset{+}{\underset{H}{\overset{..}{O}}}-\overset{..}{N}=\overset{..}{\underset{..}{O}}: \; Cl^- + H_2O$$

Fig. 5-4. The reaction of nitrous acid with primary amines to give diazonium salts.

A number of steps are involved in this reaction (Fig. 5-4). Step A is a displacement reaction and step B is an ionization reaction, whereas the remaining steps involve simple proton transfers.

The diazonium salts undergo a number of displacement reactions which are of considerable use in organic synthesis (Fig. 5-5).

An interesting reaction in which nitrogen is not lost is the so-called coupling reaction, in which diazonium salts react with phenols and with aromatic amines by electrophilic substitution to give derivatives known as **azo** compounds:

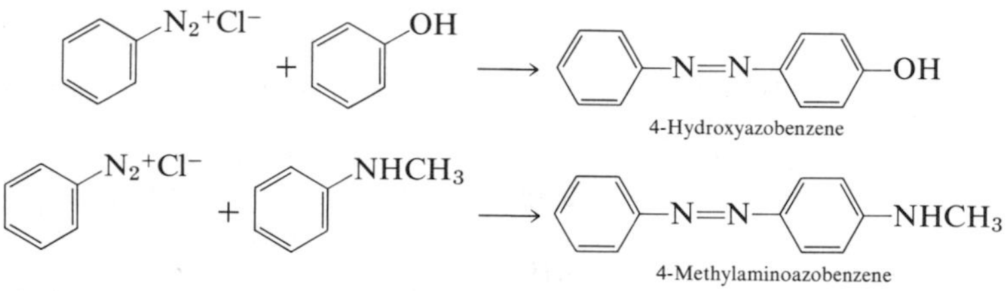

4-Hydroxyazobenzene

4-Methylaminoazobenzene

The azo compounds are all colored materials and many of the more complex ones, such as naphthol blue-black B, are used as dyes. Butter yellow (4-dimethylaminoazobenzene) was used for many years as an artificial color-

Fig. 5-5. Reactions of aromatic diazo-nium salts.

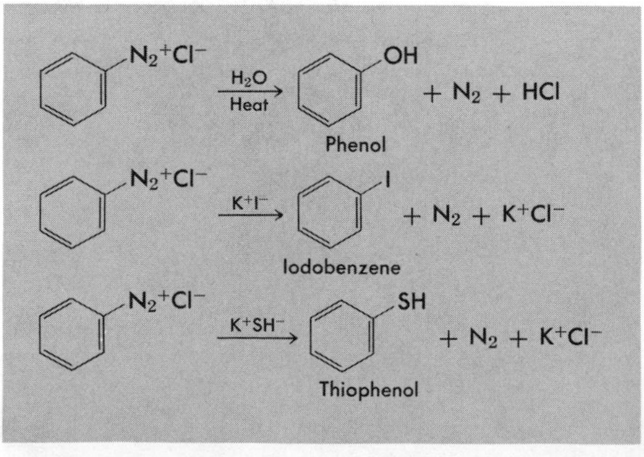

ing agent in butter and in edible oils. The compound was found to be carcinogenic, however, and it is no longer used in foods.

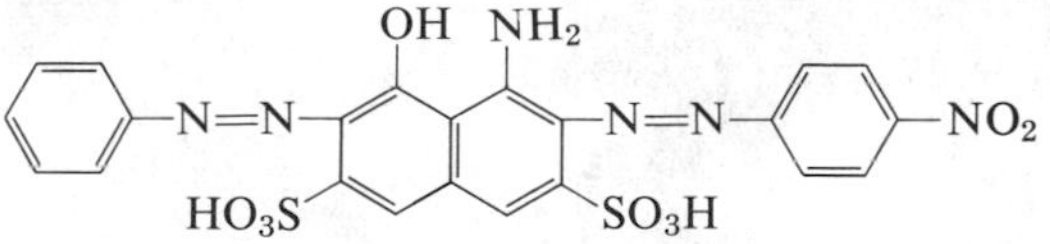

Napthol blue black B

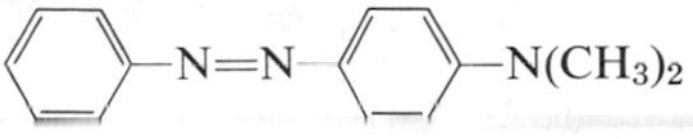

Butter yellow

Diazonium salts have been used in an ingenious way to locate in tissues and organs the sites of certain enzymes which catalyze the hydrolysis of esters. The tissue or organ is flooded with a mixture of a diazonium salt and a phenyl ester, the hydrolysis of which is catalyzed by the enzyme:

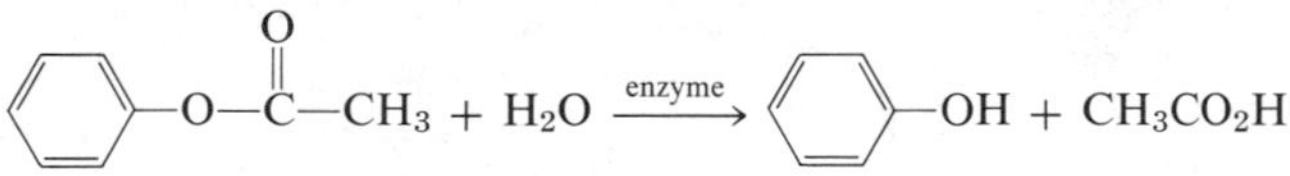

The phenol liberated reacts immediately with the diazonium salt

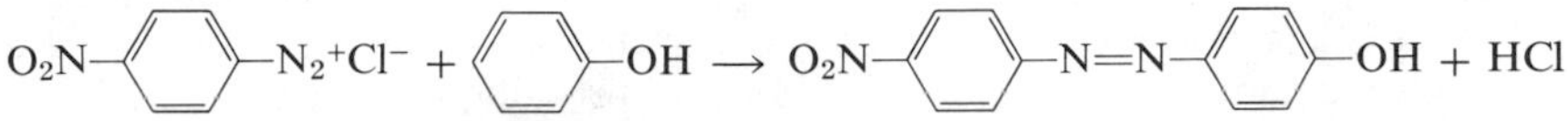

to give a dye (it should be noted that the phenol esters themselves do not react with diazonium ions). The tissues are examined and the colored areas noted; these are the areas that contained the hydrolytic enzyme.

THE REACTIONS OF ALIPHATIC AMINES WITH NITROUS ACID. The reactions of primary aliphatic and aromatic amines with nitrous acid are similar in that diazonium salts are formed as reaction intermediates in both cases. The subsequent reactions are quite different, however, in that aliphatic diazonium salts are extremely unstable (no aliphatic diazonium salt has ever been isolated). The aliphatic diazonium ions formed as reaction intermediates decompose very rapidly to give nitrogen and a carbonium ion: $RNH_2 + HONO \longrightarrow RN_2^+ \longrightarrow R^+ + N_2$. The carbonium ion then reacts in the typical carbonium-ion fashion with a nucleophile in the system, or by the elimination of a β-proton (Fig. 5-6). A third typical decomposition path for carbonium ions is indicated in Fig. 5-6. This is the isomerization

Fig. 5-6. The reaction of propylamine with nitrous acid.

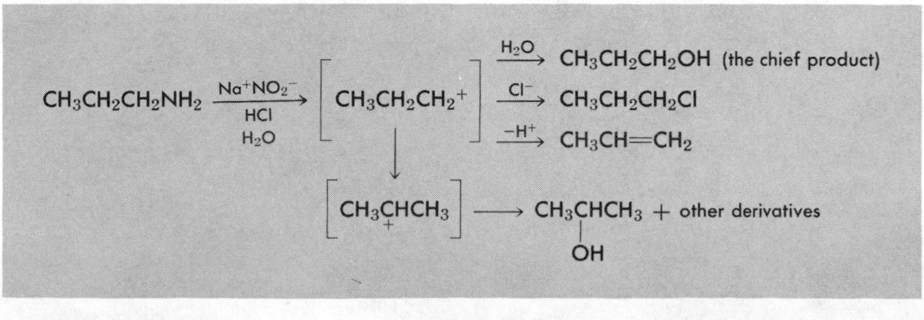

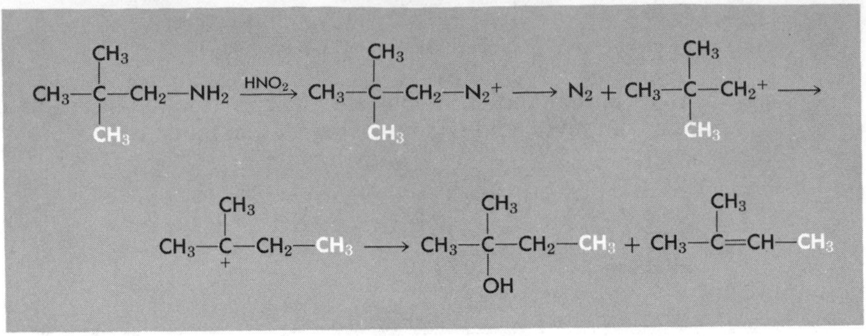

Fig. 5-7. The migration of a methyl group in the reaction of 2,2-dimethyl propylamine with nitrous acid.

reaction whereby carbonium ions rearrange to give a more stable carbonium ion (in this case, the *secondary* propyl carbonium ion). The reaction occurs by the transfer of a hydride ion ($H:^-$) from an adjacent carbon atom:

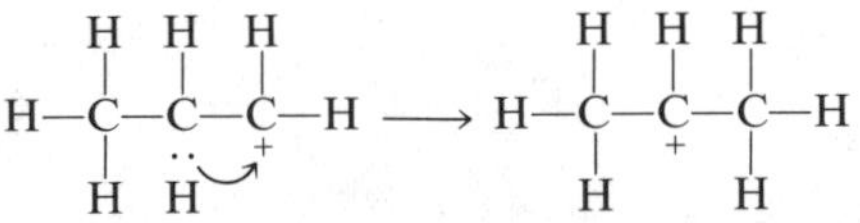

Alkyl groups also migrate to give more stable carbonium ions, and the tendency is so strong that the nitrous acid deamination of 2,2-dimethyl propylamine gives, as the only alcohol product, 2-methyl-2-butanol (Fig. 5-7).

Migrations of alkyl groups and hydrogen of this type are typical reactions of electron-deficient species. Similar reactions are found for compounds containing electron-deficient nitrogen (Fig. 5-3) and for compounds containing electron-deficient oxygen ($R—\overset{..}{O}{}^+$).

Secondary and tertiary amines react differently with nitrous acid, and the reaction serves as a convenient way to distinguish the 3 types of amines. Secondary amines (both aliphatic and aromatic) react with nitrous acid to yield a water-insoluble compound called a nitrosoamine:

$$(CH_3)_2\overset{..}{N}H + H—\overset{..}{\underset{..}{O}}—\overset{..}{N}=\overset{..}{O}: \longrightarrow (CH_3)_3\overset{..}{N}—\overset{..}{N}=\overset{..}{O}: + H_2O$$

N-Nitrosodimethylamine

Tertiary amines, on the other hand, do not react with nitrous acid other than to form a water soluble salt:

$$(CH_3)_3N: + HONO \longrightarrow (CH_3)_3NH^+NO_2^-$$

Heterocylic primary amines react with nitrous acid to give chiefly the corresponding alcohol. The reaction with cytosine (2-hydroxy-4-amino-pyrimidine)

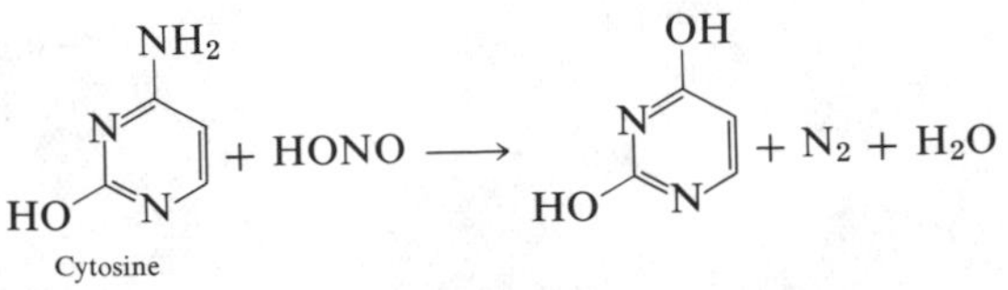

Cytosine

114

is especially interesting in that cytosine is an important constituent of the chromosomes (the genetic material) of all living things. The treatment of bacterial cells with nitrous acid yields the hydroxy derivative of cytosine in the chromosomes; this change (a mutation) causes a definite change in the progeny of the bacteria, which is passed on to all the succeeding generations!

AMIDES

Amides are derivatives of ammonia and the amines in which one or more of the hydrogen atoms are replaced by acyl groups ($R—\overset{\overset{O}{\|}}{C}—$). Examples are given in Fig. 5-8. The names of the parent compounds are derived from the carboxylic acid names by the substitution of the suffix **amide** for the **ic acid** endings. The amides have many of the properties of the amines. They are basic compounds, but much more weakly basic than the amines because of resonance delocalization of the unshared electron pair of nitrogen:

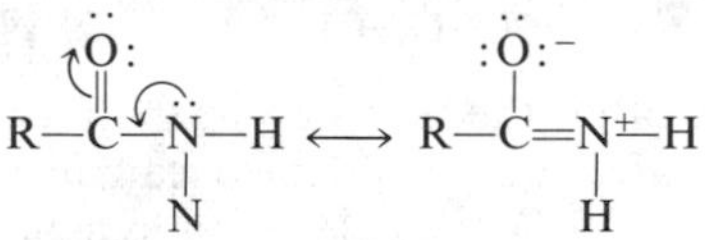

$$R—\overset{\overset{..}{O}:}{\overset{\|}{C}}\overset{\frown}{—}\overset{|}{\underset{N}{N}}—H \longleftrightarrow R—\overset{\overset{..}{O}:^-}{C}=\overset{|}{\underset{H}{N^{\pm}}}—H$$

They are prepared, principally, by the reaction of ammonia (or an amine) with an ester or an acid anhydride:

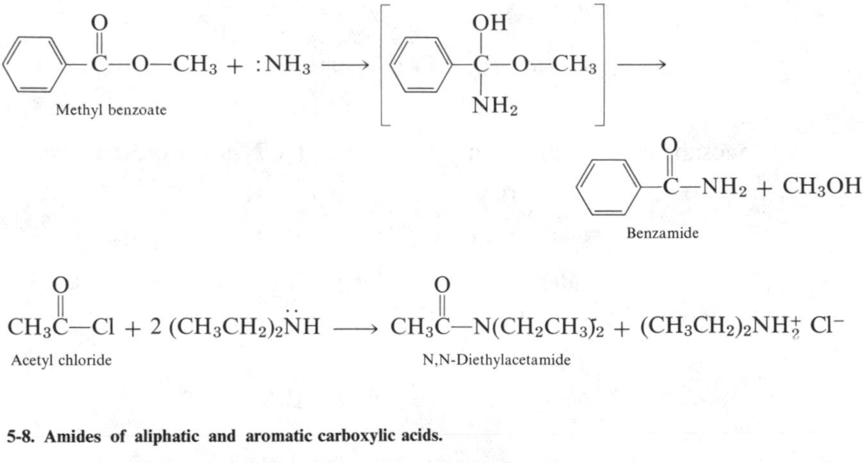

Methyl benzoate

Benzamide

$$CH_3\overset{\overset{O}{\|}}{C}—Cl + 2\,(CH_3CH_2)_2\overset{..}{N}H \longrightarrow CH_3\overset{\overset{O}{\|}}{C}—N(CH_2CH_3)_2 + (CH_3CH_2)_2NH_2^+\,Cl^-$$

Acetyl chloride   N,N-Diethylacetamide

Fig. 5-8. Amides of aliphatic and aromatic carboxylic acids.

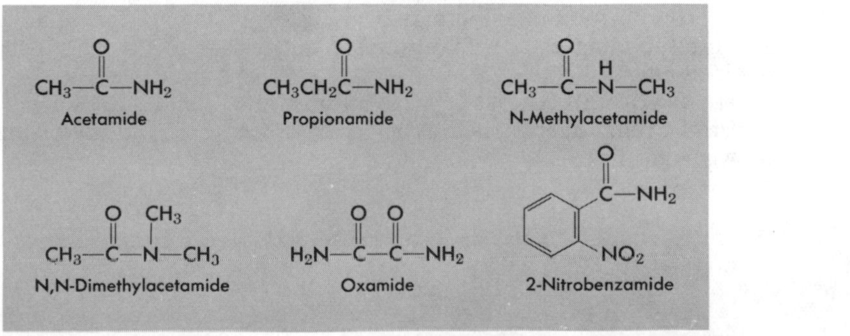

$$CH_3—\overset{\overset{O}{\|}}{C}—NH_2$$
Acetamide

$$CH_3CH_2\overset{\overset{O}{\|}}{C}—NH_2$$
Propionamide

$$CH_3—\overset{\overset{O}{\|}}{C}—\overset{\overset{H}{|}}{N}—CH_3$$
N-Methylacetamide

$$CH_3—\overset{\overset{O}{\|}}{C}—\overset{\overset{CH_3}{|}}{N}—CH_3$$
N,N-Dimethylacetamide

$$H_2N—\overset{\overset{O}{\|}}{C}—\overset{\overset{O}{\|}}{C}—NH_2$$
Oxamide

2-Nitrobenzamide

Reactions of the Amides

Amides are readily hydrolyzed in both acidic and basic solutions:

1. Acid hydrolysis
$$R-\overset{O}{\overset{\|}{C}}-NH_2 + H_3O^+Cl^- \longrightarrow R-\overset{O}{\overset{\|}{C}}-\overset{+}{N}H_3 \ Cl^- + H_2O \longrightarrow$$

$$R-\overset{O^-}{\underset{\underset{OH_2 \ Cl^-}{\overset{+}{N}H_3}}{\overset{|}{C}}} \longrightarrow R-\overset{O}{\overset{\|}{C}}-\overset{+}{O}H_2 + NH_3 \longrightarrow RCO_2H + NH_4^+Cl^-$$
$$Cl^-$$

2. Base hydrolysis
$$R-\overset{O}{\overset{\|}{C}}-N(CH_3)_2 + Na^+OH^- \longrightarrow R-\underset{\underset{OH}{}}{\overset{O^-Na^+}{\overset{|}{C}}}-N(CH_3)_2 \longrightarrow$$

$$R-\overset{O}{\overset{\|}{C}}-OH + (CH_3)_2N^-Na^+ \longrightarrow RCO_2^-Na^+ + (CH_3)_2NH$$

This reaction is often the first step in the identification of amides, since the carboxylic acid and amine obtained can usually be identified more easily than the amide itself. A second general reaction of the amides, the Hofmann rearrangement, was outlined in the section on the preparation of amines.

THE REACTION OF AMIDES WITH NITROUS ACID. Unsubstituted amides give reactions with nitrous acid similar to those of primary amines:

$$R-\overset{O}{\overset{\|}{C}}-NH_2 + HONO \longrightarrow \left[R-\overset{O}{\overset{\|}{C}}-N_2^+OH^- \right] \longrightarrow R-\overset{O}{\overset{\|}{C}}-OH + N_2$$
$$+ H_2O$$

Monosubstituted amides, in contrast, give the N-nitroso derivatives:

$$R-\overset{O}{\overset{\|}{C}}-\overset{H}{\underset{}{N}}-CH_3 \xrightarrow{HONO} R-\overset{O}{\overset{\|}{C}}-\overset{N=O}{\underset{}{N}}-CH_3 + H_2O$$

The N-nitrosoamides undergo an interesting rearrangement leading to the elimination of nitrogen at about 75° C:

$$R-\overset{O}{\overset{\|}{C}}-\underset{\underset{:O=N:}{}}{\overset{}{N}}-CH_3 \longrightarrow R-\overset{O}{\overset{\|}{C}}-\overset{..}{O}-\overset{..}{N}=\overset{..}{N}-CH_3 \longrightarrow N_2 + R-\overset{O}{\overset{\|}{C}}-\overset{..}{O}-CH_3$$

This decomposition reaction may be used for the conversion of amides into the corresponding esters. Disubstituted amides, as might be expected, are stable to nitrous acid.

DEHYDRATION OF AMIDES. Most unsubstituted amides are dehydrated by powerful drying agents such as phosphorus pentoxide to give compounds known as nitriles:

$$CH_3CH_2\overset{O}{\overset{\|}{C}}-NH_2 \xrightarrow{P_2O_5} CH_3CH_2C{\equiv}N$$
Propionitrile

The nitriles may also be prepared by the nucleophilic displacement of halide ion from alkyl halides with cyanide ion: CH_3CH_2—$Br + Na^+CN \longrightarrow$ $CH_3CH_2C{\equiv}N + Na^+Br^-$.

AMINO ACIDS

The **amino acids** (R—$\overset{\overset{\textstyle H}{|}}{\underset{\underset{\textstyle NH_2}{|}}{C}}$—$CO_2H$) are carboxylic acids substituted on the α-carbon atom by an amino group. They were originally obtained by the hydrolysis of proteins, but by the early part of this century they had all been synthesized in the laboratory. Glycine (aminoacetic acid) is the simplest amino acid, and it was also the first to have been isolated; it was obtained crystalline in 1820 by Bracconnot from the hydrolysis products of gelatin. Scientists have isolated a few dozen amino acids from natural sources since that time, largely from proteins. The 20 amino acids that are essential for the synthesis of proteins in living systems are listed in Table 5-2. Note the similarities in what are essentially the building blocks of the proteins.

Table 5-2

ESSENTIAL AMINO ACIDS $\quad R$—$\overset{\overset{\textstyle H}{|}}{\underset{\underset{\textstyle NH_2}{|}}{C}}$—$CO_2H$

R	Name	R	Name
H—	Glycine	HO—⬡—CH_2—	Tyrosine
CH_3—	Alanine		
HO—CH_2—	Serine		
HS—CH_2—	Cysteine	HN-imidazole-CH_2—	Histidine
CH_3CHOH—	Threonine		
HO_2C—CH_2—	Aspartic acid		
$(CH_3)_2CH$—	Valine	indole-CH_2—	Trypto-phane
CH_3—S—CH_2CH_2—	Methionine		
HO_2C—CH_2CH_2—	Glutamic acid		
$(CH_3)_2CHCH_2$—	Leucine		
$CH_3CH_2CH(CH_3)$—	Isoleucine	CH_2—CH_2	Proline
H_2N—$CH_2CH_2CH_2CH_2$—	Lysine	CH_2—N—CH—CO_2H	
H_2N—$\overset{\overset{\textstyle NH}{\|}}{C}$—NH—$CH_2$—$CH_2$—$CH_2$	Argenine		
HO_2C—$\underset{\underset{\textstyle NH_2}{|}}{CH}$—$CH_2$—S—S—$CH_2$—	Cystine	OH	
		CH—CH_2 CH_2—N—CH—CO_2H	Hydroxy-proline
⬡—CH_2—	Phenylalanine		

Since carboxylic acids are neutralized by amines, it is not surprising that amino acids, which contain both of these groups, exist as internal salts, or **dipolar** ions:

$$R-\overset{\overset{\textstyle H}{|}}{\underset{\underset{\textstyle H-\overset{+}{N}-H}{|}}{C}}-\overset{\overset{\textstyle O}{\|}}{C}-O^-$$

When an amino acid is treated with a base, the proton is lost from the nitrogen atom of the $-NH_3^+$ group:

$$H-\underset{\underset{H-\overset{|}{\underset{|}{N^+}}-H}{|}}{\overset{\overset{H}{|}}{C}}-\overset{\overset{O}{\|}}{C}-O^- + H_2O \rightleftharpoons H_3O^+ + H-\underset{\underset{:\overset{|}{N}-H}{|}}{\overset{\overset{H}{|}}{C}}-\overset{\overset{O}{\|}}{C}-O^-$$

As a result, the ionization constants are different from those of the carboxylic acids in which the proton is transferred from an oxygen atom to water. The ionization constant for glycine is 1.6×10^{-10} compared to the value of 1.8×10^{-5} found for acetic acid. In strong acids, the amino acids behave as bases, and a proton is transferred to the carboxylate ion:

$$R-\underset{\underset{NH_3^+}{|}}{\overset{\overset{H}{|}}{C}}-\overset{\overset{O}{\|}}{C}-O^- + H_3O^+ \longrightarrow R-\underset{\underset{NH_3^+}{|}}{\overset{\overset{H}{|}}{C}}-\overset{\overset{O}{\|}}{C}-O-H + H_2O$$

The amino acids are thus typical amphoteric compounds in that they react with both acids and bases.

Preparation of the Amino Acids

Most of the amino acids may be prepared by the displacement of a bromide ion from an α-bromo acid with ammonia:

$$CH_3-\underset{\underset{Br}{|}}{\overset{\overset{H}{|}}{C}}-CO_2H + 2 NH_3 \longrightarrow CH_3-\underset{\underset{NH_3^+}{|}}{\overset{\overset{H}{|}}{C}}-CO_2^- + NH_4^+Br^-$$

Alanine

A second general method, called the **Strecker** synthesis, involves the reaction of an aldehyde with ammonium cyanide, and the hydrolysis of the nitrile formed as an intermediate.

$$(CH_3)_2CH-\overset{\overset{O}{\|}}{C}-H + NH_4^+CN^- \longrightarrow$$

Isobutyraldehyde

$$(CH_3)_2CH-\underset{\underset{NH_2}{|}}{\overset{\overset{H}{|}}{C}}-C\equiv N \xrightarrow[H_3O^+]{H_2O} (CH_3)_2CH-\underset{\underset{NH_3}{|}}{\overset{\overset{H}{|}}{C}}-CO_2^-$$

Valine

Many other synthetic methods have been devised which are specific for one or more of the amino acids; for further information, consult the list of selected readings at the end of this volume.

Reactions of the Amino Acids

The reactions of amino acids are similar to those of the amines and carboxylic acids:

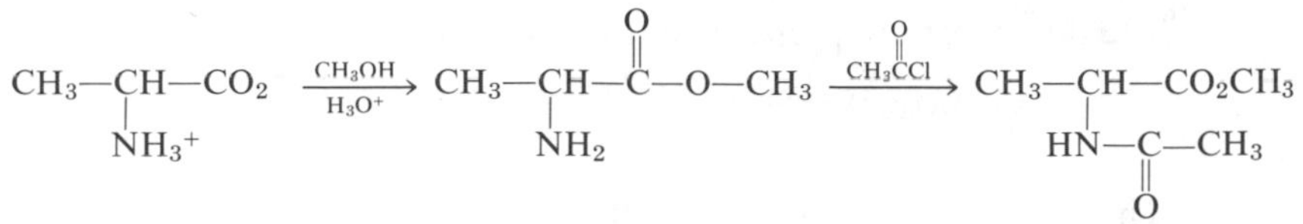

$$CH_3-\underset{\underset{NH_3^+}{|}}{CH}-CO_2 \xrightarrow[H_3O^+]{CH_3OH} CH_3-\underset{\underset{NH_2}{|}}{CH}-\overset{\overset{O}{\|}}{C}-O-CH_3 \xrightarrow{CH_3CCl} CH_3-\underset{\underset{HN-\underset{\underset{O}{\|}}{C}-CH_3}{|}}{CH}-CO_2CH_3$$

An especially important reaction of amino acids is amide formation, as we shall illustrate further in the section on proteins (Chapter 6).

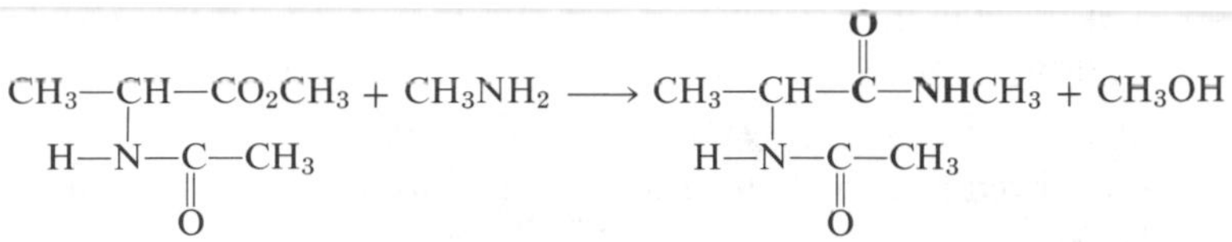

$$CH_3-\underset{\underset{H-N-\underset{\underset{O}{\|}}{C}-CH_3}{|}}{CH}-CO_2CH_3 + CH_3NH_2 \longrightarrow CH_3-\underset{\underset{H-N-\underset{\underset{O}{\|}}{C}-CH_3}{|}}{CH}-\overset{\overset{O}{\|}}{C}-NHCH_3 + CH_3OH$$

ORGANIC COMPOUNDS CONTAINING SULFUR

The compounds of sulfur at the -2 level of oxidation are, by and large, similar to those compounds of oxygen, as expected from the positions of the 2 elements in the periodic table. The chief differences stem from the greater acidity of hydrogen sulfide and its alkyl derivatives, and the greater nucleophilicity of the sulfur compounds. Sulfur compounds with a positive oxidation number, such as the sulfonic acids (RSO_3H), are also of considerable importance in chemistry.

Examples of various sulfur-containing compounds are given in Fig. 5-9. The names of these compounds are closely related to the names of the oxygen analogs; usually the term **thio** is added to indicate the presence of the sulfur atom (as an exception, however, the RSH compounds are very often called mercaptans).

The thiols are characterized by atrocious odors (butanethiol is chiefly responsible for the scent of the skunk) and by the formation of insoluble precipates with lead, mercury, and the other heavy metals. Many enzymes contain thiol groups, and it is common practice to precipitate or inactivate these enzymes with mercuric salts.

The thiols are generally prepared by displacement reactions involving alkyl halides and salts of hydrogen sulfide (H_2S):

$$CH_3CH_2-Br + K^+SH^- \longrightarrow CH_3CH_2SH + K^+Br^-$$

Fig. 5-9. Compounds of sulfur.

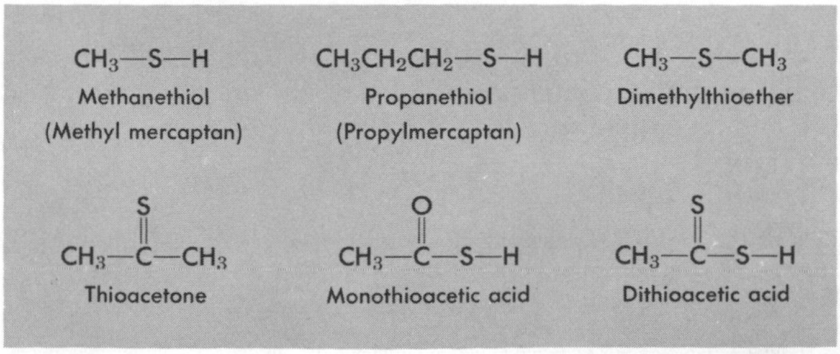

CH_3-S-H	$CH_3CH_2CH_2-S-H$	CH_3-S-CH_3
Methanethiol	Propanethiol	Dimethylthioether
(Methyl mercaptan)	(Propylmercaptan)	
$CH_3-\overset{\overset{S}{\|}}{C}-CH_3$	$CH_3-\overset{\overset{O}{\|}}{C}-S-H$	$CH_3-\overset{\overset{S}{\|}}{C}-S-H$
Thioacetone	Monothioacetic acid	Dithioacetic acid

The thioethers are prepared in a similar way:

$$CH_3CH_2—Br + CH_3S^-K^+ \longrightarrow CH_3SCH_2CH_3 + K^+Br^-$$

Methylethylthioether

The thiols are more acidic than the corresponding alcohols, although they are still weak acids; the ionization constant for ethanethiol is 10^{-12}, for example:

$$CH_3CH_2SH + H_2O \rightleftharpoons CH_3CH_2S^- + H_3O^+ \qquad K = 10^{-12}$$

Thiol anions of this type (prepared quantitatively by the reaction of the thiol with sodium hydroxide) are readily oxidized by the oxygen in air, or by oxidizing agents such as iodine to give the corresponding free radicals $(2\ CH_3—\overset{..}{\underset{..}{S}}:^-Na^+ + :\overset{..}{\underset{..}{I}}:\overset{..}{\underset{..}{I}}: \longrightarrow 2\ CH_3—\overset{..}{\underset{..}{S}}\cdot + 2\ Na^+:\overset{..}{\underset{..}{I}}:)$. The radicals are short-lived intermediates and they stabilize themselves through dimerization to yield compounds known as **disulfides.**

$$2\ CH_3—\overset{..}{\underset{..}{S}}\cdot \longrightarrow CH_3—\overset{..}{\underset{..}{S}}—\overset{..}{\underset{..}{S}}—CH_3$$

Dimethyl disulfide

Disulfides are readily formed, in addition, from other types of thiols.

$$2\ CH_3\overset{\overset{\textstyle S}{\|}}{C}—SH \xrightarrow[O_2\ or\ I_2]{NaOH} CH_3\overset{\overset{\textstyle S}{\|}}{C}—S—S—\overset{\overset{\textstyle S}{\|}}{C}CH_3$$

At least one disulfide, lipoic acid, is of considerable importance in cellular metabolism. This acid reacts as an oxidizing agent in certain cellular reactions, such as the decarboxylation of pyruvic acid (CH_3COCO_2H), and in these reactions, the lipoic acid is reduced to the corresponding dithiol; oxidation at a later stage by other components of the cell then regenerates the lipoic acid.*

$$\begin{array}{c} CH_2CH_2CHCH_2CH_2CH_2CH_2CO_2H \\ \underset{S\rule{1.5cm}{0.4pt}S}{|\qquad\qquad|} \end{array} \qquad \begin{array}{c} CH_2CH_2CHCH_2CH_2CH_2CH_2CO_2H \\ \underset{SH\qquad SH}{|\qquad\quad|} \end{array}$$

Lipoic acid   Reduced form of lipoic acid

The oxidation of thioethers with hydrogen peroxide yields monoxides called **sulfoxides,** and these in turn can be oxidized to dioxides called **sulfones:**

$$CH_3—\overset{..}{\underset{..}{S}}—CH_3 \xrightarrow{H_2O_2} CH_3—\overset{\overset{\textstyle :\overset{..}{O}:}{|}}{\underset{..}{S}}—CH_3 \xrightarrow{H_2O_2} CH_3—\overset{\overset{\textstyle :\overset{..}{O}:}{|}}{\underset{\underset{\textstyle :\overset{..}{O}:}{|}}{S}}—CH_3$$

Dimethyl sulfoxide   Dimethyl sulfone

Dimethyl sulfoxide is a highly polar solvent capable of dissolving both organic and inorganic compounds. It has shown promise as a solvent for proteins, and recently it was used in place of water as a solvent in a study of the enzyme trypsin.

---

*For details of the biological reactions of lipoic acid, see W. D. McElroy, *Cell Physiology and Biochemistry*, 2nd ed. (Englewood Cliffs, New Jersey: Prentice-Hall, 1964).

The Sulfonic Acids and Derivatives

The oxidation of thiols under acidic conditions leads to a series of acids, the most important of which are the sulfonic acids:

$$CH_3SH \longrightarrow CH_3-\overset{\cdot\cdot}{\underset{}{S}}-OH \longrightarrow CH_3-\overset{:\overset{\cdot\cdot}{O}:}{\underset{}{S}}-OH \longrightarrow CH_3-\overset{:\overset{\cdot\cdot}{O}:}{\underset{:\overset{\cdot\cdot}{O}:}{S}}-OH$$

| Methane sulfenic acid | Methane sulfinic acid | Methane sulfonic acid |

The aromatic sulfonic acids are usually prepared directly, on the other hand, by the action of sulfuric acid on the aromatic compounds:

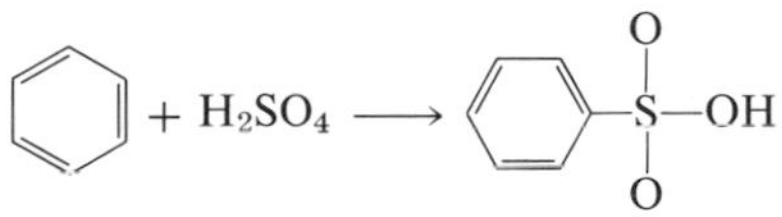

$$\bigcirc + H_2SO_4 \longrightarrow \bigcirc-\overset{O}{\underset{O}{S}}-OH$$

Benzenesulfonic acid

The synthesis of an interesting derivative of an aromatic sulfonic acid is given in Fig. 5-10. The derivative, called **saccharin,** is widely used as an artificial sweetening agent.

The sulfonic acids are related to sulfuric acid, and like sulfuric acid they are strong acids, fully ionized in water solutions: $RSO_3H + H_2O \longrightarrow RSO_3^- + H_3O^+$. The sulfonic acids show many of the chemical properties of the carboxylic acids; they are readily converted into the corresponding acid chlorides and esters, for example:

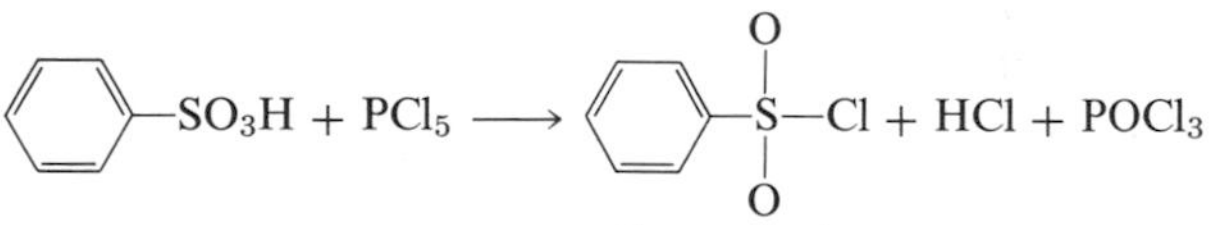

$$\bigcirc-SO_3H + PCl_5 \longrightarrow \bigcirc-\overset{O}{\underset{O}{S}}-Cl + HCl + POCl_3$$

Benzenesulfonyl chloride

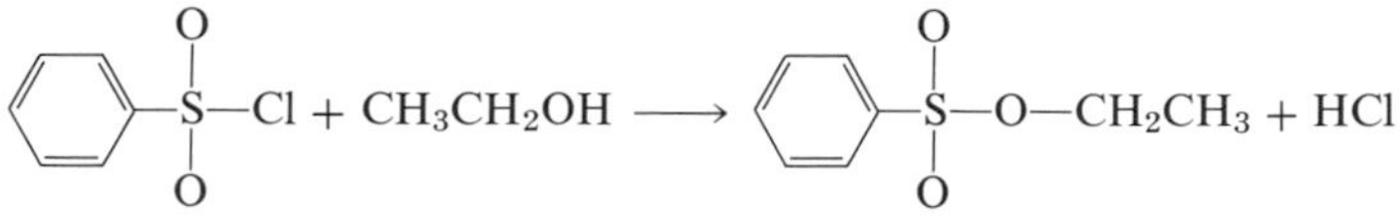

$$\bigcirc-\overset{O}{\underset{O}{S}}-Cl + CH_3CH_2OH \longrightarrow \bigcirc-\overset{O}{\underset{O}{S}}-O-CH_2CH_3 + HCl$$

Ethyl benzenesulfonate

Fig. 5-10. The synthesis of saccharin.

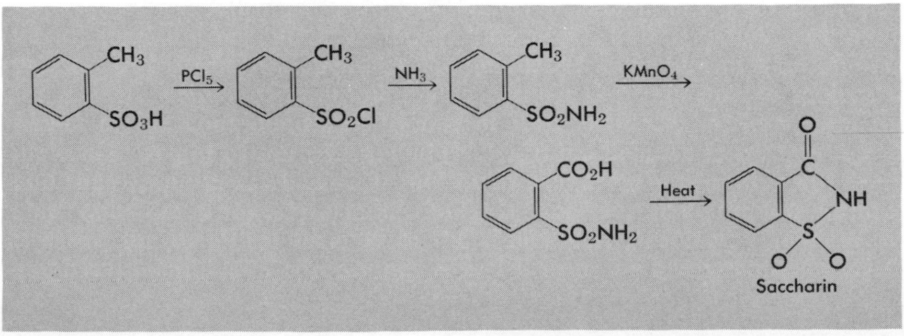

Saccharin

Esters of sulfuric acid itself may also be prepared by reactions of this type:

$$\underset{\text{Sulfuryl chloride}}{Cl-\overset{\displaystyle O}{\underset{\displaystyle O}{S}}-Cl} + 2\ CH_3OH \longrightarrow \underset{\text{Dimethyl sulfate}}{CH_3-O-\overset{\displaystyle O}{\underset{\displaystyle O}{S}}-O-CH_3} + 2\ HCl$$

Esters of sulfuric acid, especially those involving the hydroxyl group of a sugar molecule, are of considerable biological importance. The anticlotting agent, heparin, for example, is a polysaccharide (see p. 140) which contains such an ester linkage to sulfuric acid.

Nucleophilic Displacement Reactions of Compounds Containing Sulfur

The alkyl sulfates and sulfonates react as alkylating agents with nucleophiles:

$$CH_3CH_2\overset{..}{\underset{K^+}{S}}:^- \longrightarrow CH_3-O-\overset{\displaystyle O}{\underset{\displaystyle O}{S}}-O-CH_3 \longrightarrow CH_3CH_2\overset{..}{S}CH_3 + K^+\,{}^-O-\overset{\displaystyle O}{\underset{\displaystyle O}{S}}-O-CH_3$$

and as such can be used interchangeably with the alkyl halides (CH_3I, for example). A closely related alkylation reaction occurs with the thioethers to yield salts that are similar in structure to the hydronium and quaternary ammonium ions.

$$CH_3-\overset{\displaystyle CH_3}{\underset{..}{S}}: \longrightarrow CH_3\overset{\frown}{-Br} \longrightarrow \underset{\text{Trimethylsulfonium bromide}}{CH_3-\overset{\displaystyle CH_3}{\overset{+}{S}}-CH_3\ Br^-}$$

Compounds of this type are also alkylating agents:

$$CH_3-\overset{\displaystyle CH_3}{\underset{\displaystyle Br^-}{\overset{+}{S}}}-CH_3 \longleftarrow :NH_3 \longrightarrow CH_3-\overset{..}{S}-CH_3 + CH_3-\overset{\displaystyle H}{\underset{\displaystyle H}{\overset{+}{N}}}-H\ \ Br^-$$

The sulfonium salts constitute the third group of alkylating agents that have been discussed. A general reaction can be written for these reactions,

$$H_3N:\frown CH_3 \overset{\frown}{-}X^{+\text{ or }0} \longrightarrow CH_3NH_3^+\ X^{0\text{ or }-}$$

where $X = I^-$, $R-SO_3^-$, or $R-\overset{..}{\underset{..}{S}}-R$. The group displaced, X, is generally called the leaving group, and in the examples cited, it is either a neutral species or the negative ion of a strong acid (HI or RSO_3H, for example). These species are all weak bases, and in fact, the correlation of the basicity of the leaving group (this, in turn, is related to the stability of the groups) with the rate of the displacement reaction is generally good. Alkyl nitrates (CH_3-O-NO_2) and quaternary salts ($CH_3-NR_3^+$) are also good alkylating agents, for example. Similar arguments account for the fact that methanol is a very poor alkylating agent (methanol does not react with sodium iodide), whereas the protonated form is a rather good alkylating agent.

$$CH_3-\ddot{O}-H + HI \longrightarrow I^- + CH_3-\overset{+}{\underset{|}{\ddot{O}}}-H \longrightarrow CH_3I + H_2O$$
$$\phantom{CH_3-\overset{+}{\underset{|}{\ddot{O}}}}H$$

It is interesting to note that certain compounds necessary in the diet of animals are methyl-transfer agents (that is, alkylating agents), and their structures are very similar to those outlined above. One compound of this type, chlorine, was given on page 108; other examples are given below:

$$(CH_3)_2\overset{+}{\ddot{S}}-CH_2CH_2\overset{H}{\underset{NH_2}{\overset{|}{C}}}-CO_2H \qquad (CH_3)_3\overset{+}{N}CH_2CO_2^-$$

Methyl sulfonium derivative of methionine   Betaine

The mechanism of alkylation in a cell is almost certainly related to the mechanism of the alkylations carried out in the test tube; that is, nucleophilic substitution is involved in both cases.

ORGANIC COMPOUNDS CONTAINING PHOSPHORUS

A vast number of different types of phosphorus compounds are known. In this volume, we shall mention only those with oxidation numbers of -3 and $+5$. The phosphorus analog of ammonia is called phosphine, PH_3, and the derivatives of this compound are named largely as derivatives of phosphine (Fig. 5-11).

Ammonia and phosphine are similar in the types of reactions they undergo; they differ qualitatively, however, in the greater acidity and nucleophilicity of phosphine—a result of the lower position of phosphorus in the periodic table. Most of the alkyl derivatives of phosphine are prepared from the alkyl halides; typical nucleophilic displacements are involved:

$$PH_3 + 3\ CH_3I \xrightarrow{\ 3\ KOH\ } (CH_3)_3P + 3\ K^+I^- + 3\ H_2O$$

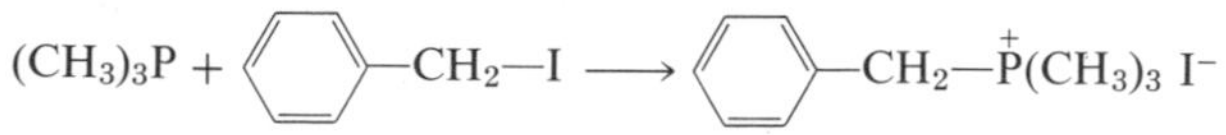

$$(CH_3)_3P + \langle \bigcirc \rangle -CH_2-I \longrightarrow \langle \bigcirc \rangle -CH_2-\overset{+}{P}(CH_3)_3\ I^-$$

Benzyltrimethylphosphonium iodide

An extremely valuable reaction of the phosphonium halides known as the **Wittig** reaction has been developed recently (Fig. 5-12); in effect, this reaction is a direct method for the conversion of carbonyl compounds into alkene derivatives. In the example cited, the proton adjacent to the phenyl ring is

Fig. 5-11. Organic compounds of phosphorus in the -3 stage of oxidation.

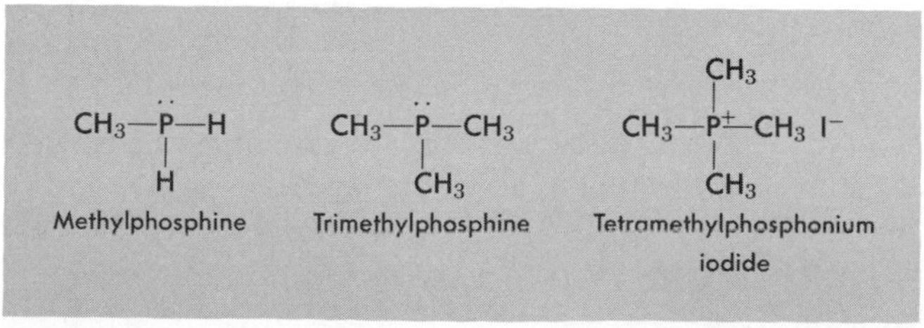

$$CH_3-\overset{\cdot\cdot}{\underset{H}{\overset{|}{P}}}-H \qquad\qquad CH_3-\overset{\cdot\cdot}{\underset{CH_3}{\overset{|}{P}}}-CH_3 \qquad\qquad CH_3-\overset{\overset{\displaystyle CH_3}{|}}{\underset{CH_3}{\overset{|}{P^{\pm}}}}-CH_3\ I^-$$

Methylphosphine   Trimethylphosphine   Tetramethylphosphonium iodide

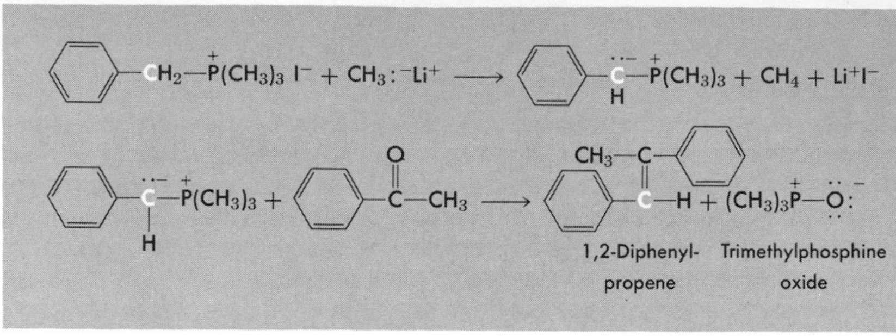

Fig. 5-12. The Wittig reaction, a synthesis of alkenes from the corresponding carbonyl compounds.

removed by the base methyl lithium, because this is the most acidic proton; the electron pair formed in this position is stabilized by resonance:

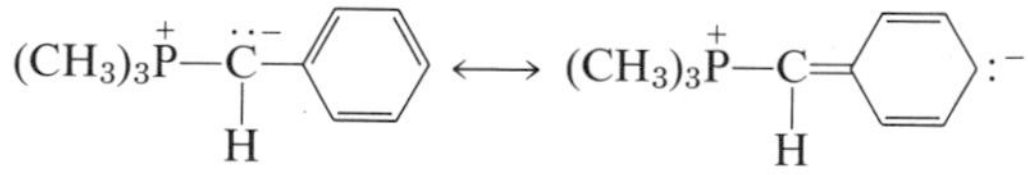

The reaction is a general one, and by the use of different phosphonium compounds, it can be used to introduce the $=CH_2$, $=CHR$, and $=CR_2$ groups in place of the doubly bonded oxygen atoms in most carbonyl compounds.

Derivatives of Phosphoric Acid

Another group of compounds of interest to the biochemist are the derivatives of phosphoric acid, H_3PO_4. Alkyl esters of phosphoric acid are prepared in much the same way as esters of sulfuric acid and the carboxylic acids. One of the simplest methods involves the reaction of a phosphoric acid chloride with an alcohol:

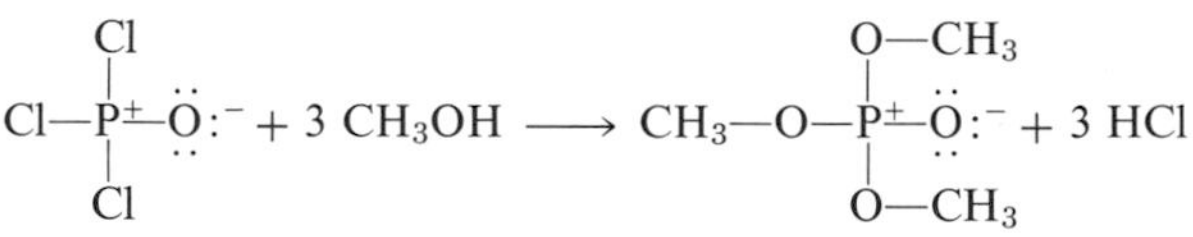

Trimethyl phosphate

The heating of phosphoric acid yields first a monoanhydride known as pyrophosphoric acid ($H_4P_2O_7$), and then higher anhydrides, some of which are high-molecular-weight polymers (known collectively as metaphosphoric acid, HPO_3). Pyrophosphoric acid can be readily converted into its methyl ester by the methods outlined before.

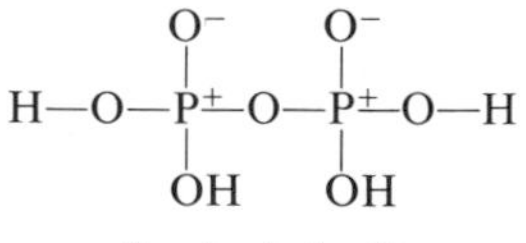

Pyrophosphoric acid 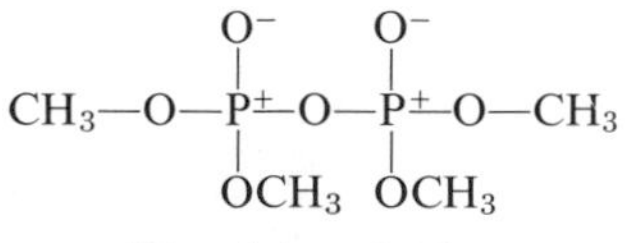   Tetramethyl pyrophosphate

These simple esters of the phosphoric acids resemble the corresponding esters of sulfuric acid in reacting as alkylating agents.

Phosphoric acid forms derivatives of the carboxylic acids which are typical

124

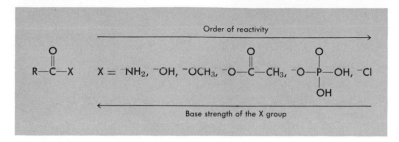

Fig. 5-13. The reactivity of various carboxylic acid derivatives.

anhydrides; compounds of this type, such as acetyl phosphate, have also been isolated from natural sources. The reactions that these anhydrides undergo are similar to those of the corresponding acid chlorides (see p. 96 and below).

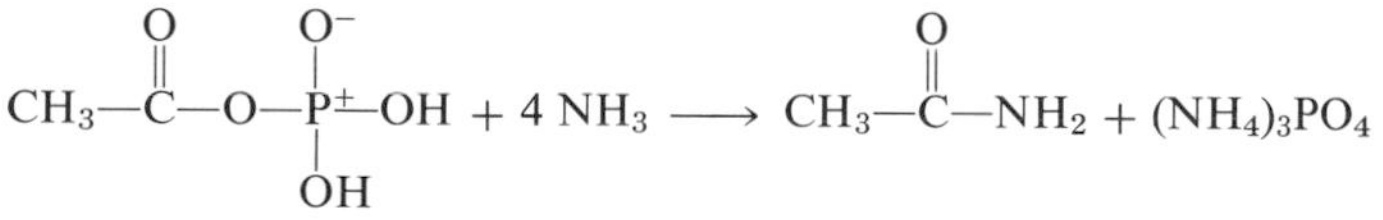

$$CH_3-\overset{\overset{O}{\|}}{C}-O-\overset{O^-}{\underset{\underset{OH}{|}}{P^\pm}}-OH + 4\,NH_3 \longrightarrow CH_3-\overset{\overset{O}{\|}}{C}-NH_2 + (NH_4)_3PO_4$$

Acetyl phosphate

Fig. 5-14. Reactions of acid anhydrides and "activated" acids of biological interest.

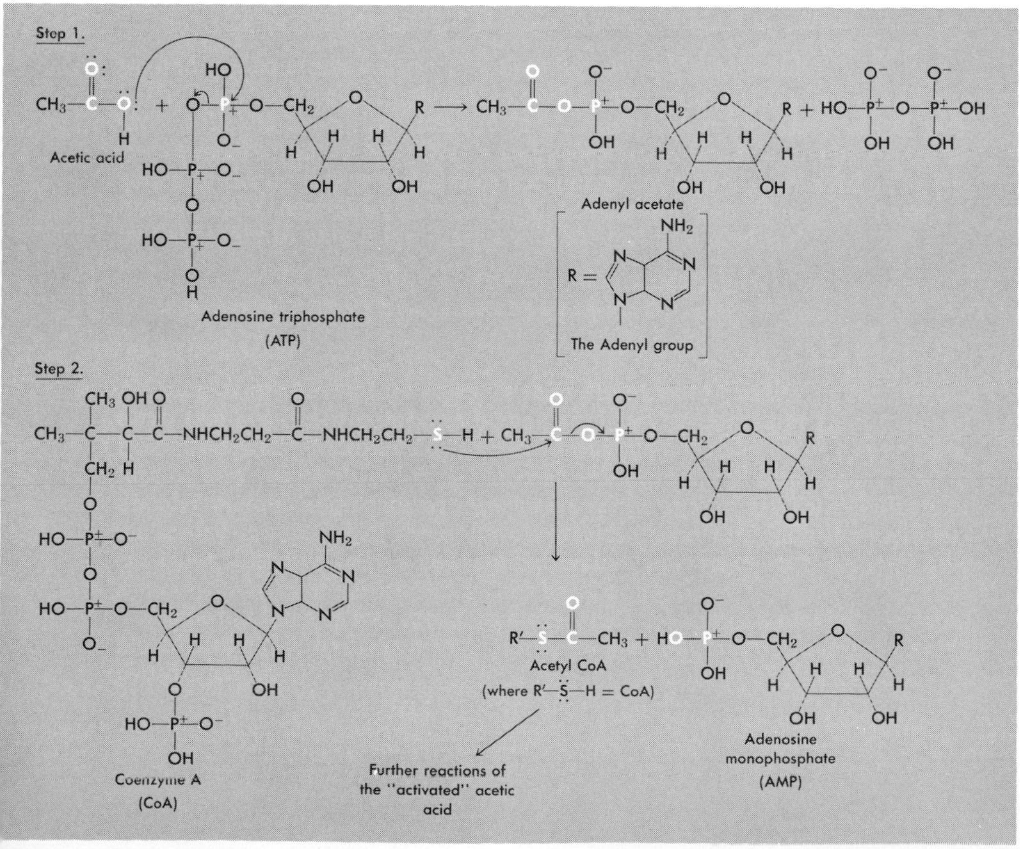

Step 1.

CH₃—C—O + O—P—O—CH₂ ... R → CH₃—C—O—P—O—CH₂ ... R + HO—P—O—P—OH

Acetic acid

Adenosine triphosphate (ATP)

Adenyl acetate

R = The Adenyl group

Step 2.

Coenzyme A (CoA)

Acetyl CoA (where R'—S—H = CoA)

Adenosine monophosphate (AMP)

Further reactions of the "activated" acetic acid

A number of derivatives of the carboxylic acids (RCOX) have been discussed (in this chapter and the preceeding one) in which the sole difference is the group X lost in the displacement reaction. It is instructive to see how the reactivity of these compounds with nucleophiles is related to the nature of the group X (Fig. 5-13). Notice that the more active the derivative, the more weakly basic (and therefore the more stable) the leaving group (X). Precisely the same series is involved in the reactivity of alkylating agents in nucleophilic displacement reactions, as we have seen in the previous section on sulfur compounds:

$$H_3N: \quad\longrightarrow\quad CH_3{-}X \quad\longrightarrow\quad CH_3NH_3{}^+X^-$$

Acid anhydrides involving phosphoric acid are very important in biological systems. An example of a reaction involving an anhydride of this type (an "activated acid," see Chapter 4) is given in Fig. 5-14, along with a similar reaction of a sulfur derivative; these reactions are key steps in the metabolism of the fatty acids.

Natural Products

CHAPTER SIX

Natural products are compounds derived from living or once-living organisms. An infinite variety of natural products has been isolated, but we can group most of these compounds into about a dozen classes. Of this dozen, three classes—proteins, carbohydrates, and fats—are especially important since they are the three main types of foodstuffs; principal emphasis in this chapter will be on these natural products.

PEPTIDES AND PROTEINS

Proteins are probably the most important of the chemical constituents of living organisms. They are the chief component of muscle fibre, skin, tendons, nerves, blood, etc. In addition, enzymes, antibodies, and certain hormones are proteins. The proteins have been investigated intensively for many years and they may be defined, in a chemical sense, as high-molecular-weight polymers in which the building blocks are the amino acids.

The acid-catalyzed hydrolysis of proteins yields predominantly a mixture of the amino acids. Chromatographic methods are available today for the separation of the amino acids in mixtures of this type, and for the determination of the ratios in which the amino acids occur in the protein. It is interesting to note that each protein is composed of a different assortment of amino acids and that these are linked together in a unique sequence. The amino acid compositions of certain proteins are given in Table 6-1.

Table 6-1

THE DISTRIBUTION OF AMINO ACIDS IN CERTAIN PROTEINS
(Grams of amino acid/100 g protein)

Protein	Glycine	Alanine	Valine	Leucine	Isoleucine	Methionine	Phenylalanine	Tryptophane	Lysine
Fibroin (silk)	44	30	4	1	1	—	3	—	1
Keratin (wool)	7	4	5	11	—	1	4	2	3
Albumin (hen)	3	7	7	9	7	5	8	1	6
Hemoglobin (horse)	6	7	9	15	—	1	8	2	9
Insulin (ox)	4	5	8	13	3	—	8	—	3

Adapted from L. F. Fieser and M. Fieser, *Advanced Organic Chemistry* (New York: Reinhold Publishing Corp., 1961), p. 1025.

The fact that proteins are hydrolyzable to amino acids gives us no clue, of course, to how the amino acids are bound together in the protein. Modern physical methods of analysis (principally infrared spectroscopy), on the other hand, have shown quite clearly that in a protein the nitrogen of one amino acid is bonded to the carbonyl group of another (to form an amide linkage) and that the carbonyl group of the first amino acid is bonded to the amino group of the third amino acid, etc., etc.:

$$\cdots\cdots -\underset{R}{\underset{|}{\overset{H}{\overset{|}{N}}}}-\underset{R}{\underset{|}{\overset{H}{\overset{|}{C}}}}-\overset{O}{\overset{||}{C}}\left[-\underset{R}{\underset{|}{\overset{H}{\overset{|}{N}}}}-\underset{}{\overset{H}{\overset{|}{C}}}-\overset{O}{\overset{||}{C}}-\right]_n\underset{R}{\underset{|}{\overset{H}{\overset{|}{N}}}}-\overset{H}{\overset{|}{C}}-\overset{O}{\overset{||}{C}}-\cdots\cdots \text{ etc.}$$

The proteins are polymers of the amino acids, and the acid hydrolysis of the proteins, therefore, involves merely the hydrolysis of typical amide linkages. The polymers made up of a small number of amino acids (2,3,4 $\cdots$ to about 100) are commonly called **peptides,** whereas those formed of a larger number of units (up to 10,000 units or more!) are called **proteins.**

Since thousands of amino acid residues, representing possibly a dozen different amino acids, are present in a single molecule, and since the sequence of the amino acids does not appear to be regular, the structures of the proteins are extremely complex and only a few structures of the simple proteins have been determined. The peptides are much less complex, and considerable progress has been made in this field. The structure of a cyclic peptide containing 8 amino acids is given in Fig. 6-1. This compound, oxytocin, is highly active in regulating uterine contraction in childbirth. It was synthesized recently in the laboratory from the individual amino acids.

The activity of the proteins in cellular processes is a function of both the chemical properties and the shapes of these very high-molecular-weight compounds. The mechanism of action of the enzymes is of particular interest

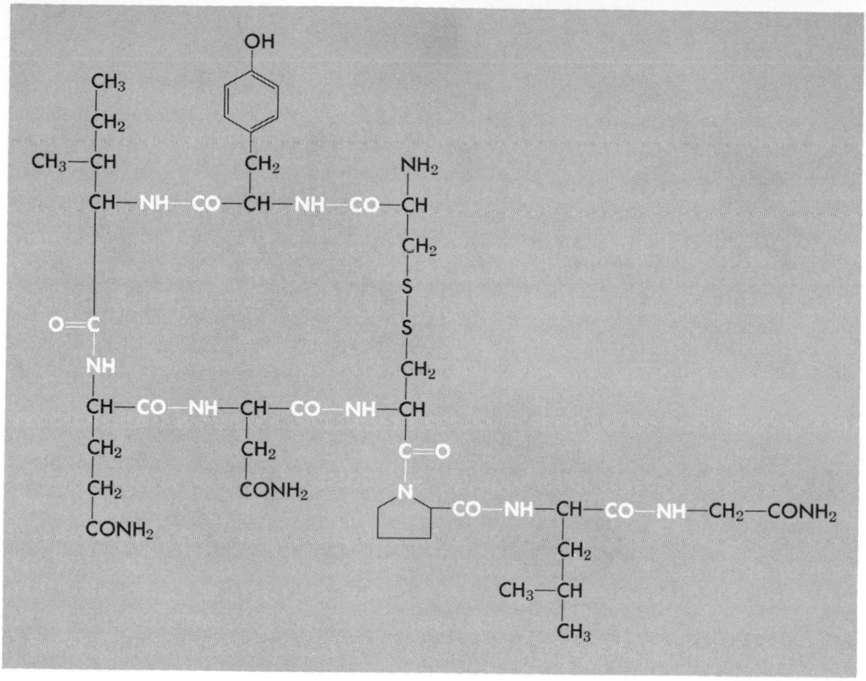

Fig. 6-1. Oxytocin (the peptide linkages are given in white).

in this respect. The enzymes are catalysts that regulate the many chemical reactions occurring in a living organism; several hundred have been isolated, some in crystalline form, and each has a particular role to play in the catalysis of a particular reaction or set of reactions. Most enzymes are highly specific in their action; the enzyme urease catalyzes only the hydrolysis of urea, for example, and the enzyme fumarase catalyzes the addition of water to fumaric acid (to yield malic acid), but it does not catalyze the addition of water to its geometrical isomer, maleic acid (the formulas of these acids are given in Fig. 4-10). The mechanism of enzyme catalysis is not known with certainty at the present time although considerable effort has been expended on the problem. More detailed accounts of the mode of action of the enzymes in various biological processes are given in the other volumes of this series.

The methods used in the synthesis of peptides involve a great deal of ingenuity. In general, the amino acids are added one at a time to the peptide chain by typical amide-forming reactions in which a free amino group and an acid anhydride (or other "active" acid) group (Chapters 4 and 5) react to give the amide linkage; the detailed account of these steps is beyond the scope of this volume, however.

One curious fact about proteins and amino acids remains. It has been found that the amino acids isolated from the hydrolysis of proteins are the same as the synthetic amino acids with <u>one important exception</u>:

$$CH_3CH_2CO_2H \xrightarrow{Cl_2} CH_3CHClCO_2H \xrightarrow{NH_3} CH_3CHCO_2H$$
$$\underset{\displaystyle NH_2}{|}$$

Propionic acid   Synthetic alanine

129

The amino acids isolated from proteins rotate the plane of plane-polarized light, whereas the corresponding synthetic amino acids do not rotate this plane! This difference in behavior has its origins in a type of isomerism called optical isomerism. This topic will be outlined in the next section, where we shall see that there are 2 kinds of amino acids—those that rotate the plane of polarized light to the right, and those that rotate the plane to the left. An equimolar mixture of these forms, furthermore, does not rotate this plane. In living systems, the behavior of the 2 forms is quite different and in extreme cases, one form may be active, whereas the other form may actually be a poison.

OPTICAL ISOMERISM

The study of optical isomerism began with the observation that most compounds isolated from natural sources are able to rotate the plane of polarized light. Plane-polarized light may be obtained by passing ordinary light through certain minerals such as Iceland spar (a form of $CaCO_3$). Ordinary visible light is a form of electromagnetic radiation for which the vectors used to represent the changes in the electrical or magnetic fields are randomly oriented (Fig. 6-2A); the view here is a cross-section of a pencil-shaped beam of light. A properly prepared section of Iceland spar has the property of transmitting only light with these vectors oriented in one particular direction (Fig. 6-2B); light of this type is called plane-polarized light.

Materials such as Iceland spar may be used not only to form plane-polarized light, but also to determine the change in the inclination of this plane brought about by amino acids, etc.; the instrument used to measure these rotations is called a polarimeter (Fig. 6-3). The polarizer and analyzer are sections of Iceland spar that transmit plane-polarized light in 1 direction. If the sample tube in the polarimeter is empty, a maximum amount of light will reach the observer when the polarizer and analyzer are aligned and passing light vibrating in the same plane. If the analyzer is turned, less and less light will reach the observer until a minimum is reached when the analyzer is at right angles to the polarizer; at this point the field will be dark (Fig. 6-3A). This is our starting point (0° on the scale). Now if an optically active compound such as an amino acid is introduced into the sample tube, the plane of the polarized light will be tilted by the compound (to the right in Fig. 6-3B) and a certain amount of light will pass through the analyzer to the observer. The analyzer is now rotated a few degrees to the right (as in Fig. 6-3B) until the field is dark again; at this point, the plane of the polarized light is again at right angles to the analyzer. The analyzer, then, has been turned a certain number of degrees (α), which is equal to the degrees of tilting of the polarized light by the compound in the sample cell.

Fig. 6-2. The magnetic vectors of ordinary and plane-polarized light.

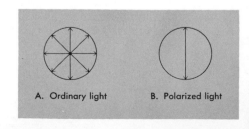

A. Ordinary light   B. Polarized light

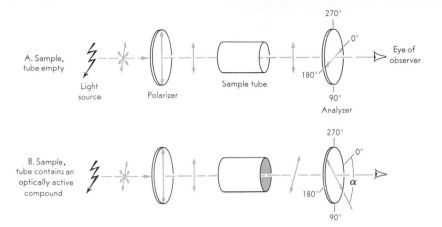

Fig. 6-3. Schematic diagram of a polarimeter.

Since α is dependent on the concentration of the compound in the sample tube and also on the length of the sample tube, optical activity is usually reported in terms of the specific rotation, $[\alpha]_D$, which is independent of these variables, but characteristic of a given compound: $[\alpha]_D = \dfrac{\alpha}{l \cdot c}$, where $\alpha =$ the observed reading, $l =$ the length of the cell in decimeters, $c =$ the concentration in g/cc, and the subscript $_D$ refers to the wavelength of the polarized light used.

If the compound rotates plane-polarized light to the right, and the analyzer must be moved to the right (or in a clockwise direction), the compound is said to be **dextrorotatory** (or $+$) and if it rotates plane-polarized light in the opposite direction, it is said to be **levorotatory** (or $-$). In either case, the compounds are called **optically active** compounds. The specific rotations $[\alpha]$ of optically active compounds range from values just above the error of the instrument (about $.01°$) to values of thousands of degrees. It should be emphasized at this point that, in general, most of the compounds that chemists use (such as ethanol, benzene, etc.,) are optically inactive; that is, they do not rotate the plane of polarized light.

Optical Activity

The ability of a compound to rotate the plane of plane-polarized light has been traced back to the symmetry of the molecules of that compound. We can illustrate this relationship with the aid of models of the molecules; it is recommended that the reader construct these models out of balls and sticks or wires and clay.

Suppose, for example, that we were to construct a ball-and-stick model of a carbon atom bearing 2 different types of substituents (as in CH_3Cl). We would find that we could superimpose the mirror image on this model (this merely requires a movement of the mirror image to the left until it coincides with the model, Fig. 6-4), and that there is only one model of this compound that can be constructed (Fig. 6-4). The various models represented in Fig. 6-4 are identical; for example, model b may be converted into a by a rotation of $120°$ about the Y axis. Simple rotations of the other models will show that forms c and d are also identical with form a. The situation is similar if 3 different substituents are attached; for example, a model of CH_2ClBr can be superimposed on its mirror image and only one model of

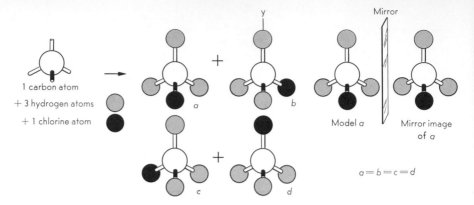

Fig. 6-4. Various ways of assembling a model of a carbon atom bearing 2 different substituents.

the compound can be constructed. In this connection, it has been determined in the laboratory that the compounds CH_3Cl and CH_2ClBr are not optically active.

If the carbon atom bears 4 different substituents, however (as in CHClBrI), a model of the compound is not superimposable on its mirror image (Fig. 6-5). Although we can superimpose the models so that the carbon atom and the hydrogen and iodine atoms coincide, the chlorine and bromine atoms occupy different regions in space; by no amount of rotation can the the 2 models be superimposed. Further, 2 different models of CHClBrI can be constructed (Fig. 6-6), but only 2. Furthermore, one of these 2 forms turns out to be identical to the model *a* constructed earlier (Fig. 6-5), and the other is identical to the mirror image of model *a*. A simple but useful rule concerning these comparisons is that any model of a carbon atom bearing 4 different substituents is converted into its mirror image when the positions of any 2 substituents are exchanged.

Precisely the same behavior occurs at the molecular level. We find that there is only one kind of CH_3Cl (and of CH_2ClBr), but 2 kinds of CHClBrI. We can separate these 2 kinds (corresponding to forms *a* and *b* in Fig. 6-5), and study them independently. If we do, we find that they differ only by the way in which they rotate the plane of plane-polarized light. One form is dextrorotatory, the other is levorotatory. The *magnitude* of the rotation is the same, and therefore an equimolar mixture of the 2 forms has a zero specific rotation. The 2 optically active forms are called **enantiomers**—

Fig. 6-5. Model, and its mirror image, of a carbon atom bearing 4 different substituents.

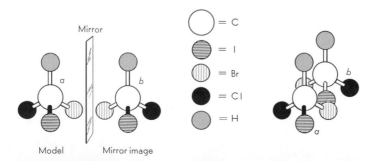

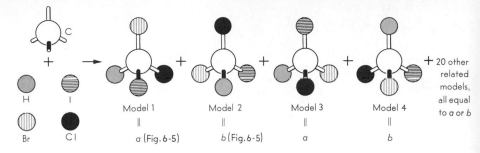

Fig. 6-6. Molecular models of CHClBrI which show that only 2 forms of this compound can be constructed.

which is a general term used to designate mirror-image forms that are not superimposable—and the 50-50 mixture is called a **racemic mixture.** A carbon atom bearing 4 different substituents is called an **asymmetric** carbon atom and it can lead to a maximum of 2 optical isomers. Most compounds bearing an asymmetric carbon atom are optically active, although there are a few exceptions to this rule. The *maximum* number of optical isomers possible in compounds bearing more than 1 asymmetric carbon is given by the term 2^n, where n is the number of asymmetric carbon atoms in the molecule (in a few instances of cyclic or else highly symmetrical compounds, fewer isomers than predicted by this rule may exist).

Optical isomerism is the third type of isomerism we have outlined; in Chapter 3, we covered geometrical isomerism and structural isomerism. The 3 types together make up the science of **stereoisomerism,** the study of the distribution of atoms in space.

SYMMETRY. The determination of whether a molecule is superimposable on its mirror image is often inconvenient to carry out, and therefore a shortcut has been devised for determining whether or not a compound is capable of optical activity. If a molecule has a plane of symmetry or a center of symmetry, it is not optically active, and it is called a **symmetric** molecule. But if a molecule does not have these elements of symmetry, in the vast majority of cases it is optically active, and the molecules are called **asymmetric** compounds. A **plane of symmetry** is defined as a plane (conveniently visualized as a mirror) cleaving a molecule in such a way that one side of the molecule is a mirror image of the other. A **center of symmetry** is defined as a point (at the center of a molecule) so situated that any straight line through it passes through the same environment in both directions extending from that point.

We can illustrate these elements of symmetry with the aid of a few common objects (Fig. 6-7). The average coffee pot (*a*) has a plane of symmetry that bisects the handle, pot, and spout. A specially constructed coffee pot with the spout at 90° from the handle (*b*) would have no symmetry elements, and it could be termed an asymmetric pot. A cube (*c*) is a highly symmetric object with a center of symmetry and several planes of symmetry (9 to be exact). A cube bearing 4 different pairs of balls at the corners arranged as in Fig. 6-7(*d*), on the other hand, has a center of symmetry as its only symmetry element.

Living things also possess certain symmetry elements; most animals and most plants (other than those with alternate leaves) possess planes of sym-

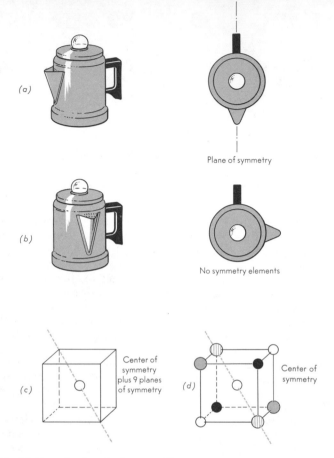

(a)

Plane of symmetry

(b)

No symmetry elements

(c) Center of symmetry plus 9 planes of symmetry

(d) Center of symmetry

Fig. 6-7. Symmetry elements of common objects.

metry, for example. To return to the molecular level, examples of optically active compounds are given in Fig. 6-8, and examples of inactive compounds are given in Fig. 6-9 to illustrate the symmetry rules.

In calculating the number of isomers a compound has, we assume that there is free rotation about single bonds. Usually that conformation is chosen which has the maximum amount of symmetry; that is, the compound

Fig. 6-8. Optically active compounds.

$$CH_3—\overset{\displaystyle H}{\underset{\displaystyle NH_3{}^+}{C}}—CO_2{}^-$$

Alanine

2 optical isomers ($+$ and $-$)

($2^n = 2$)

$[\alpha]_D = +8.5°$ and $-8.5°$

$$CH_3—\overset{\displaystyle H}{\underset{\displaystyle OH}{C}}—\overset{\displaystyle H}{\underset{\displaystyle NH_2}{C}}—CH_3$$

3-Amino-2-butanol

4 optical isomers

($2^n = 4$)

2 $+$ isomers and

2 $-$ isomers

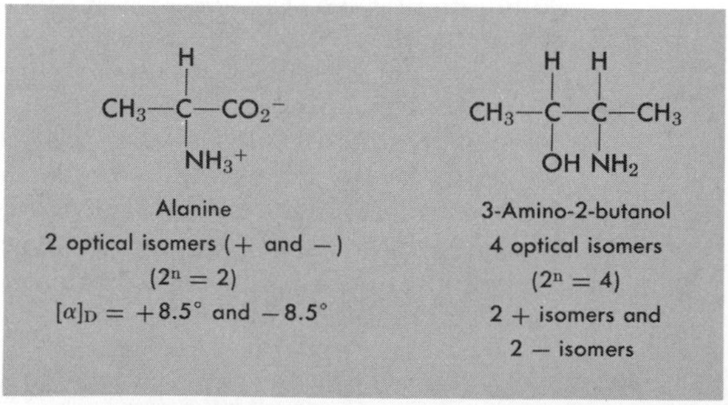

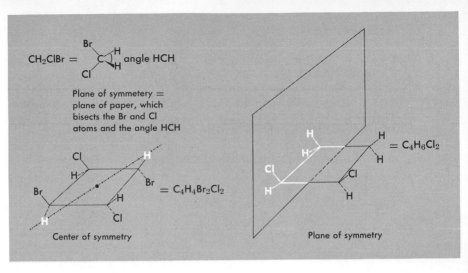

Fig. 6-9. Optically inactive compounds.

CH_2ClCH_2Cl is not optically active although a casual examination might suggest that it is:

Conformation I   ⟺   Conformation II

1,2-Dichloroethane

Conformation II has a plane of symmetry in the plane of the paper.

RESOLUTION.   If enantiomers have exactly the same chemical properties, the question arises, how can they be separated? Several methods have been developed, but the most common procedure depends on the 3-dimensional structure of asymmetric compounds. If a pure enantiomer of an amine is obtained from natural sources—for example ($+$) 2-butylamine (CH_3CHNH_2-CH_2CH_3)—it can be reacted with a racemic mixture of ($+$) and ($-$) alanine; the result is a mixture of salts, necessarily formed in equal molar quantities. It can be seen from the 3-dimensional representation in Fig. 6-10 that the salts are made up of different partners. The forms shown will have different rotations, and the ($++$) form will have a higher rotation than the ($-+$) form. Molecules that are not enantiomeric (that is, not mirror images) yet contain 2 or more asymmetric centers are called **diastereomers.** The enantiomer of form *a* would be the ($--$) salt prepared from the ($-$) acid and the

Fig. 6-10. The 2 diastereomeric salts of ($+$)2-butylamine and ($+$ and $-$) alanine.

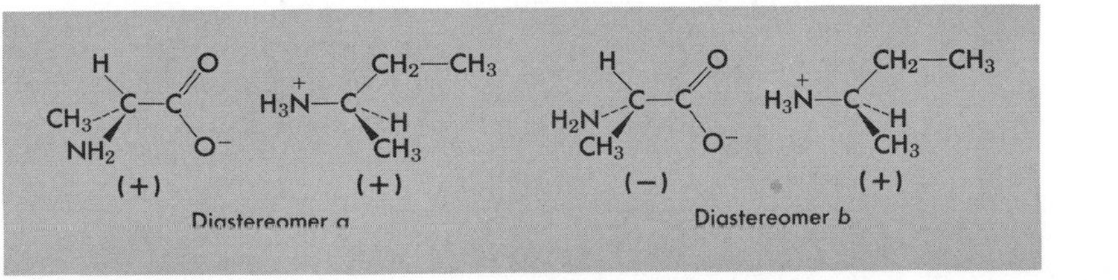

($-$) amine, and the enantiomer of form b would be the ($+$ $-$) salt prepared in turn from the correct components.

Diastereomers (a and b, for example, in Fig. 6-10) have different physical properties. Usually one form is less soluble than the other, and on fractional crystallization, one diastereomer can usually be obtained pure. If, for example, our ($+$ $+$) 2-butylammonium alanate were less soluble than the ($-$ $+$) form, it would crystallize out of the reaction mixture first; treatment of this salt with concentrated base would then liberate the free amine:

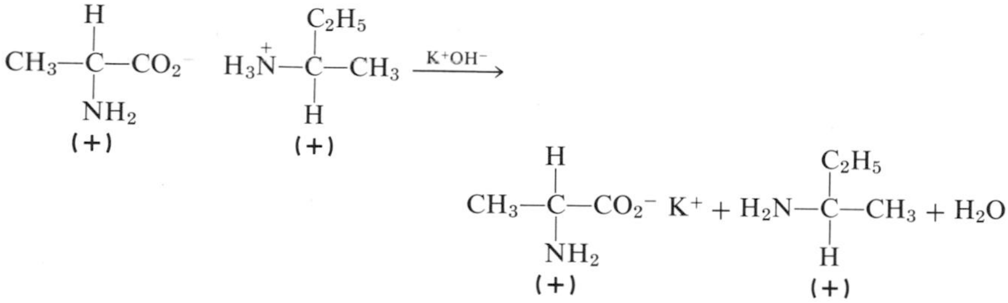

$$CH_3-\underset{\underset{(+)}{\overset{|}{NH_2}}}{\overset{\overset{H}{|}}{C}}-CO_2^-\quad \underset{\underset{(+)}{\overset{|}{H}}}{\overset{\overset{C_2H_5}{|}}{H_3\overset{+}{N}-C}}-CH_3 \xrightarrow{\ K^+OH^-\ }$$

$$CH_3-\underset{\underset{(+)}{\overset{|}{NH_2}}}{\overset{\overset{H}{|}}{C}}-CO_2^-\ K^+ + \underset{\underset{(+)}{\overset{|}{H}}}{\overset{\overset{C_2H_5}{|}}{H_2N-C}}-CH_3 + H_2O$$

The amine is very volatile, and it could be removed by distillation. The residual potassium salt would then be treated with a strong acid to yield ($+$) alanine, a pure enantiomer of alanine. The ($-$) form can usually be obtained in a similar way from the more soluble diastereomer. In effect, therefore, by this procedure the optically inactive mixture has been separated, and the 2 pure enantiomers isolated.

The reaction of single enantiomers with a racemic mixture always leads to the formation of diastereomers. All enzymes and related species in the body are optically pure (note that the hydrolysis of proteins gives the constituent amino acids which are optically pure, and not racemic). Therefore, when living organisms are fed racemic mixtures of compounds, the 2 enantiomers will interact differently with the enzyme and very often only 1 enantiomer will be metabolized. In this method, an asymmetric molecule is being used, in effect, to destroy preferentially one enantiomer in a racemic mixture. The other enantiomer remains in the reaction mixture and it can often be isolated in a pure form. The separation of a racemic mixture into its constituent enantiomers is called **resolution.** By the use of these 2 methods of resolution, a very large number of optically active compounds have been isolated and characterized.

In the previous section, we have seen that an asymmetric molecule reacts differently with enantiomers. In contrast, symmetric molecules react with enantiomers at the same rate—or if asymmetric carbon atoms are being generated from symmetric molecules, the enantiomers are produced at the same rate. It is for the latter reason that materials prepared in the laboratory from optically inactive compounds are always racemic mixtures. For example, a racemic cyanide is obtained from the addition of HCN to methyl ethyl ketone:

Fig. 6-11. The enantiomers of glyceraldehyde.

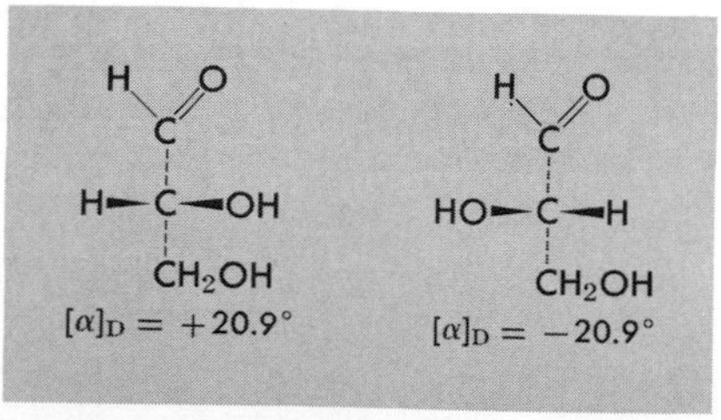

$[\alpha]_D = +20.9°$ $[\alpha]_D = -20.9°$

$$HCN + H_2O \rightleftharpoons H_3O^+ + CN^-$$

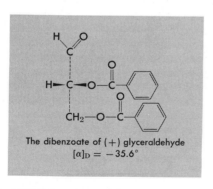

Methyl ethyl ketone

$$CH_3—\overset{\overset{OH}{|}}{\underset{\underset{CN}{|}}{C}}—CH_2CH_3 + H_2O$$

Racemic 2-hydroxy-2-cyanobutane

There is an equal probability that the cyanide ion will attack from the back side or from the front side (defined in terms of the plane of the paper) of the essentially planar methyl ethyl ketone molecule. This means that ions *a* and *b* are formed in equal quantities: ions *a* and *b* are enantiomers, and the protonation of these species then yields racemic 2-hydroxy-2-cyanobutane.

CONFIGURATION. If a compound bearing one asymmetric carbon atom such as glyceraldehyde (α, β-dihydroxypropanal, Fig. 6-11) can exist in either the (+) or the (−) form, does form *a* rotate the plane of polarized light to the right, and form *b* rotate the plane to the left? Or is the situation reversed? The answer is that form *a* is the enantiomer of glyceraldehyde that rotates the plane of polarized light to the right. This assignment was made arbitrarily at first by the German chemist Emil Fisher in 1891. Fisher had, of course, a 50/50 chance of being right, but his choice was proved to be the correct one in 1952 by Dutch scientists using a special type of X-ray analysis.

Optically active compounds can give a wide variety of optically active derivatives; an example is given in Fig. 6-12. In the formation of the benzoate ester shown, no bond to the asymmetric carbon has been broken, and it has the same distribution of H, CHO, O, $CH_2O(H)$ in space about the asymmetric carbon atom as (+) glyceraldehyde. This derivative is said to have the same configuration as (+) glyceraldehyde, where **configuration** is defined as the arrangement of atoms that characterize a stereoisomer. This family relationship is indicated with the prefixes D and L. (+) Glyceraldehyde is <u>defined</u> as D-glyceraldehyde and all compounds with the same configuration as D-glyceraldehyde (for example, the benzoate in Fig. 6-12) are defined as members of the D family of optically active compounds. The mirror image compounds belong to the L family; an example is given in Fig. 6-13. Note that members of the same family often have rotations of opposite sign,

The dibenzoate of (+) glyceraldehyde
$[\alpha]_D = -35.6°$

Fig. 6-12. A levorotatory derivative of D(+)glyceraldehyde.

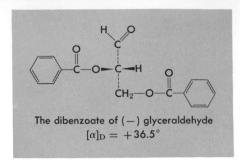

The dibenzoate of (−) glyceraldehyde
$[\alpha]_D = +36.5°$

Fig. 6-13. A derivative of L(−)glyceralde-hyde.

or to state it differently, that the sign of rotation does not tell what family a compound belongs to or what the distribution in space of the groups attached to the asymmetric carbon is. In these compounds (Figs. 6-12 and 6-13), the configuration of the compound is given by the D or L label, whereas the (+) or (−) sign gives the actual sign of the specific rotation.

The distribution in space of these groups (the configuration of the asymmetric carbon, that is) is usually determined experimentally by one of 3 methods. Method 1 (rarely used) is the absolute X-ray method mentioned before. Method 2 is based on the principle that if a derivative of an asymmetric compound is prepared without breaking a bond to the asymmetric carbon atom in the reference compound, then the derivative belongs to the same family as the reference compound. This was true of D-glyceraldehyde and the benzoate illustrated in Fig. 6-12. Further examples are given in Fig. 6-14; all of the compounds illustrated have the D configuration.

In Method 3, bonds to the asymmetric carbon atoms are made, and broken, but it is known from other lines of research whether the new group comes in on the same side of the asymmetric carbon atom as the leaving group—or whether it comes in on the opposite side. For example, it has been established that nucleophilic displacement reactions proceed with **inversion** of configuration—which means that the reaction of a D molecule yields an L product (or vice versa, of course) (Fig. 6-15). The species "Z" is the half-way point in the reaction, and the process shown in the figure for the inversion of the H, CH_3, and CH_3CH_2 groups resembles the movements of the ribs of an umbrella when they are inverted in a high wind.

The nucleophilic displacement of bromide ion by hydroxide ion will now give us the D alcohol (Fig. 6-16) and this can be esterified to give us our starting derivative (in Fig. 6-15). These transformations illustrate the

Fig. 6-14. Derivatives of D(−)-2-butanol.

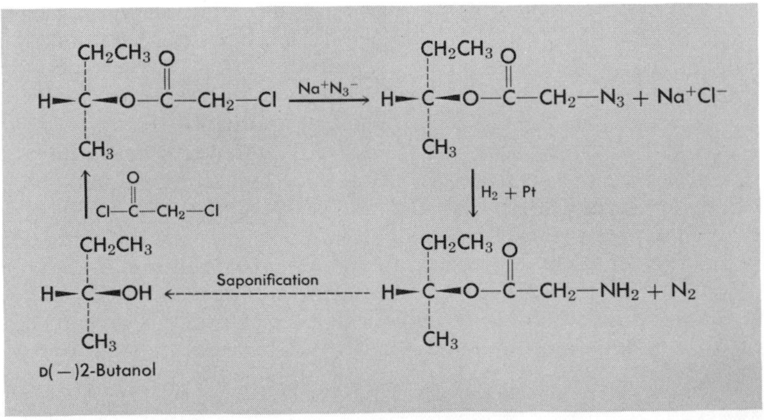

$$\text{H}-\overset{\overset{\displaystyle CH_2CH_3}{|}}{\underset{\underset{\displaystyle CH_3}{|}}{C}}-\text{O}-\overset{\overset{\displaystyle O}{\|}}{C}-CH_2-Cl \xrightarrow{Na^+N_3^-} \text{H}-\overset{\overset{\displaystyle CH_2CH_3}{|}}{\underset{\underset{\displaystyle CH_3}{|}}{C}}-\text{O}-\overset{\overset{\displaystyle O}{\|}}{C}-CH_2-N_3 + Na^+Cl^-$$

$\uparrow$ $Cl-\overset{\overset{\displaystyle O}{\|}}{C}-CH_2-Cl$

$\downarrow H_2 + Pt$

$$\text{H}-\overset{\overset{\displaystyle CH_2CH_3}{|}}{\underset{\underset{\displaystyle CH_3}{|}}{C}}-\text{OH} \xleftarrow{\text{Saponification}} \text{H}-\overset{\overset{\displaystyle CH_2CH_3}{|}}{\underset{\underset{\displaystyle CH_3}{|}}{C}}-\text{O}-\overset{\overset{\displaystyle O}{\|}}{C}-CH_2-NH_2 + N_2$$

D(−)2-Butanol

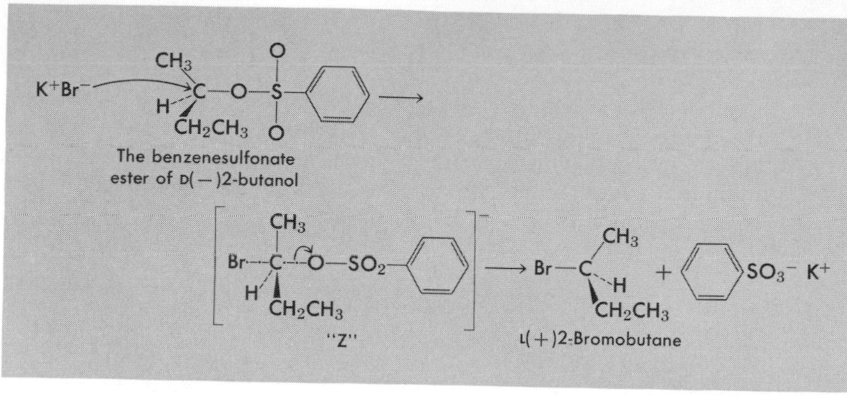

Fig. 6-15. The inversion of configuration attending the nucleophilic displacement of benzenesulfonate ion by bromide ion. (The dot-dash lines represent partial bonds.)

rule that 2 inversions of configuration (once by the bromide ion and once by the hydroxide ion) have the same effect as 1 retention of configuration (that is, no net effect on the configuration).

Carbonium ion reactions, on the other hand, normally lead to a loss of optical activity; that is, racemic or largely racemic products are usually obtained from reactions of this type (Fig. 6-17). We can attribute the formation of these racemic products to the fact that carbonium ions are planar (because of the sp^2 hybridization of the electron-deficient carbon). A carbonium ion intermediate therefore possesses a plane of symmetry (in Fig. 6-17, this plane is perpendicular to the plane of the paper) and any product formed from the carbonium ion must be optically inactive.

The study of optically active compounds is very important since it allows

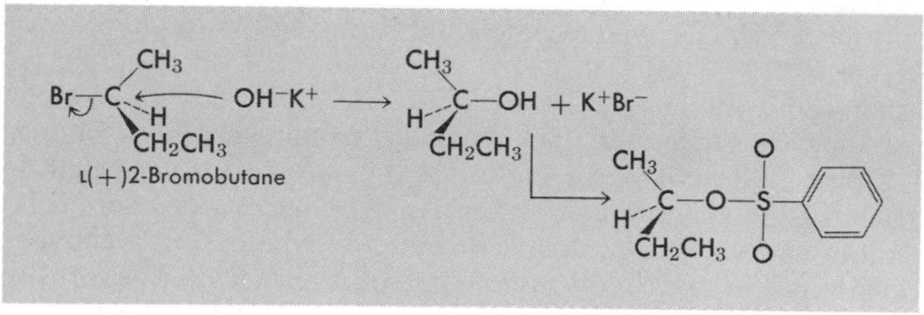

Fig. 6-16. Inversion of configuration in the displacement of bromide ion by hydroxide ion.

Fig. 6-17. The formation of racemic products in a carbonium ion reaction.

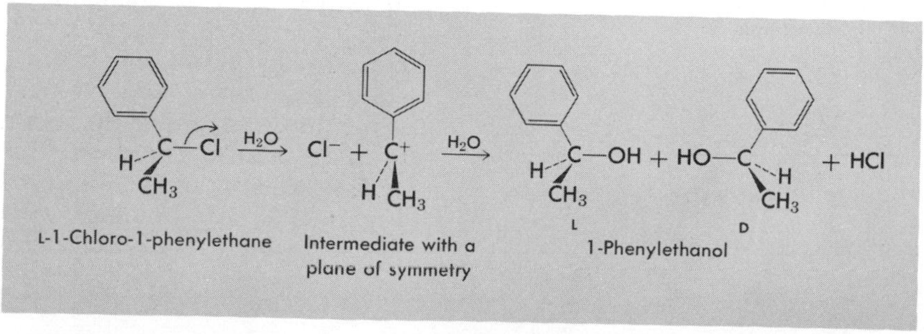

us to determine whether a reagent molecule has entered on the front side of the molecule or on the back side. Although most of the reactions that are known proceed with inversion of configuration (accompanied occasionally by more or less racemization) a few are known that proceed with retention of configuration (Fig. 6-18).

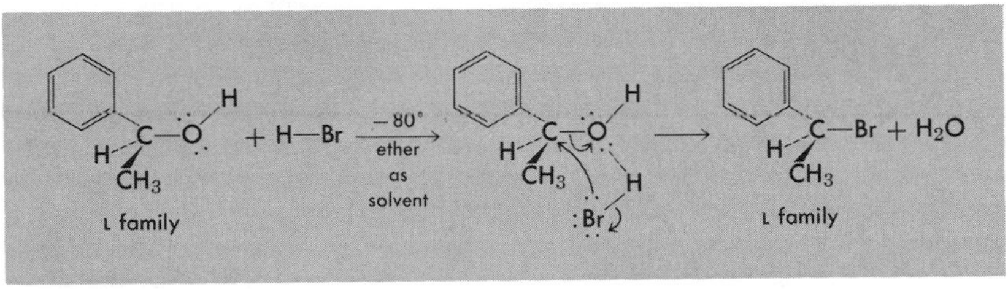

Fig. 6-18. A reaction that proceeds with retention of configuration.

CARBOHYDRATES

Carbohydrates are compounds of carbon, hydrogen, and oxygen derived more or less directly from carbon dioxide and water in photosynthesis. Sugar, starch, and cellulose are examples of carbohydrates that illustrate the importance of this class of compounds to life. Cellulose is the principal constituent of wood (and paper), starch is the principal constituent of the grains and other seeds, and the sugars, in addition to their widespread use as a foodstuff, are important functioning parts of all living organisms. The term carbohydrates stems from the fact that many of the sugars have the empirical formula $C_nH_{2n}O_n$, which corresponds technically to a "hydrate of carbon" $C_n(H_2O)_n$.

Structurally, the sugars are hydroxylated aldehydes and ketones; if the compounds are single units they are called **monosaccharides,** whereas if more than 1 unit is present in the molecule, they are called **disaccharides, trisaccharides,** and in general **polysaccharides.** The saccharides are further broken down into **aldoses** and **ketoses** depending on whether an aldehyde group or a keto group is present in the molecule. The monosaccharides are further subdivided to indicate the number of carbon atoms in the molecule. A **tetrose** contains 4 carbon atoms, a **pentose** 5, a **hexose** 6, etc.

Monosaccharides

Fig. 6-19. A projection formula and a schematic diagram for D-glyceraldehyde.

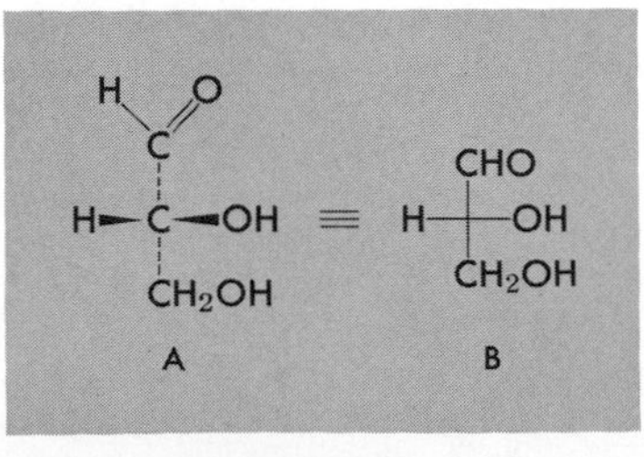

In the previous sections, we have discussed the stereochemistry of the aldotriose glyceraldehyde. This compound (Fig. 6-11), which has only two stereoisomers (+ and −) plays a central role in assigning the configuration of the other saccharides. It is inconvenient to draw projection formulas (see Fig. 6-19A) for complex compounds. Consequently, molecules of this type

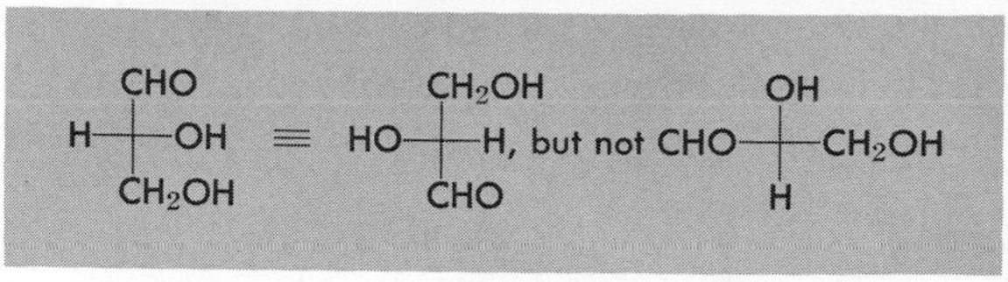

Fig. 6-20. Schematic diagrams of D(+)-glyceraldehyde.

$$\begin{array}{c} CHO \\ H-\!\!\!-OH \\ CH_2OH \end{array} \equiv \begin{array}{c} CH_2OH \\ HO-\!\!\!-H, \text{ but not } \\ CHO \end{array} \begin{array}{c} OH \\ CHO-\!\!\!-CH_2OH \\ H \end{array}$$

are often represented by schematic diagrams as shown in Fig. 6-19B. In these diagrams, the vertical line represents bonds going away from the reader (behind the plane of the paper) whereas the horizontal lines represent bonds coming out of the paper toward the reader. In working with these diagrams, certain rules must be followed: (1) the diagrams may be rotated in the plane of the paper by 180° but *not* by 90° (Fig. 6-20), and (2) the exchange of any 2 groups gives the enantiomeric configuration for that particular asymmetric carbon atom (Fig. 6-21). These rules should be verified through the use of

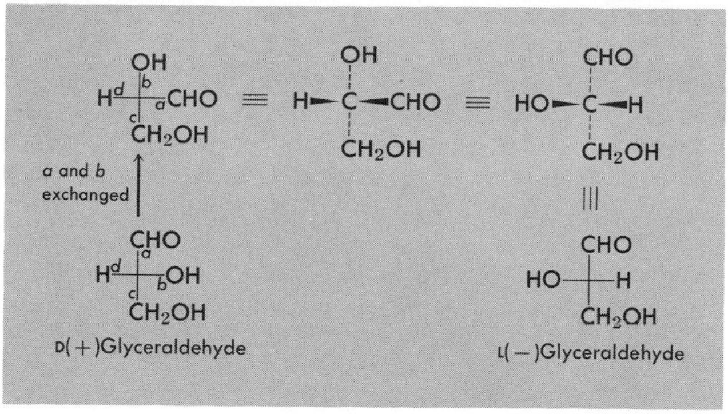

Fig. 6-21. An illustration of the fact that exchange of any 2 groups on an asymmetric carbon atom gives the enantiomeric configuration.

ball-and-stick models. The schematic diagrams are useful in that they clearly illustrate mirror-image relationships (Fig. 6-22).

D-glyceraldehyde reacts readily with HCN to give a mixture of 2 cyanohydrins (one new asymmetric carbon atom is generated in this reaction):

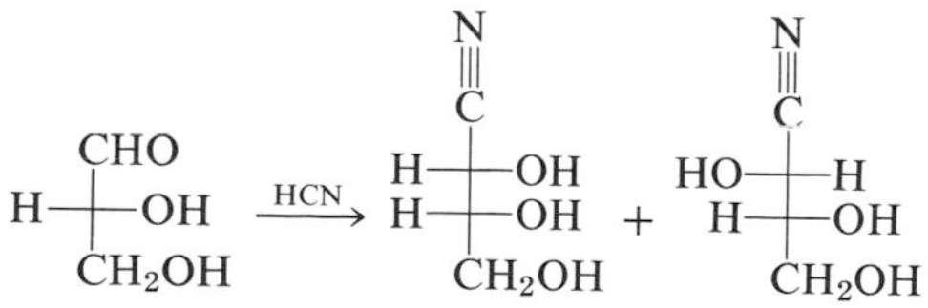

The ratio of isomers is not 50-50 because the glyceraldehyde molecule already contains an asymmetric carbon atom and the asymmetric forces set up with the incoming cyanide ion favor one form slightly over the other. In any event, each cyanohydrin can be converted into the corresponding tetrose (Fig. 6-23).

By methods of this type, the four aldotetroses have been synthesized. Their configurations and names are given in Fig. 6-24. The number of isomers could have been predicted from the expression (2^n) discussed in the

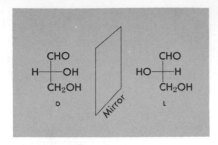

Fig. 6-22. D- and L-Glyceraldehyde. Each is the mirror image of the other.

last section, where n = the number of asymmetric carbon atoms in the molecule.

It should be noted that, by definition, the family relationships of the higher saccharides are assigned on the basis of the configuration of the bottommost asymmetric carbon atom in the schematic diagrams of the compounds (oriented so that the aldehyde group is at the top). That is, the tetroses with an OH group on the number 3 carbon atom on the right side of the formula are members of the D family. It can be seen from Fig. 6-22 that the 2 tetroses synthesized from D-glyceraldehyde must be D-tetroses, whereas the 2 synthesized from L-glyceraldehyde must be L-tetroses.

By an extension of the cyanohydrin synthesis (Fig. 6-23), the 8 aldopentoses (Fig. 6-25) have been synthesized from the tetroses. By similar procedures, furthermore, the 16 aldohexoses have been synthesized from the aldopentoses. The 3 most common aldohexoses are given in Fig. 6-26; also listed is the most common ketohexose, fructose.

Glycosides

We have represented the pentoses and hexoses as linear molecules, but in fact, they exist largely in a cyclic hemi-acetal form. Glucose, for example, has the structure shown in Fig. 6-27, in which the OH group on carbon atom number 5 has added to the carbonyl group. A new asymmetric center has been formed in this process, and the OH group on the number 1 carbon atom either points to the right or to the left on our schematic diagram.

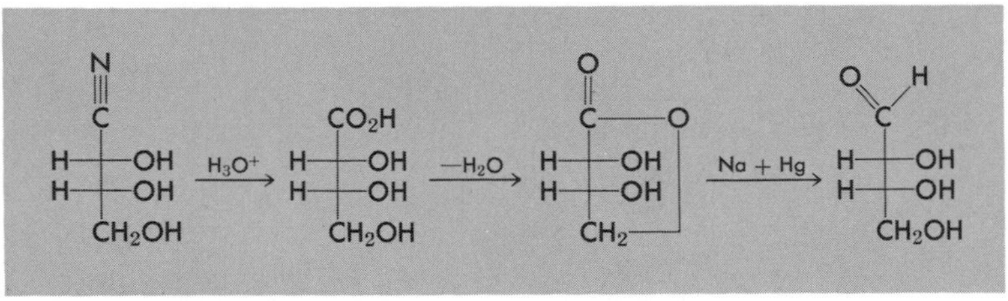

Fig. 6-23. The conversion of a cyanohydrin into an aldose.

Fig. 6-24. The aldotetroses.

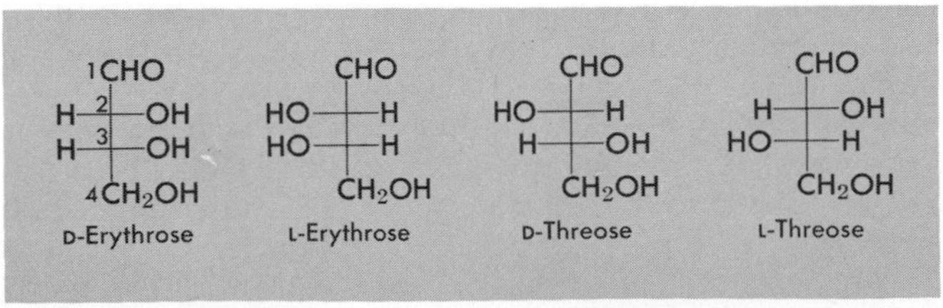

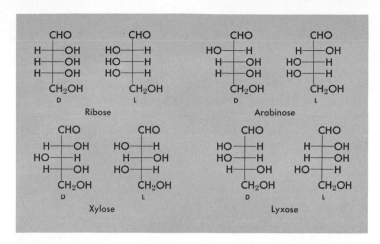

Fig. 6-25. The aldopentoses.

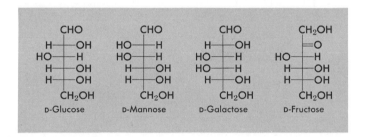

Fig. 6-26. Three common aldohexoses and one ketohexose.

Both forms of glucose have been isolated; the former is called α-D-glucose, (Fig. 6-27A), the latter β-D-glucose (Fig. 6-27B). Similarly, the pentoses exist largely as 5-membered cyclic hemi-acetals.

As typical hemi-acetals, the cyclic forms of the saccharides react with alcohols to form acetals (Fig. 6-28). The acetals of sugars are called **glycosides**, in general, although specifically the acetals of glucose are called **glucosides**. Glucose is widely distributed in nature, where it is found not in the free state, but usually bound to other compounds through a glucoside linkage. Pentose glycosides are also widely distributed in nature; an example of a riboside was given in Fig. 5-14.

Fig. 6-27. (A) α-D-Glucose. (B) β-D-Glucose.

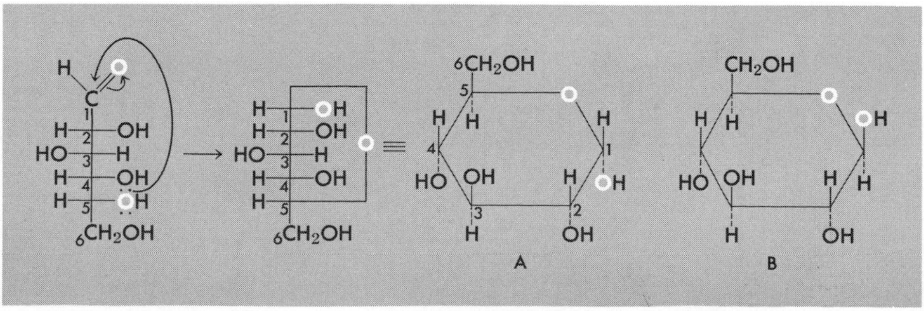

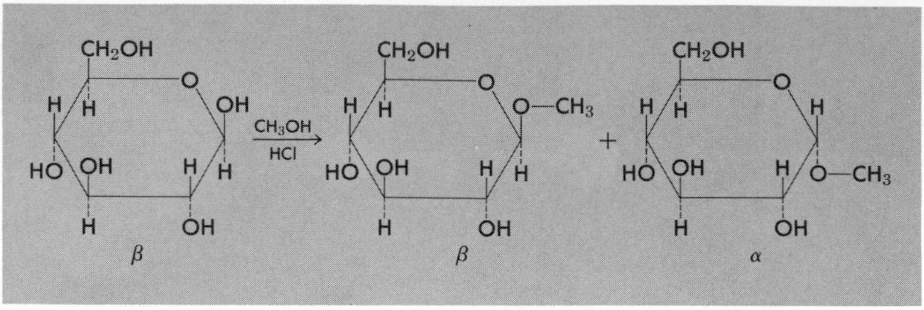

Fig. 6-28. The 2 methyl glucosides.

Polysaccharides

If the acetal of a monosaccharide is formed with the hydroxyl group of a second monosaccharide, a disaccharide results. The common "sugar" of commerce is the disaccharide called sucrose in which the hydroxyl group of a fructose molecule is used in forming the acetal of glucose (Fig. 6-29). Trisaccharides, tetrasaccharides, and the higher saccharides, in which all combinations of the monosaccharides may be found, also have structures of this type.

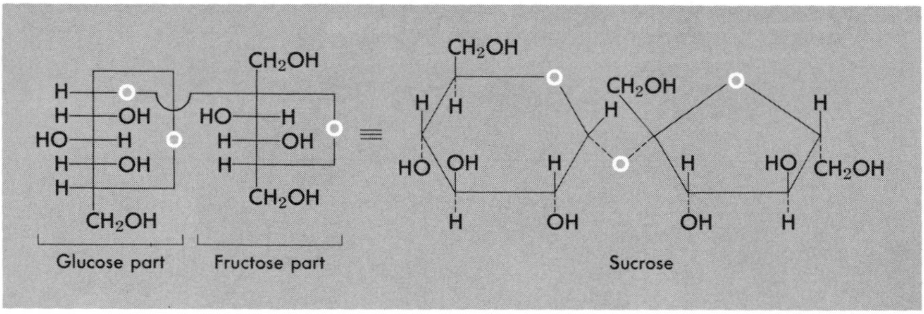

Fig. 6-29. Sucrose.

The complete hydrolysis of starch and also cellulose yields only D-(+)-glucose indicating that these compounds are polysaccharides of D-glucose. Starch is largely the polymer with an α glycoside linkage (Fig. 6-30). About 200–1000 glucose molecules are linked together to form a starch molecule. The structure of cellulose is similar except that the β-glycoside linkage is involved and the molecular weight is higher, the molecule being made up of about 1500 glucose residues.

Fig. 6-30. A representative chain in the giant molecule of starch.

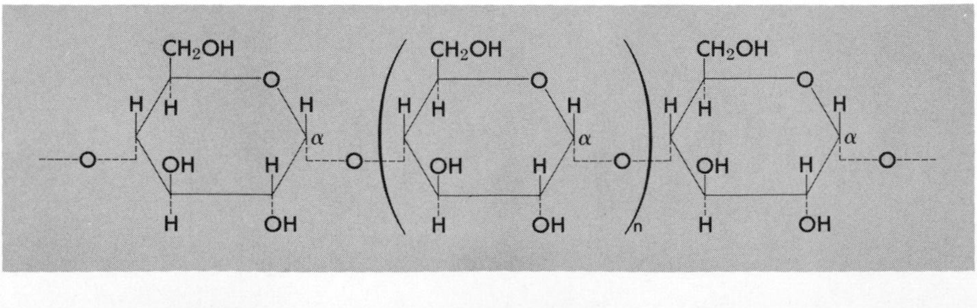

FATS

Fats such as lard and butter, and vegetable oils such as corn oil and olive oil, are composed principally of esters of the alcohol glycerol and various high-molecular-weight carboxylic acids (called fatty acids); esters of this type are usually referred to as **glycerides:**

$$
\begin{array}{c}
\underset{H}{HC}-O-\overset{\displaystyle O}{\overset{\|}{C}}-R \\
| \\
\underset{}{IIC}-O-\overset{\displaystyle O}{\overset{\|}{C}}-R' \\
| \\
\underset{H}{HC}-O-\overset{\displaystyle O}{\overset{\|}{C}}-R''
\end{array}
$$

The R groups in the glycerides may all be alike ($R = R' = R''$), or else any combination may be present; some of the more common fatty acids found in glycerides are given in Table 6-2. Most of the fatty acids are long-chain acids with an even number of carbon atoms. Odd carbon acids are not

Table 6-2

FATTY ACIDS

Name of the Acid	Formula
Lauric	$CH_3(CH_2)_{10}CO_2H$
Myristic	$CH_3(CH_2)_{12}CO_2H$
Palmitic	$CH_3(CH_2)_{14}CO_2H$
Stearic	$CH_3(CH_2)_{16}CO_2H$
Oleic	$CH_3(CH_2)_7CH{=}CH(CH_2)_7CO_2H$ (cis)
Linoleic	$CH_3(CH_2)_4CH{=}CHCH_2CH{=}CH(CH_2)_7CO_2H$ (cis,cis)
Ricinoleic	$CH_3(CH_2)_5CH(OH)CH_2CH{=}CH(CH_2)_7CO_2H$ (cis)

common in nature, presumably because the fatty acids are synthesized in biological systems from a C_2 unit, acetate ion. Most common fats are complex mixtures of glycerides containing several different fatty acids. In a few cases, however, a single fatty acid predominates and it can be recovered after hydrolysis. Myristic acid, for example, can be readily isolated from the fat of the nutmeg, palmitic acid from coconut oil, and stearic acid from beef tallow.

The glycerides of the unsaturated fatty acids tend to have lower melting points than the glycerides of saturated fatty acids and most oils are composed of predominantly the glycerides of unsaturated fatty acids. The hydrogenation of the double bonds of the fatty acids present in oils (converting them into saturated acid chains) raises the melting point of the glycerides. The "hardening" of vegetable oils such as corn and cottonseed oil to yield cooking fats such as Crisco and Spry is an important commercial process today:

$$
\text{Oils} + H_2 \xrightarrow[\text{catalyst}]{\text{Ni}} \text{saturated fats}
$$

An interesting application of this melting point dependence on the degree of unsaturation is found in the fat composition of the sea anemone (*Metridium dianthus*). Sea anemones contain large amounts of fats, and in the species living off the shores of Florida, these fats are largely glycerides of saturated fatty acids. In contrast, the related sea anemones living in colder waters off the coasts of New England contain fats made up largely of the unsaturated fatty acids; a Florida sea anemone deposited in the waters off New England would stiffen to the point of immobility.

Lipids

The term lipids refers to materials obtained from plant and animal sources that are soluble in oil but insoluble in water. The principal constituents of the lipids are fats, but also present are a number of more complex glycerides. The phosphorus-containing lipids, or **phospholipids,** such as sphingomyelin, are important examples of complex pseudoglycerides; they are found principally in nerve and brain tissues.

$$CH_3-(CH_2)_{12}-CH{=}CH-\overset{H}{\underset{|}{C}}-OH$$

$$HC-NH-\overset{O}{\overset{\|}{C}}-(CH_2)_{16}-CH_3$$

$$CH_2-O-\overset{O^-}{\underset{\underset{O_-}{|}}{\overset{|}{P}}}-O-CH_2-CH_2-\overset{+}{N}(CH_3)_3$$

Sphingomyelin

Soaps

One of the most important of the chemical reactions of the glycerides is saponification (the hydrolysis with sodium hydroxide). The products are glycerol and the sodium salts of the fatty acids present in the glyceride:

$$
\begin{array}{l}
CH_2O-\overset{O}{\overset{\|}{C}}-R \\[1em]
CHO-\overset{O}{\overset{\|}{C}}-R + 3\,Na^+OH^- \longrightarrow \\[1em]
CH_2O-\overset{O}{\overset{\|}{C}}-R
\end{array}
\qquad
\begin{array}{l}
CH_2OH \\[1em]
CHOH \quad + 3\ R-\overset{O}{\overset{\|}{C}}-O^-Na^+ \\[1em]
CH_2OH \\[0.5em]
\text{Glycerol}
\end{array}
$$

The sodium salts of long-chain fatty acids are soaps, and the soap of commerce is prepared by this saponification procedure. Before the chemical era of the twentieth century and the ready availability of NaOH, soap was customarily prepared by the interaction of animal fats with water extracts of wood ashes (which contain sodium and potassium carbonates). This process, which is saponification brought about by the carbonates reacting as weak bases, has been in use since the days of the early Babylonians, and even today it is still used in primitive countries.

A soap molecule has 2 features that are essential for its cleansing action: a long hydrocarbon chain and a polar group (the carboxylate group). Modern detergents, such as sodium laurel sulfate, although they differ considerably from soaps in a structural sense, retain these 2 features.

$$CH_3(CH_2)_{10}CH_2-O-\overset{\displaystyle O}{\underset{\displaystyle O}{\overset{\displaystyle |}{\underset{\displaystyle |}{S}}}}-O^-Na^+$$

Sodium laurel sulfate

OTHER NATURAL PRODUCTS

In addition to the 3 major classes of natural products, a number of other types exist, which, although they are not foodstuffs, are no less important in the proper functioning of living things. A full exposition of each type is beyond the scope of this volume; instead, a brief introduction to several types will be given along with the formulas of representative members.

Alkaloids

Alkaloids are complex amines that are found in plants; the function of these compounds in the plant is unknown at the present time. Many of the alkaloids produce interesting physiological reactions in man (ranging from the relief of pain to the production of hallucinations) and for this reason, and also because alkaloids are easy to isolate, they were among the earliest natural products studied by chemists. Examples are given in Fig. 6-31, along with the principle sources.

Steroids

Steroids are compounds containing a pentanohydrophenanthrene ring system (Fig. 6-32). They occur in most plants and animals, and in animals, at least, they are essential for the functioning of the organism. Members of this class include the sex hormones, the bile acids, the toad poisons, and also complex steroids that are used in the treatment of arthritis and heart ailments. Members of this last group are often found attached to sugar molecules (as glycosides) and certain others contain alkaloids as integral parts of their molecules. The formula given in Fig. 6-32 is that of cholesterol, the most common steroid in mammals; it has been estimated that a 140-pound man contains about 0.5 of a pound of cholesterol.

Fig. 6-31. Alkaloids.

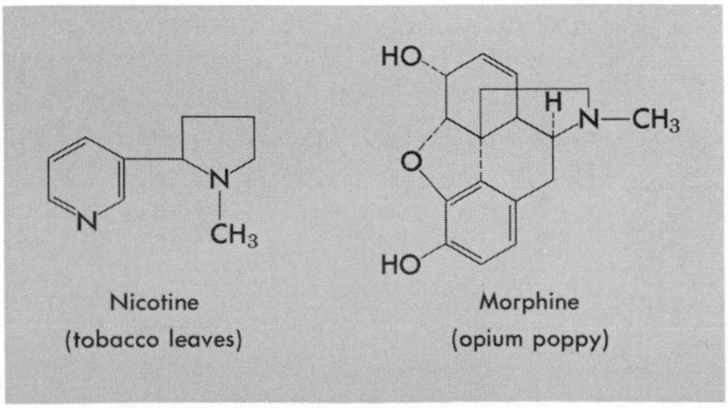

Nicotine
(tobacco leaves)

Morphine
(opium poppy)

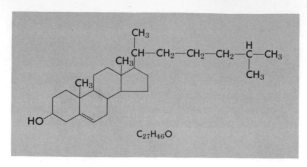

Fig. 6-32. Cholesterol.

Terpenes

The terpenes are compounds built up of units of isoprene (2-methylbuta-diene, $CH_2=C(CH_3)-CH=CH_2$). They have been isolated chiefly from plants, but certain important terpenes have also been isolated from animal sources. Squalene ($C_{30}H_{50}$), for example, is a terpene isolated from the liver of sharks; it is an intermediate in the synthesis of cholesterol in mammals. Two examples of terpenes have been given elsewhere in this volume (Fig. 3-13 and Vitamin A, p. 76); other examples appear in Fig. 6-33.

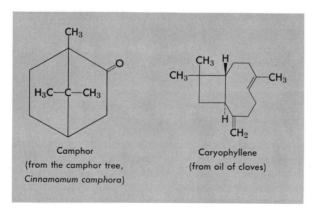

Fig. 6-33. Terpenes.

Porphyrins

Porphyrins are complex tetrapyrrole derivatives. The structure of heme, a member of this class, is given in Fig. 6-34. Heme and a protein (globin) together make up the hemoglobin molecule, the oxygen-carrier in blood. Chlorophyll, the key molecule in photosynthesis, is a related porphyrin containing magnesium (the structure of chlorophyll is given in the volume in this series on plant life*). Still other porphyrins are involved in electron transport and possibly in free-radical reactions in the cell.

The chemistry of the natural products is usually subdivided further to

---

* A. W. Galston, *The Life of the Green Plant*, 2nd ed. (Englewood Cliffs, N.J.: Prentice-Hall, 1964).

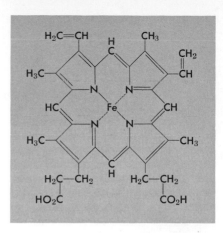

Fig. 6-34. The heme molecule.

include classes such as the vitamins, antibiotics (and other compounds used in chemotherapy, such as sulfanilamide), hormones, nucleotides, compounds responsible for the coloring matter of flowers, etc. It should be pointed out, however, that these are extreme definitions, and that many compounds are known that could fit equally well into several of these categories.

SELECTED READINGS

ATOMS, MOLECULES, CHEMICAL REACTIONS AND INORGANIC CHEMISTRY

Grunwald, E., and R. H. Johnsen, *Atoms, Molecules and Chemical Change.* Englewood Cliffs, New Jersey: Prentice-Hall, 1960. An introductory volume for those with little or no background in science.

Sienko, M. J., and R. A. Plane, *Chemistry,* 2nd. ed. New York: McGraw-Hill Book Company, Inc. 1961. A good treatment of general chemistry at the college level.

Andrews, D. H., and R. J. Kokes, *Fundamental Chemistry.* New York: John Wiley and Sons, Inc., 1962. A rigorous treatment of the subject (at the college level) which stresses thermodynamics.

ORGANIC CHEMISTRY

English, J., Jr., and H. G. Cassidy, *Principles of Organic Chemistry,* 3rd ed. New York: McGraw-Hill Book Company, Inc., 1961. A brief, introductory treatment of the subject.

Fieser, L. F., and M. Fieser, *Advanced Organic Chemistry.* New York: Reinhold Publishing Corp., 1961. A thorough treatment of organic chemistry at the college level. Contains a number of chapters on biochemistry.

Cram, D. J., and G. S. Hammond, *Organic Chemistry,* 2nd ed. New York: McGraw-Hill Book Company, Inc., 1964. Organic chemistry organized in terms of reaction mechanisms.

Wilson, E. O., "Pheromones," *Scientific American,* **208,** Issue 5, p. 100 (1963). A popular account of the organic compounds used by insects in communication.

PHYSICAL CHEMISTRY

Moore, W. J., *Physical Chemistry,* 3rd. ed. Englewood Cliffs, New Jersey: Prentice-Hall, 1962. An interesting and comprehensive coverage of physical chemistry.

APPENDIX A: THE METRIC SYSTEM

Length

1 meter = 10 decimeters = 100 centimeters = 1000 millimeters

1 centimeter = 10 millimeters

1 kilometer = 1000 meters

English Equivalents

1 meter = 39.4 inches

2.5 centimeters = 1 inch

1.6 kilometers = 1 mile

Mass

1 kilogram = 1000 grams = 1,000,000 milligrams

1 gram = 1000 milligrams

1 kilogram = 2.2 pounds

28.3 grams = 1 ounce

Volume

1 liter = 1000 milliliters

1 liter = 1.06 quart

TEMPERATURE EQUIVALENTS

Degrees Centigrade ($C°$) = 5/9($F°$ − 32)   Degrees Fahrenheit ($F°$) = 9/5 $C°$ + 32
Degrees Absolute or Kelvin ($K°$) = $C°$ + 273.2

APPENDIX B: A FEW MATHEMATICAL OPERATIONS

General

The exponent of 10^2 = 2, and 10^2 means 10 times 10 = 100   123,000 = 1.23×10^5

$1 = 10^0$, $10 = 10^1$, $100 = 10^2$, etc. $1/10 = 0.1$, $1/100 = 0.01$, etc.

Exponents

Multiplication (exponents are added):

$10 \times 10 \times 10 = 10^3 = 1000$

$10^4 = 10 \times 10^3 = 100 \times 10^2$, etc., = 10,000

$(8 \times 10^6)(9 \times 10^{-2}) = 72 \times 10^4 =$
$7.2 \times 10 \times 10^4 = 7.2 \times 10^5$

Division (exponents are subtracted):

$1/10 = 10^0/10^1 = 10^{(0-1)} = 10^{-1}$,

$1/10^3 = 10^{-3}$, etc.

$\dfrac{7 \times 10^{-4}}{2 \times 10^3} = 3.5 \times 10^{-7}$ [that is, (7×10^{-4})

$(1/2 \times 10^{-3}) = 7/2 \times 10^{-7}$]

Exponents of exponents (exponents are multiplied)

$(10^2)^3 = 10^6$ $\sqrt{10^4} = (10^4)^{1/2} = 10^{4/2} = 10^2$

Subtraction and addition (the exponents are made identical and the operation is performed):

$(4.5 \times 10^{-3}) - (2 \times 10^{-4}) = (45 \times 10^{-4}) - (2 \times 10^{-4}) = 43 \times 10^{-4} = 4.3 \times 10^{-3}$

Logarithms (to base 10)

(The logarithm of a number is the exponent to which 10 must be raised to equal the number)

Log 1000 = log (10^3) = 3   Log 0.001 = log (10^{-3}) = −3

Multiplication (add logarithms):

Log (100 × 100) = log ($10^2 \times 10^2$) = log (10^2) + log (10^2) = 2 + 2 = 4

Log 1300 = log (1.3×10^3) = .11 + 3 = 3.11 [the value .11 is obtained from a table of logarithms]

Division (subtract logarithms):

Log (1000/100) = log (1000) − log (100) = 3 − 2 = 1

Index